D1242362

Degradation
of Herbicides

DEGRADATION OF HERBICIDES

Edited by

P. C. KEARNEY and D. D. KAUFMAN

UNITED STATES DEPARTMENT OF AGRICULTURE
AGRICULTURAL RESEARCH SERVICE
CROPS RESEARCH DIVISION
BELTSVILLE, MARYLAND

1969

MARCEL DEKKER, INC., New York

Preface

The introduction and subsequent destruction of foreign substances in biological systems has formed the basis for many phases of modern chemistry. Drugs, insecticides, detergents, and a myriad of other substances have received major attention. The foreign substances under consideration in the present book are the organic herbicides which are making an ever-increasing contribution to modern agriculture. The fate of herbicides and, in a larger sense, of all organic pesticides in our environment, is currently a subject of intense investigation. Part of this flurry of activity can be traced to the publication of *Silent Spring*, by Rachel Carson, and the subsequent debates on the real and/or imaginary hazards of pesticides.

The herbicides constitute a large and very diverse group of organic compounds. It is currently estimated that 125 or more herbicides are commercially available. This large number of compounds can be roughly categorized under 10 to 12 major groups. Each chapter in *Degradation of Herbicides* is devoted to a discussion of the pertinent findings concerning the degradation of one particular group of herbicides. The chapters are organized so as to cover first a brief history of the compounds and some of their physical and chemical properties. Next, a detailed treatment of herbicide degradation in plant, soil, and animal systems is presented. A brief discussion of mode of action is included where appropriate to degradation. The last chapter is a slight departure from the others in that it describes an important degradative process affecting a large number of herbicides, i.e., photodecomposition.

Just a word about the use of the term "degradation." All too often, alterations of organic substances in biological systems have been erroneously ascribed to "metabolism" in the sense of enzyme-catalyzed reactions. Numerous examples of pesticide transformations are currently appearing in which purely chemical systems are involved. We have attempted to avoid this pitfall and use the more generalized term "degradation" to cover all transformations of organic herbicides without particularly trying to ascribe these to enzyme or particulate systems. The text does not attempt detailed coverage of all degradation reactions pertaining to the 125 or more herbicides presently on the market. Rather, it attempts to look at classes of compounds and note similarities of reactions between major groups of herbicides. Such an approach should serve as an excellent basis for predicting the behavior of future synthetic compounds falling into a class or major group of organic herbicides presently in use. Nomenclature in the text follows the style recommended by the Weed Society of America. This book does not make recommendations for uses of the herbicides discussed.

Degradation of Herbicides is directed at the needs of biochemists, chemists, plant physiologists, and microbiologists who are concerned with the effects and transformations of pesticides and other compounds introduced into the environment.

P.C.K.
D.D.K.

Beltsville, Maryland
January 1969

Contributors to This Volume

Dagmar Berrer, *Pesticides Research Laboratories, J. R. Geigy S. A., Basel, Switzerland*

Mason C. Carter, *Department of Forestry, Auburn University, Auburn, Alabama*

Donald G. Crosby, *Agricultural Toxicology and Residue Research Laboratory, University of California, Davis, California*

Gerard Dupuis, *Pesticides Research Laboratories, J. R. Geigy S. A., Basel, Switzerland*

Herbert Esser, *Pesticides Research Laboratories, J. R. Geigy S. A., Basel, Switzerland*

S. C. Fang, *Department of Agricultural Chemistry, Oregon State University, Corvallis, Oregon*

C. L. Foy, *Department of Plant Pathology and Physiology, Virginia Polytechnic Institute, Blacksburg, Virginia*

H. H. Funderburk, Jr., *Botany and Plant Pathology Department, Auburn University Agricultural Experiment Station, Auburn, Alabama*

Hans Geissbuhler, *Agrochemical Division Ciba Ltd., Basel, Switzerland*

Richard A. Herrett, *Union Carbide Corporation, Clayton, North Carolina*

Ernest G. Jaworski, *Agricultural Division, Monsanto Company, St. Louis, Missouri*

Enrico Knuesli, *Pesticides Research Laboratories, J. R. Geigy S. A., Basel, Switzerland*

Ming-Yu Li, *Agricultural Toxicology and Residue Research Laboratory, University of California, Davis, California*

M. A. Loos, *Department of Microbiology and Plant Pathology, University of Natal, Pietermaritzburg, South Africa*

G. W. Probst, *Eli Lilly and Company, Greenfield Laboratories, Greenfield, Indiana*

C. R. Swanson, *Crops Research Division, Agricultural Research Service, USDA, Delta Branch Experiment Station, Stoneville, Mississippi*

J. B. Tepe, *Eli Lilly and Company, Greenfield Laboratories, Greenfield, Indiana*

Contents

PREFACE   v

CONTRIBUTORS TO THIS VOLUME   vii

1. Phenoxyalkanoic Acids   1
   M. A. Loos

1-1.   Introduction: Chemical and Physical Properties   1
1-2.   Degradation of Phenoxyacetic Acids   6
1-3.   Degradation of Higher Phenoxyalkanoic Acids   31
1-4.   Degradation of Ester, Amide, and Nitrile Derivatives of
       Phenoxyalkanoic Acids   41
1-5.   Degradation of Sodium 2,4-Dichlorophenoxyethyl Sulfate   44
1-6.   Summary and Conclusions   44
References   45

2. *s*-Triazines   51

   *Enrico Knuesli, Dagmar Berrer, Gerard Dupuis, and
   Herbert Esser*

2-1.   Introduction: Chemical and Physical Properties   51
2-2.   Degradation of Triazine Herbicides by Nonbiological Systems   57
2-3.   Degradation of Triazine Herbicides by Biological Systems   62
2-4.   Conclusions   74
References   74

3. The Substituted Ureas   79

   Hans Geissbuhler

3-1.   Introduction   79
3-2.   Soil and Plant Factors Affecting Degradation   83
3-3.   Degradation   89
3-4.   Biochemical and Enzymatic Mechanisms Involved in Degradation   104
References   108

4. **Methyl- and Phenylcarbamates**   **113**

   Richard A. Herrett

   4-1. Introduction   113
   4-2. Pathways of Degradation   121
   4-3. Degradation in Plants   132
   4-4. Degradation in Soils   134
   4-5. Enzymatic Studies   136
   4-6. Metabolism and Selective Phytotoxicity   139
   4-7. Summary   140
   References   142

5. **Thiolcarbamates**   **147**

   S. C. Fang

   5-1. Introduction   147
   5-2. Degradation   148
   5-3. Summary and Conclusions   163
   References   164

6. **Chloroacetamides**   **165**

   Ernest G. Jaworski

   6-1. Introduction   165
   6-2. Degradation of CDAA   167
   6-3. Degradation of 2-Chloro-*N*-isopropylacetanilide   174
   6-4. Uptake and Metabolism of Other 2-Chloroacetamides   177
   6-5. Mode of Action   182
   6-6. Conclusion   184
   References   184

7. **Amitrole**   **187**

   Mason C. Carter

   7-1. Introduction   187
   7-2. Degradation   188
   7-3. Mode of Action   198
   References   204

8.   **The Chlorinated Aliphatic Acids**   **207**
      C. L. Foy

8-1. Introduction   207
8-2. Degradation   212
8-3. Mode of Action   238
References   249

9.   **Trifluralin and Related Compounds**   **255**
      G. W. Probst and J. B. Tepe

9-1. Introduction   255
9-2. Chemical and Physical Properties   256
9-3. Degradation   258
9-4. Mode of Action   277
9-5. Summary   279
References   280

10. **Diquat and Paraquat**   **283**
      H. H. Funderburk, Jr.

10-1. Introduction   283
10-2. Degradation   286
10-3. Mode of Action   294
References   296

11. **The Benzoic Acid Herbicides**   **299**
      C. R. Swanson

11-1. Introduction   299
11-2. Degradation in Plants and Soils   302
References   317

12. **Herbicide Photodecomposition**   **321**
      Donald G. Crosby and Ming-Yu Li

12-1. Introduction   321
12-2. Photodecomposition   322
12-3. Photochemistry of Herbicides and Plant-Growth Regulators   335
12-4. Discussion   358
References   360

AUTHOR INDEX   365
SUBJECT INDEX   383

CHAPTER 1

Phenoxyalkanoic Acids

M. A. LOOS

DEPARTMENT OF MICROBIOLOGY AND PLANT PATHOLOGY
UNIVERSITY OF NATAL
PIETERMARITZBURG, SOUTH AFRICA

1-1. Introduction: Chemical and Physical Properties	1
1-2. Degradation of Phenoxyacetic Acids	6
A. Degradation in Plants	6
B. Degradation by Microorganisms	18
1-3. Degradation of Higher Phenoxyalkanoic Acids	31
A. Degradation in Plants	31
B. Degradation by Microorganisms	38
1-4. Degradation of Ester, Amide, and Nitrile Derivatives of Phenoxyalkanoic Acids	41
A. Degradation in Plants	41
B. Microbial Degradation of 2,4-D Esters	43
1-5. Degradation of Sodium 2,4-Dichlorophenoxyethyl Sulfate . .	44
1-6. Summary and Conclusions	44
References	45

1-1. INTRODUCTION: CHEMICAL AND PHYSICAL PROPERTIES

The phenoxyalkanoic acids are compounds with the basic structure:

$$\text{(benzene ring, positions 1-6)}-O-(CH_2)_n-COOH$$

The more important phenoxyalkanoic acid herbicides are listed in Table 1-1. The table also indicates the abbreviated and common names that are used for these herbicides, their structural formulas, and some of their

1

TABLE 1-1

Phenoxyalkanoic Acid Herbicides: Names, Structural Formulas, and Properties[a]

Chemical name	Abbreviated or common name[b]	Structural formula	Molecular weight	Melting point, °C	Solubility in water
Phenoxyacetic acids		CH_2-COOH structure with $O-CH$ linkage to ring; X, Y, Z positions			
2-Methyl-4-chlorophenoxyacetic acid	MCPA	X = CH₃, Y = Cl, Z = H	200.6	119	825 ppm Sodium salt: 27%
2,4-Dichlorophenoxyacetic acid	2,4-D	X, Y = Cl, Z = H	221.1	140.5	620 ppm Sodium salt: 4.5%
2,4,5-Trichlorophenoxyacetic acid	2,4,5-T	X, Y, Z = Cl	255.5	158	251 ppm

2-Phenoxypropionic acids

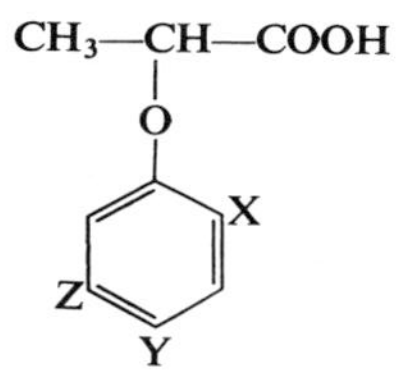

2-(2-Methyl-4-chlorophenoxy)-propionic acid	MCPP Mecoprop	X = CH$_3$ Y = Cl Z = H	214.7	94–95	620 ppm (20°C) Sodium salt: 42.0% a.e. w/v (15°C) Potassium salt: 79.5% w/v (0°C)
2-(2,4-Dichlorophenoxy)pro-pionic acid	2,4-DP Dichlorprop	X, Y = Cl Z = H	235.1	117.5–118.1	350 ppm (20°C) Sodium salt: 66% a.e. w/v (20°C) Potassium salt: 90% a.e. w/v (20°C)
2-(2,4,5-Trichlorophenoxy)pro-pionic acid	Silvex	X, Y, Z = Cl	269.5	179–181	140 ppm (25°C)

4-Phenoxybutyric acids

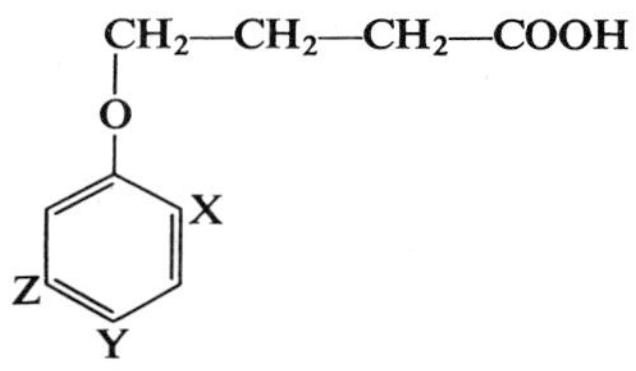

TABLE 1-1 –continued

Chemical name	Abbreviated or common name[b]	Structural formula	Molecular weight	Melting point, °C	Solubility in water
4-(2-Methyl-4-chlorophenoxy)-butyric acid	MCPB	X = CH$_3$ Y = Cl Z = H	228.7	100	44 ppm
4-(2,4-Dichlorophenoxy)butyric acid	2,4-DB	X, Y = Cl Z = H	249.1	117–119	46 ppm (25°C)
4-(2,4,5-Trichlorophenoxy)-butyric acid	2,4,5-TB	X, Y, Z = Cl	283.6	114–115	Sodium salt: > 20% (25°C)
Phenoxyalkanoic acid derivatives Sodium 2,4-dichlorophenoxy-ethyl sulfate	Sesone		309.1	170	25% (room temp.)

^{a} Data from Ref. 1.

^{b} Other phenoxyacetic acids abbreviated in the text are 2-chlorophenoxyacetic acid (2-CPA), 4-chlorophenoxyacetic acid (4-CPA), 2,5-dichlorophenoxyacetic acid (2,5-D), 2,6-dichlorophenoxyacetic acid (2,6-D), 2,4,6-trichlorophenoxyacetic acid (2,4,6-T), 4-hydroxy-phenoxyacetic acid (4-OH-PA), 2-hydroxy-4-chlorophenoxyacetic acid (2-OH-4-CPA), 6-hydroxy-2,4-dichlorophenoxyacetic acid (6-OH-2,4-D), and 6-hydroxy-2-methyl-4-chlorophenoxyacetic acid (6-OH-MCPA).

physical properties. The herbicide sesone is not a phenoxyalkanoic acid, but due to its conversion in soil to 2,4-D, it clearly belongs to the same class. Many other phenoxyalkanoic acids and their derivatives show plant-growth-regulating activity (2–4) but have not become important commercially.

The chlorine-substituted phenoxyacetic acids, 2,4-D, MCPA, and 2,4,5-T, were introduced as selective weed killers at the end of World War II, following the publication of wartime research on their growth-regulating and herbicidal activities (5,6). They are highly active against many broad-leaved weeds but not against graminaceous species, thus they are commonly used for weed control in cereal crops and lawns (1,6). Many woody broad-leaved plants are effectively controlled with 2,4,5-T (1,6). During 1966 the U.S. production of 2,4-D, the most widely used phenoxy herbicide, exceeded 68,182,000 lb (7).

The 2-phenoxypropionic acid herbicides were introduced mainly to control certain weed species not readily controlled by the phenoxyacetic acid herbicides (1). Also, on the other hand, the 4-phenoxybutyric acids are particularly useful because of their lack of toxicity to certain crop plants that are damaged by low concentrations of the phenoxyacetic acids (1,6). Thus, the phenoxybutyric acid herbicides may be used for weed control in many legume crops. The selectivity of these herbicides, which is related to their degradation by β oxidation, will be discussed later. Sesone is active only when applied to soil, where it is converted to 2,4-dichlorophenoxyethanol and 2,4-D. It is used to prevent germination of weed seeds and the growth of weed seedlings in deep-rooted crops, where there is little chance of the crop roots absorbing 2,4-D from the surface layers of the treated soil (1,6,8). Sesone applied to the leaves of the crop has no harmful effect.

Many commercial herbicide formulations contain salts, amine salts, or esters of phenoxyalkanoic acids rather than the free acids (1,6). It is believed that the esters are active only after they have been hydrolyzed in the plant to the free acid.

Degradation of the phenoxyalkanoic acid herbicides, after they have been applied to plants or soil, is of great importance. Degradation by plant enzymes may be a major factor determining the lack of toxicity of these compounds for certain plants; decomposition by soil microorganisms is obviously important in controlling their persistence. Phenoxy herbicides that are not active per se may be activated by the action of plant or microbial enzymes.

This chapter discusses the investigations conducted during the past two decades on the degradation of phenoxyalkanoic acids and their derivatives by plants and soil microorganisms. Special attention is given to degradation pathways.

1-2. DEGRADATION OF PHENOXYACETIC ACIDS

A. Degradation in Plants

The ability of plants to degrade phenoxyacetic acid herbicides has been known since 1950, when Holley et al. (9) and Weintraub et al. (10) reported the metabolism of ^{14}C-labeled 2,4-D by beans (*Phaseolus vulgaris*). Both groups of investigators observed limited degradation of the 2,4-D side chain, as indicated by the liberation of $^{14}CO_2$ from 2,4-D labeled in the carboxyl (9–11) or methylene positions (10,11); in addition, 2,4-D-1-^{14}C-treated beans accumulated large amounts of a water-soluble, ether-insoluble, radioactive metabolite within the plant (9). This metabolite, which accounted for about 60% of the radioactivity present in the bean plants after 1 week, was hydrolyzed with acid or alkali to yield a radioactive organic acid that was more water soluble than 2,4-D, or was a stronger acid (12). Holley (12) suggested that the acid metabolite was a hydroxy-2,4-dichloro-phenoxyacetic acid.

These early studies with bean suggested three mechanisms for the metabolism of phenoxyacetic acids by plants, namely, degradation of the acetic acid side chain, hydroxylation of the aromatic ring, and conjugation with a plant constituent. Subsequent investigations, many of which have been reviewed previously (13–18), have confirmed the occurrence of these degradation mechanisms in many different plant species. The importance of degradation as a detoxication mechanism in certain plants was also indicated.

1. Side-Chain Degradation

Degradation of the side chain of phenoxyacetic acid herbicides has been observed in many plants besides bean (19–31), but in only a few species or varieties does it appear to play a major role in herbicide breakdown. Such plants include red currant (19), certain apple varieties (20,21), strawberry, and garden lilac (20)—all of which showed high rates of $^{14}CO_2$ release from 2,4-D labeled with ^{14}C in the side chain. Thus, excised leaves or leafy shoots of these plants released 7 to 33% of the ^{14}C label from 2,4-D-1-^{14}C as $^{14}CO_2$ in 20 to 24 hours (19–21). In experiments lasting several days, up to 50% of the 2,4-D-1-^{14}C label and up to 20% of the 2,4-D-2-^{14}C label was released as $^{14}CO_2$ by red currant and strawberry leaves (*19,20*). Red currant, straw-berry, and Cox's Orange Pippin apple leaves also decarboxylated 2,4,5-T–1-^{14}C, 4-CPA-1-^{14}C, and MCPA-1-^{14}C at rates comparable to those ob-served for the decarboxylation of 2,4-D-1-^{14}C, but little or no decarboxyla-tion of 2-CPA-1-^{14}C was observed (*19,20*).

Leafe (*22*) showed that side-chain degradation was a mechanism in the metabolism of MCPA by *Galium aparine* (bedstraw), although only 7% of the radioactivity of MCPA-1-^{14}C or MCPA-2-^{14}C supplied to the plants was evolved as $^{14}CO_2$. However, most of the radioactive carbon of the MCPA side chain was cleaved from the aromatic portion of the molecule, some of it being incorporated into cell constituents such as starch, proteins, and nucleic acids. The extent of side-chain degradation was thus greater than the decarboxylation data indicated. Weintraub et al. (*32*) reported that ^{14}C released from 2,4-D-1-^{14}C and 2,4-D-2-^{14}C in the bean was incorporated into plant acids, sugar, dextrins, starch, pectin, protein, and cell-wall substances. It is not known whether the ^{14}C was released from the MCPA or 2,4-D side chain as $^{14}CO_2$ and incorporated into the cell com-ponents by CO_2 fixation or whether a radioactive MCPA or 2,4-D fragment was directly incorporated into the cell material.

Many plants are capable of a slow or limited side chain degradation of phenoxyacetic acid herbicides, which is probably not of any great signifi-cance in herbicide metabolism. For example, many of the plants studied by Luckwill and Lloyd-Jones (*20*), including several apple varieties, liberated less than 8% of the ^{14}C from 2,4-D-1-^{14}C as $^{14}CO_2$ in 20 or 21 hours. A daily release of only 1 to 2% of the 2,4-D-1-^{14}C label as $^{14}CO_2$ was reported for the bean (*11,23*), corn (*23*), and cotton (*24*), while the release of less than 1% per day was observed with Stayman apples (*21*), sorghum (*24*), black-jack oak, persimmon, green ash, sweet gum, winged elm (*25*), and big leaf maple (*26*). The results of Fang et al. (*33*) with bean, indicating release of 17.5% of the radioactivity of 2,4-D-2-^{14}C as $^{14}CO_2$ in 3 days, were criticized by Weintraub et al. (*11*), who believed that this rate of $^{14}CO_2$ release was much too high. Other plants exhibiting a slow decarboxylation of 2,4-D are black currant (*19*), tick bean (*27*), cocklebur, smartweed, jimsonweed, and bur cucumber (*28*) and cultivated cucumber (*29*). Bur and cultivated cucumbers can also slowly decarboxylate 2,4,5-T (*29*), as can bean (*23*) and big leaf maple (*26*).

Fluorine-containing phenoxyacetic acids, like their chlorine-containing counterparts, also undergo side-chain degradation in plants. The rate of degradation may be similar to that of the corresponding chlorine-containing acids, as in the case of 4-fluorophenoxyacetic acid and 2,4-difluorophenoxyacetic acid decarboxylation in bean (23), or it may be quite different. Thus, in contrast to their rapid decarboxylation of 2,4-D, McIntosh Apple shoots decarboxylated 2-chloro-4-fluorophenoxyacetic acid only very slowly (21). On the other hand, blackjack oak decarboxylated this compound considerably faster than 2,4-D, although the amount of radioactivity released as $^{14}CO_2$ from the carboxyl-labeled 2-chloro-4-fluorophenoxy-acetic acid amounted in 22 hours to only 7% of the applied dose (25).

Several 2-phenoxypropionic acids, which can be regarded as phenoxy-acetic acids substituted in the side chain with a methyl group, are slowly decarboxylated in plants, for example, dichlorprop in the big leaf maple (26) and silvex in the big leaf maple (26) and prickly pear (30). Degradation of these compounds was extremely slow, and the success that was obtained with silvex in the control of prickly pear was ascribed to the long persistence of this compound in the plant (30). Similarly, mecoprop was resistant to side-chain degradation in bedstraw (22).

Loss of the side chain from a phenoxyacetic acid without further metabolic changes to the molecule would yield the corresponding phenol. Luckwill and Lloyd-Jones (20), investigating 2,4-D metabolism in strawberry, demonstrated the formation of a phenol which they assumed was 2,4-dichlorophenol. The amount of phenol formed agreed closely with the amount of 2,4-D–2-^{14}C that lost its label as $^{14}CO_2$. Moreover, the symptoms that developed in 2,4,5-T-treated strawberries suggested that 2,4,5-tri-chlorophenol, which would be formed by loss of the side chain from 2,4,5-T, was damaging the plants rather than 2,4,5-T itself. Recently Chkanikov et al. (34), using paper chromatography, demonstrated the production of 2,4-dichlorophenol from 2,4-D in bean, sunflower, corn, and barley (Fig. 1-1). Using red raspberry homogenates, they demonstrated that 2,4-di-chlorophenol and 2,4,5-trichlorophenol could be metabolized in plants. However, these phenols were not metabolized by black raspberry homo-genates.

Two different mechanisms of side-chain degradation appear to occur among plants metabolizing phenoxyacetic acids. Thus, tick beans meta-bolizing 2,4-D (27) and bedstraw metabolizing MCPA (22) released both side-chain carbons as CO_2 at the same rate. These observations suggest removal of the 2,4-D or MCPA side chain as a 2-carbon unit through cleavage of the molecule at the ether linkage. Alternatively, the methylene carbon might be released immediately after the carboxyl carbon. By con-trast, a definite stepwise degradation of the side chain occurred in bean (11), red currant (19), strawberry (20), cotton, and sorghum (24), with the carboxyl carbon being released as CO_2 about twice as fast as the methylene carbon.

Stepwise degradation of the phenoxyacetic acid side chain would involve the formation of an intermediate containing only one carbon from the original side chain. Luckwill and Lloyd-Jones (*19,20*) obtained evidence that such an intermediate was formed in 2,4-D-treated red currant and strawberry leaves, but they were unable to extract it from the leaf residue for identification. They suggested that it might be a bound form of 2,4-dichloroanisole, which could be formed by the decarboxylation of 2,4-D. The hypothetical pathway involving the formation of 2,4-dichloroanisole in the conversion of 2,4-D to 2,4-dichlorophenol is shown in Fig. 1-1 (pathway B), but the existence of this pathway in plants has still to be established.

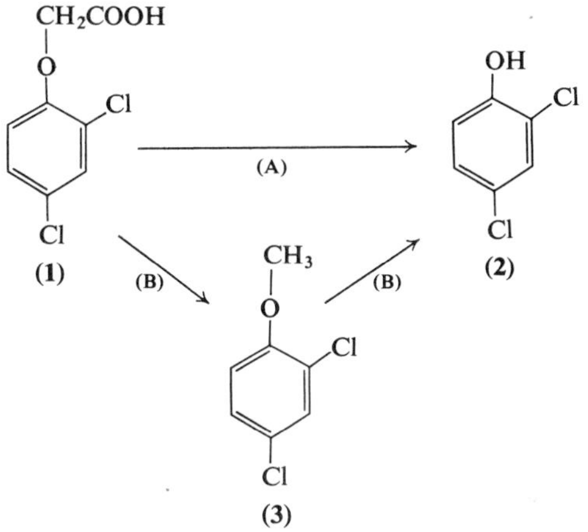

Fig. 1-1. Conversion of 2,4-D (**1**) in plants to 2,4-dichlorophenol (**2**). Hypothetical pathways involving (A) cleavage of the 2,4-D at the ether linkage and (B) the intermediary formation of 2,4-dichloroanisole (**3**).

2. Ring Hydroxylation

The early work of Holley (*12*) suggested that 2,4-D was metabolized in bean to a hydroxy-2,4-dichlorophenoxyacetic acid. The hydroxy acid metabolite was not identified (*12*).

Fawcett et al. (*4*), using paper chromatography, showed that wheat and pea tissue hydroxylated unsubstituted phenoxyalkanoic acids, including phenoxyacetic acid, in the 4 position (Fig. 1-2, pathway A). In addition, the higher phenoxyalkanoic acids were β-oxidized. Similar reactions were observed in oats, barley, and corn, but not in peanuts, soybeans, and alfalfa (*35*). In the oats, barley, and corn, the higher phenoxyalkanoic acids with an even number of carbons in the side chain appeared to be β-oxidized to phenoxyacetic acid, then hydroxylated to yield 4-hydroxyphenoxyacetic acid. The 4 hydroxylation of phenoxyacetic acid in oats was confirmed by Thomas et al. (*36*).

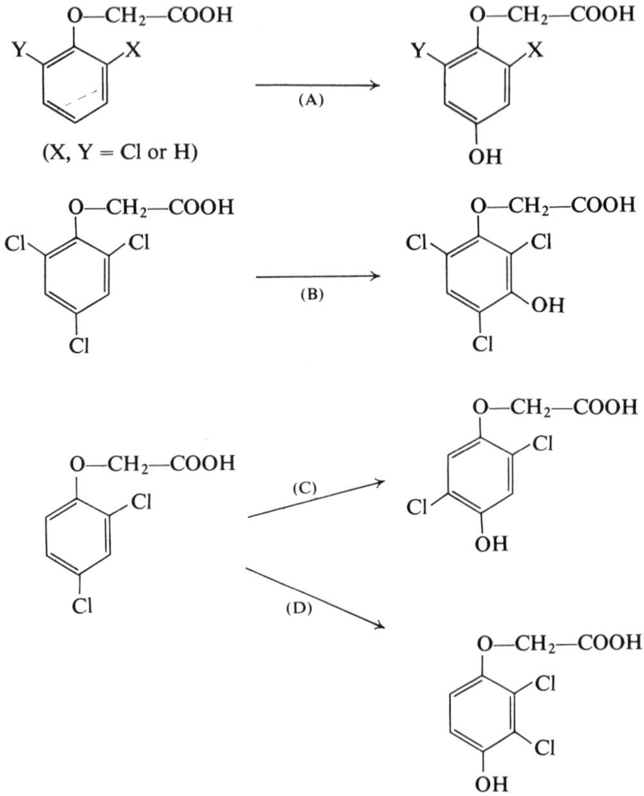

Fig. 1-2. Ring hydroxylation of phenoxyacetic acids by plants. (A) 4 Hydroxylation of phenoxyacetic acid, 2-CPA, and 2,6-D; (B) 3 hydroxylation of 2,4,6-T; (C) and (D) 4 hydroxylation of 2,4-D with chlorine shift to the 5 or 3 position.

Thomas et al. (*37*) also investigated the hydroxylation of chlorine-substituted phenoxyacetic acids in oats. If the 4 position of the ring was unsubstituted, the phenoxyacetic acid was hydroxylated in that position (Fig. 1-2, pathway A); the hydroxylated phenoxy acids were than conjugated to glucose to form the 4-O-β-D-glucosides (Fig. 1-3). Thus, 2-chloro-phenoxyacetic acid (2-CPA) was converted to the glucoside of 2-chloro-4-hydroxyphenoxyacetic acid and 2,6-dichlorophenoxyacetic acid (2,6-D) to the glucoside of 2,6-dichloro-4-hydroxyphenoxyacetic acid. Chlorine-substituted phenoxyacetic acids with no unsubstituted 4 position, for example, 2,4-D and 4-chlorophenoxyacetic acid (4-CPA), were not hydroxylated by oats. The fate of 2,4,6-trichlorophenoxyacetic acid was exceptional, with hydroxylation occurring in the 3 position (Fig. 1-2, pathway B). The 3-hydroxy-2,4,6-trichlorophenoxyacetic acid then combined with glucose to form the glucoside.

The identity of the principal 2,4-D metabolite in bean, which was believed by Holley (*12*) and Crosby (*38*) to be a hydroxyphenoxyacetic acid, was reinvestigated (*39*). The ether-insoluble fraction of alcohol extracts from 2,4-D-treated beans contained metabolites of 2,4-D, which on treatment with β-glucosidase yielded two phenolic acids that were separated by thin-layer chromatography. The major phenolic acid was identified as 2,5-dichloro-4-hydroxyphenoxyacetic acid and the minor phenolic acid as 2,3-dichloro-4-hydroxyphenoxyacetic acid. The hydroxylation of 2,4-D in bean was thus accompanied by a chlorine shift from the 4 to the 5 or 3 position (Fig. 1-2, pathways C and D). Such a reaction had previously been reported only in the fungus *Aspergillus niger* (*40*). The two dichloro-4-hydroxyphenoxyacetic acid metabolites accumulated in bean as the glucosides.

3. Conjugation with Plant Constituents

The formation of glucosides of hydroxyphenoxyacetic acids, mentioned in the previous section, is an example of degradation involving conjugation with plant constituents. The structure of the 4-O-β-D-glucoside of 2-chloro-4-hydroxyphenoxyacetic acid (**4**) is indicated in Fig. 1-3. The glucosides of other hydroxyphenoxyacetic acids are similar.

The esterification of glucose with phenoxyacetic acids has also been observed (*37,41*). Klämbt (*41*) reported the formation of the glucose ester of 2,4-D in wheat, while Thomas et al. (*37*) reported that oats converted 2,4-D, 4-CPA, and 2,6-D to their β-D-glucose esters. The structure of the β-D-glucose ester of 2,4-D (**5**) is illustrated in Fig. 1-3.

Aspartic acid combined with 2,4-D to form 2,4-dichlorophenoxyacetyl-aspartic acid (**6**) (Fig. 1-3) in wheat (*41*), peas (*42*), red and black currants (*19*), and probably also in wild and cultivated cucumbers (*29*), according to paper chromatographic evidence. Conjugation of phenoxyacetic acids with other amino acids has not yet been detected, but it is reasonable to suppose that it can occur (*19*). Conjugates of phenoxyacetic acids and many naturally occurring amino acids have been prepared by chemical synthesis (*43–46*).

The identity of the conjugates discovered by Butts and his colleagues (*47, 48*), which were designated "unknowns 1 and 3," is uncertain. Unknown 1 is a major metabolite of 2,4-D in beans (*47,49*) and in peas during the early stages of 2,4-D metabolism (*50*). Unknown 3 is the major 2,4-D metabolite in corn and wheat (*48*), as well as in tomatoes and peas during the later stages of 2,4-D metabolism (*50*). Unknowns 1 and 3 were distinguished

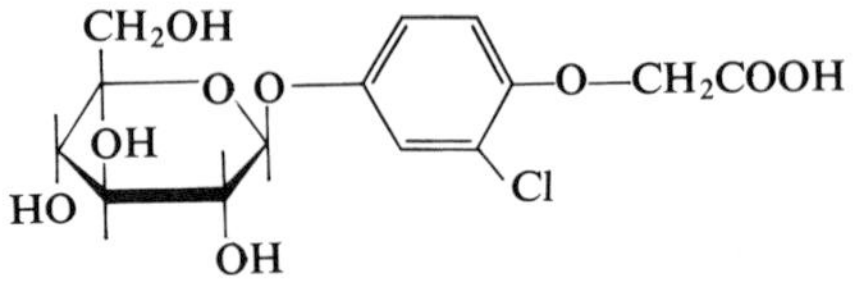

Fig. 1-3. Conjugated forms of phenoxyacetic acids detected in plants. (**4**), β-D-glucoside of 4-hydroxy-2-chlorophenoxyacetic acid; (**5**), β-D-glucose ester of 2,4-D; and (**6**), 2,4-dichlorophenoxyacetylaspartic acid.

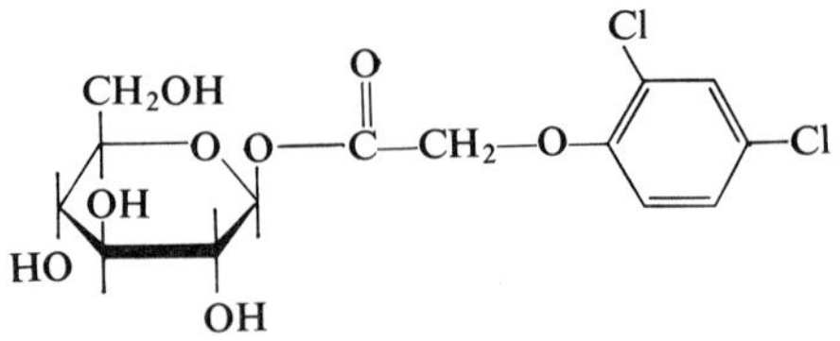

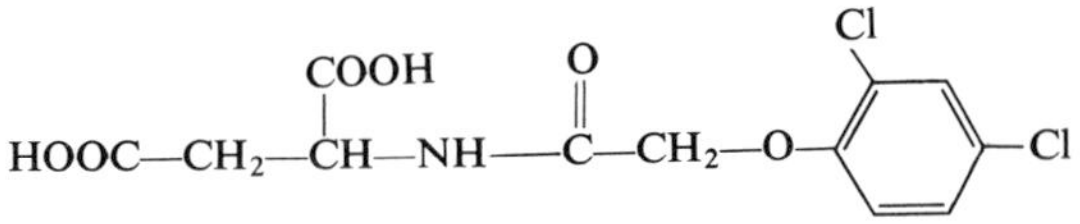

from 2,4-D and from each other by their R_f values on paper chromatograms. Both were hydrolyzed by acid or emulsin and unknown 1 was hydrolyzed by takadiastase to yield 2,4-D (*47,48*). These observations suggested that the two conjugates were glycosides of 2,4-D (*47,48*). However, Butts and Fang (*51*) subsequently suggested that the plant constituent of the complex was a protein. They isolated 2,4-D– and 2,4,6-T–"protein" complexes from beans treated with 2,4-D or 2,4,6-T which were found to contain at least 12 amino acids. The relative amounts of the amino acids from each complex were rather similar. When the 2,4-D–protein complex was injected into the stems of beans, 2,4-D was decarboxylated about three times as fast as when free 2,4-D was injected, suggesting that the complex was a product of a detoxication process and perhaps an intermediate in the metabolism of 2,4-D (51).

Bach and Fellig (52) and Bach (53) did not accept the conclusion that unknowns 1 and 3 are 2,4-D–protein complexes. In agreement with Jaworski and Butts (47), they found that after a few days most of the 2,4-D was converted into a biologically inactive complex that chromatographed on paper more slowly than 2,4-D (52,54). On hydrolysis with acid, this complex yielded a substance with a similar R_f to 2,4-D. Further work (53,55) indicated that the complex, which was the major radioactive component of the water-soluble, ether-insoluble fraction of bean extracts, consisted of several radioactive metabolites. These metabolites were separated by elution from a charcoal column (55). The heterogeneity of the complex was also demonstrated by paper chromatography, at least six major radioactive components appearing on the chromatograms (53). On hydrolysis each of these six components yielded a number of amino acids and two radioactive, ether-soluble compounds which were identical to the two major radioactive components of the ether-soluble fraction of the bean extracts. Some 10 amino acids were detected among the hydrolysis products. Bach (53) did not believe that the ether-insoluble, radioactive products of 2,4-D metabolism were polypeptides or proteins, as proposed by Butts and Fang (51), as their behavior on ion-exchange chromatography, paper chromatography, and extraction into organic solvents could not be reconciled with a polypeptide structure. He proposed instead that the actual metabolites were probably still contaminated with relatively large amounts of "bound" amino acids, for example, amino acid amides of miscellaneous plant metabolites. Thus, there was not necessarily a direct correlation between the amino acids that were identified following hydrolysis of the various radioactive fractions and the amino acids which were presumably bound to the radioactive acids produced from the 2,4-D.

Bach (53) found no 2,4-D in the ether-soluble fraction of his extracts, nor in the hydrolysis products of the ether-insoluble metabolites, although the major ether-soluble metabolite was indistinguishable from 2,4-D by paper chromatography with 30 different solvents and countercurrent distribution. However, it differed from 2,4-D when tested chemically for functional groups. All radioactive products in both the ether-soluble and ether-insoluble fractions were therefore metabolites of 2,4-D. The ether extract contained 10 radioactive components, which all seemed to have retained the aromatic nucleus of 2,4-D. Some possessed phenol and alcohol groups but there was no evidence for aliphatic unsaturation. To account for the presence of aliphatic hydroxyl groups, Bach (53) proposed a lengthening of the 2,4-D side chain in a manner similar to that involved in fatty acid biosynthesis. He suggested that this mechanism could be a means of 2,4-D detoxication, but emphasized that it needed verification.

It seems likely, in view of subsequent findings, that 2,5- and 2,3-dichloro-4-hydroxyphenoxyacetic acid occurred among the metabolites detected by Bach (53). When Bach (53) reported his experiments, the formation of these compounds by plants was unknown.

The work of Bach (53) raises doubts as to whether the unknown 1 complex in beans contained 2,4-D, as reported by Jaworski and Butts (47), or a metabolite of 2,4-D that was chromatographically indistinguishable from 2,4-D. However, in cotton there is evidence that a conjugate resembling the unknown 1 of beans does contain 2,4-D (56). This conjugate, when injected into cotton seedlings, produced symptoms similar to those produced by 2,4-D, suggesting that the conjugate was hydrolyzed in the plant with the release of free 2,4-D. The conjugate had no effect when applied externally to the cotton seedlings, eliminating the possibility that it was contaminated with free 2,4-D.

Meagher (57) recently reported evidence for the conjugation of 2,4-D to pectic acid in citrus peel. A portion of the 2,4-D taken up by citrus peel was bound in the acetone-insoluble fraction. The herbicide was released from this fraction in a conjugated form by prolonged heating. Pectic acid isolated from the acetone-insoluble fraction of the 2,4-D-treated citrus peel and subjected to the same heat treatment liberated a conjugate of 2,4-D, thus suggesting conjugation of at least some of the "bound" 2,4-D with pectic acid.

4. Formation of Unidentified Metabolites

In addition to the metabolites discussed in the foregoing sections, many unidentified radioactive metabolites originating from ^{14}C–carboxyl- or methylene-labeled phenoxyacetic acids have been reported in plants. The unidentified metabolites have usually been distinguished from the parent phenoxyacetic acids by their solubility characteristics and paper chromatography. Examples of such compounds are the metabolites found in 2,4-D-treated cotton (24,56) and 2,4-D- or 2,4,5-T-treated big leaf maple (26) that were similar in their chromatographic behavior to the unknown 1 complex of Jaworski and Butts (47), and the metabolite found in 2,4-D-treated sorghum (24) that resembled the unknown 3 complex of Fang and Butts (48). An unidentified metabolite of 2,4-D detected in bean by Weintraub et al. (32) was a relatively volatile or unstable, ether-soluble, acidic material. *Oxalis pes-caprae* (Bermuda buttercup) also produced unstable metabolites and probably volatile metabolites from 2,4-D (*31*). Metabolites of 2,4-D or silvex, that were possibly sugar esters, were detected by Crosby (*38*) in bean and by Meagher (*57*) in citrus peel. Erickson et al. (*58*) reported the formation of an ester-like complex from 2,4-D in lemons. Other plants in which unidentified metabolites of 2,4-D have been detected are young cherry trees (*59*), red and black currants (*19*), apples and strawberries (*20*), tick beans (*27*), ironweed (*60*), jimsonweed (*61*), wild and cultivated cucumbers (*29*), and blackjack oak (*62*).

Several plants that produced unidentified metabolites from 2,4-D also produced metabolites from other phenoxyacetic acids. For example, red and black currants produced unidentified metabolites from 2,4,5-T, 2-CPA, and 4-CPA (*19*). Metabolites of 2,4,5-T were detected in wild and cultivated cucumbers (*29*), mesquite seedlings (*63*), and blackjack oak (*62*). Blackjack oak also produced several unidentified compounds from 2-chloro-4-fluorophenoxyacetic acid (*62*). MCPA metabolites were detected in bedstraw (*22*). The metabolism of silvex to a number of products in the prickly pear (*30*) can also be mentioned, as this compound can be regarded as a side-chain-substituted phenoxyacetic acid.

The unidentified metabolites discussed in this section were probably formed by the known degradation mechanisms outlined in previous sections. However, some may perhaps be the products of degradation mechanisms that have not yet been described.

5. Degradation as a Detoxication Mechanism

The ability of a plant to degrade phenoxyacetic acid herbicides will obviously influence its susceptibility to the action of these herbicides. In many cases degradation serves as a detoxication mechanism, making the plant resistant to the herbicide that is degraded.

The rapid degradation of the 2,4-D side chain appears to be responsible for the lack of toxicity of this compound toward red currants (*19*), Cox's Orange Pippin (*20*) and McIntosh apples (*21*), several strawberry varieties, and the garden lilac (*20*). By contrast, 2,4-D is highly toxic to black currants (*19*), Bramley's Seedling (*20*), and Stayman apples (*21*), which degrade the side chain of the herbicide only very slowly. However, not all 2,4-D-resistant plants decarboxylate 2,4-D at a rapid rate (*20*), indicating that side-chain degradation is not the only mechanism involved in resistance to 2,4-D. Replacement of the *p*-chlorine in 2,4-D with fluorine makes the molecule resistant to degradation by McIntosh apples; hence, 2-chloro-4-fluorophenoxyacetic acid is an effective growth regulator for this apple variety (*21*).

Red currant is relatively resistant to 4-CPA and MCPA, which it decar-boxylates at a rapid rate, but it is highly susceptible to 2,4,5-T, although this compound is decarboxylated as rapidly as 2,4-D, 4-CPA, and MCPA (*19*). Luckwill and Lloyd-Jones (*20*) suggested that 2,4,5-trichlorophenol was mainly responsible for the damage to 2,4,5-T-treated red currants, which produced quite different symptoms than 2,4,5-T-treated black currants that could not degrade the 2,4,5-T side chain. Formation of the chlorophenols might also be responsible for the toxic effects of 4-CPA and MCPA on red currants and for the high toxicity of 2,4,5-T, 4-CPA, and MCPA on strawberries (*20*). The resistance of bedstraw to MCPA was attributed to the ability of the plant to remove the MCPA side chain; resistance and side-chain degradation were both overcome by the intro-duction of a methyl group into the side chain to give the 2-phenoxypropionic acid herbicide mecoprop (*22*).

The slow and limited degradation of the side chain of phenoxyacetic acids, that is a feature of so many plants, is apparently of little value as a resistance mechanism. Thus, it occurs in several plants which are highly susceptible to the action of 2,4-D, such as bean (*11*), black currant (*19*), certain apple varieties (*20,21*), and cotton (*24*). Plants which are resistant to 2,4-D but metabolize the 2,4-D side chain as slowly or more slowly than susceptible plants (*20,23–25*) presumably owe their resistance to other mechanisms. Nevertheless, Slife et al. (*29*) postulated that the ability of the wild (bur) cucumber to decarboxylate 2,4-D more rapidly than 2,4,5-T might have some effect in determining the resistance of the plant to 2,4-D and its susceptibility to 2,4,5-T, although decarboxylation of 2,4-D was not rapid (*28*). The slow decarboxylation of 2,4-D, 2,4,5-T, dichlor-prop, and silvex (fenoprop) in big leaf maple (*26*) and of silvex in prickly pear (*30*) was not considered to be of any importance as a detoxication mechanism.

Wilcox et al. (*35*) and Thomas et al. (*36*) suggested that the hydroxylation of phenoxyacetic acids might serve as a detoxication mechanism. No direct evidence to support this proposal was reported, but the ability of gramin-aceous species and the inability of several legumes to hydroxylate phen-oxyacetic acid was observed (*35*). The resistance of graminaceous species to phenoxyacetic acids was perhaps related to their ability to hydroxylate these compounds (*35*). In the experiments of Fawcett et al. (*4*), wheat and peas both hydroxylated phenoxyacetic acid and its higher homologs, but the hydroxy acids were not the main products of metabolism. It is therefore impossible to conclude from these data (*4*) whether they were detoxication products or not.

The conjugation of phenoxyacetic acid herbicides with plant constituents appears, in some cases, to be a detoxication mechanism. Fang and Butts (*48*) suggested that the formation of the unknown 3 complex in 2,4-D-treated corn and wheat might be responsible for the resistance of these plants to 2,4-D; beans, which are susceptible to 2,4-D, failed to form this conjugate, although they did form the complex designated unknown 1 (*47*). However, further work (*50*) showed that 2,4-D-susceptible tomatoes also formed unknown 3 as the major 2,4-D metabolite, as did peas after the initial formation of unknown 1. Resistance of the cereals to 2,4-D, therefore, could not be attributed to the formation of a specific conjugate. The resistance was perhaps determined by the rate of conjugate formation, as 2,4-D-resistant graminaceous species formed 2,4-D conjugates much more rapidly than 2,4-D-susceptible beans, tomatoes, and cotton (*24,51*).

The observations of Bach and Fellig (*52,54*) are consistent with these conclusions. Cessation of the growth-stimulating activity of 2,4-D in excised bean stems was correlated with the formation of a conjugate containing 2,4-D (*52,54*) or a 2,4-D metabolite with similar chromatographic characterstics to 2,4-D (*53*). The conjugate had no growth-regulating activity (*54*). The formation of this conjugate, which was probably the unknown 1 of Jaworski and Butts (*47*), was therefore a detoxication mechanism. However, a slow rate of conjugate formation would explain the toxicity of 2,4-D for bean.

The resistance of red and black currants to 2-CPA (*19*) and of wild cucumbers to 2,4-D (*29*) was correlated with the rapid formation of unidentified metabolites of these phenoxyacetic acids. By contrast, wild cucumbers were susceptible to 2,4,5-T, which was converted to unidentified metabolites only very slowly (*29*). Cultivated cucumbers also metabolized 2,4-D rapidly and 2,4,5-T slowly, but were susceptible to the action of both herbicides (*29*). The susceptibility of the cultivated cucumber to 2,4-D was ascribed to rapid uptake of the herbicide, resulting in higher 2,4-D concentrations in this plant than in 2,4-D-resistant wild cucumber.

The conversion of phenoxyacetic acids to metabolic products does not necessarily imply detoxication. For example, a nonacidic metabolite produced from 2,4-D by red and black currants, apples, and strawberries exhibited auxin activity (*19,20*). Other 2,4-D metabolites produced in the same plants showed no growth-regulating activity and were regarded as detoxication products. One of these metabolites may have been 2,4-dichlorophenoxyacetylaspartic acid (*19*), although this compound should show growth-regulating activity (*43*). Analogous active and inactive metabolites were formed from 2,4,5-T and 2-CPA by red and black currants (*19*).

Inactive metabolites predominated in 2-CPA-treated currants which were not damaged by this phenoxyacetic acid.

The glucose ester derivatives of 2,4-D, detected by Klämbt (41) in wheat, were believed to be detoxication products.

The percentage kill of 2,4,5-T-treated blackjack oak, which increased with increasing 2,4,5-T translocation, was inversely proportional to the percentage breakdown of the chemical (64). The high resistance of Oxalis pes-caprae to 2,4-D was attributed in part to the rapid metabolism of the herbicide to volatile or unstable metabolites (31).

The rapid degradation of 2,4-D in the roots of tick beans (27) and big leaf maple (26), compared with the slow degradation in the stems and leaves, explains the resistance of these plants to the herbicidal action of 2,4-D. Applications of 2,4-D that kill the tops of the plants often fail to kill the roots, which later give rise to regrowth. Big leaf maple roots were less effective in degrading 2,4,5-T (26), but data on the relative resistance of the trees to 2,4,5-T and 2,4-D were not reported.

Degradation is not the only factor determining the susceptibility or resistance of plants to the phenoxyacetic acid herbicides. Absorption and translocation are also important (see Refs. 23, 29, 30, 48, 51, 61, and 64–66), but a discussion of these factors falls outside the scope of this chapter.

B. Degradation by Microorganisms

Early studies (67–75) of the persistence of 2,4-D, MCPA, and 2,4,5-T in soil established that these compounds are rapidly (2,4-D) or slowly (MCPA and 2,4,5-T) degraded. Warm, moist conditions and the addition of organic matter to the soil accelerated disappearance of the herbicides (69–73), while autoclaving the soil inhibited their disappearance (71–73). The herbicides were apparently degraded by the soil microorganisms, which flourish under warm, moist conditions in the presence of organic matter and are destroyed by autoclaving. In agreement with this hypothesis, the rate of 2,4-D degradation in several Hawaiian soils appeared to be correlated with the numbers of aerobic bacteria present in the soil (76).

The role of microorganisms in the degradation of phenoxyacetic acid herbicides in soil was conclusively demonstrated by Audus (14,77–82). The kinetics of 2,4-D, MCPA, and 2,4,5-T detoxication in soil-perfusion experiments were exactly what would be expected if microorganisms were the detoxicating agents (77,79,80); in addition, detoxication was blocked by the bacterial inhibitor sodium azide (79,80). The ultimate proof that microorganisms were the detoxication agents was the isolation from 2,4-D-perfused soil of a bacterium able to degrade 2,4-D in pure culture (*78,79*). Subsequently, other bacteria capable of degrading phenoxyacetic acids were isolated from soil and intensive studies of the microbial degradation of phenoxyacetic acids were undertaken (*14,16,81–83*).

1. Organisms Degrading Phenoxyacetic Acids

The bacteria and actinomycetes known to decompose phenoxyacetic acids are listed in Table 1-2. The table also indicates the phenoxyacetic acids that were metabolized by the various organisms. All the intensively studied species metabolized several phenoxyacetic acids, although the rate and extent of metabolism were not the same for all substrates (*87–91,97–99*). Many phenoxyacetic acids were degraded completely, or almost completely, with loss of their aromatic structure and release of their chlorine as inorganic chloride (*88,90,94,97–99*).

The fungus *Aspergillus niger* metabolizes phenoxyacetic acids by introducing a hydroxyl group into the aromatic ring (*40,103–107*). The hydroxylated phenoxyacetic acids are not further degraded by the fungus.

2. Adaptation of Organisms to Phenoxyacetic Acid Substrates

The phenoxyacetic-acid-decomposing bacteria and actinomycetes listed in Table 1-2 were isolated from soil by the enrichment culture technique. The phenoxyacetic acid substrates used in the enrichment media are indicated in the table. The soil-perfusion experiments of Audus (*77,79–82*) show the course of substrate disappearance in such enrichment cultures. Initially a small amount of substrate is removed by adsorption on soil colloids. This phase is followed by a lag period, during which no appreciable change in herbicide concentration is observed. The length of the lag period varies according to the substrate; for example, 2,4-D, MCPA, and 2,4,5-T characteristically exhibit short, long, and extremely long lag phases, respectively. Finally, there is the phase of rapid substrate disappearance. Subsequent additions of substrate disappear rapidly without a lag. The observations of Newman and Thomas (*74*) on 2,4-D decomposition in pots of soil confirm this course of breakdown.

The lag phase is the time required for the development in the soil of an effective population of herbicide-degrading organisms (*80–82*). The origin of the active organisms is unknown, but it has been postulated (*80–82*) that the ability to degrade phenoxyacetic acid herbicides might arise through a mutation. Alternatively, it may merely involve the induction of the appropriate enzymes in organisms that already have the capacity to degrade these

TABLE 1-2

Bacteria and Actinomycetes which Degrade Phenoxyacetic Acids

Organism	References	Phenoxyacetic acid	2-Chlorophenoxyacetic acid	4-Chlorophenoxyacetic acid	2,4-Dichlorophenoxyacetic acid	2,6-Dichlorophenoxyacetic acid	2,4-Dibromophenoxyacetic acid	4-Bromo-2-chlorophenoxy-acetic acid	2-Methyl-4-chlorophenoxy-acetic acid	4-Hydroxyphenoxyacetic acid	2-Hydroxy-4-chloro-phenoxyacetic acid	6-Hydroxy-2,4-dichloro-phenoxyacetic acid	2,4,5-Trichlorophenoxy-acetic acid
Bacteria													
Pseudomonas sp.	84,85										+		
Pseudomonas sp.	84,86			+[a]	+[a]						+		
Mycoplana sp.	87	+	+	+	+[a]						+		
Achromobacter sp.	88			+[a]					+				+

Phenoxyacetic acids metabolized

Achromobacter sp.	88,89		+	+	+	+		+	+	+	+
Achromobacter sp.	90,91	+	+	+	+	+[a]	+	+	+[a]	+	+
Flavobacterium peregrinum	88,89		+	+	+	+[a]	+	+			
F. peregrinum	92,93				+[a]				+[a]		
F. peregrinum	99										
Corynebacterium sp.	94				+[a]						
Corynebacterium-like organism	95,96				+[a]			+			
Arthrobacter globiformis (*Bacterium globiforme*)	78,79	+	+	+	+[a]					+	
Arthrobacter sp.	97,98				+[a]			+	+		
Sporocytophaga congregata (*Flavobacterium aquatile*)	95,96,100				+[a]						
Actinomycetes											
Nocardia sp.	82			+	+						
Streptomyces viridochromogenes	101				+						+

[a] Substrate in enrichment and isolation media.

herbicides (*80–82*). As soon as an organism has gained the ability to utilize the phenoxyacetic acid substrate, it will proliferate rapidly. By the end of the lag period, the population of active organisms is sufficiently large to degrade the substrate at a detectable rate.

The mutation hypothesis for the origin of active organisms is contradicted by certain experimental observations (*81,82*). Very consistent and reproducible lag periods are observed for the degradation of 2,4-D and other phenoxy acids; if the responsible organisms developed as a result of mutations, a much greater variability would be expected (*81,82*). Furthermore, samples of any one soil, when enriched quite independently, seem to produce active populations of the same organism (*81*). This result can be reconciled with the mutation hypothesis only by assuming that a particular bacterial species in the soil is more prone than other species to undergo the mutation(s) leading to activity (*81*).

It has been shown in several organisms that the enzymes degrading phenoxyacetic acids are inducible (*88–91,97,108*). The role of enzyme induction in the development of populations of 2,4-D-decomposing bacteria in soil was investigated by Pearce (*81,82*). The drug sulfanilamide inhibits bacterial proliferation but not enzyme induction; hence, if enzyme induction in a few preexisting bacteria was the first stage in the development of a 2,4-D-decomposing population, the lag phase normally observed during the breakdown of 2,4-D might be shortened by preincubating the soil with 2,4-D and sulfanilamide. Such a result was obtained with low concentrations of sulfanilamide (0.005 and 0.01 %) but not with a higher concentration (0.05 %). Since a limited proliferation of 2,4-D-decomposing bacteria might have occurred at the lower sulfanilamide concentrations, the experiment was inconclusive. However, the inhibition (or retardation) of 2,4-D degradation in the presence of sulfanilamide clearly demonstrated the role of cell proliferation in the development of 2,4-D-decomposing bacterial populations.

Soil that has been "enriched" in bacteria able to decompose a particular phenoxyacetic acid retains for long periods the ability to rapidly degrade the enrichment substrate (*74,81,82*). Thus, the ability to rapidly degrade 2,4-D without a long lag persisted in soil in the absence of 2,4-D for at least 1 year after the initial 2,4-D treatment. The perfusion of 2,4-D-treated soil with distilled water for periods up to 60 days resulted in little loss of 2,4-D-decomposing ability (*81,82*). These results provide additional evidence that bacterial proliferation and not just enzyme induction is involved in the development of herbicide-degrading populations of soil bacteria (*81*). However, the results do not support or contradict either the mutation hypothesis or the enzyme-induction hypothesis for the origin of the active organisms.

Enrichment populations of bacteria that develop in soil in response to a particular phenoxyacetic acid substrate are often adapted to degrade other phenoxyacetic acid substrates (74,79–82,88). Soils perfused with 2,4-D until degradation was complete rapidly detoxicated MCPA and vice versa (79,80,88). Both MCPA- and 2,4-D-treated soils degraded 4-CPA, while 4-CPA-treated soil degraded 2,4-D and MCPA (88). In all cases the rate of degradation of the second molecule was slower than its rate of degradation in soil in which it had induced its own enrichment microflora. Audus (79–82) postulated that 2,4-D and MCPA each induced their own specific degradation enzymes, either in the same bacterial species or in different species, and that these enzymes could incidentally degrade the other molecule. The efficiency of degradation was greatest, in each case, with the substrate that induced the formation of the enzymes. The observation that 2,4,5-T was degraded in soil enriched with MCPA, but not in soil enriched with 2,4-D, confirmed that two distinct enzyme systems were induced by 2,4-D and MCPA (80–82).

Patterns of "cross-adaptation" in soils treated with phenoxyacetic acids were extensively studied by Brownbridge (see Refs. 81 and 82). The most striking feature of the experiments was the ability of MCPA-enriched soil to rapidly degrade all phenoxyacetic acids supplied to it. Degradation was often as rapid in the MCPA-enriched soils as in soils enriched with the test compound itself. The degradation of 2,5-dichlorophenoxyacetic acid (2,5-D) was more rapid in MCPA-enriched soil than in 2,5-D-enriched soil. The MCPA-enriched soil readily degraded 2-CPA, which was unable to induce its own enrichment microflora when perfused through soil for almost 1 year. Soils perfused with 2,4-D were less efficient than the MCPA-enriched soils in degrading other phenoxyacetic acids. Thus, replacement of the 2-chlorine in the 2,4-D molecule with a methyl group had two consequences: It increased the lag phase in the development of an enrichment population (79–82), but once the MCPA enrichment population had developed, it had a greater ability to metabolize other phenoxyacetic acids than the 2,4-D enrichment population. Brownbridge (in Refs. 81 and 82) suggested that high activation energies were required for enzymatic attack on 2-methyl-substituted molecules. An enzyme generating these energies could therefore act on homologous molecules requiring similar or smaller energies.

The ability to metabolize more than one phenoxyacetic acid is common among bacteria isolated from 2,4-D or MCPA enrichment cultures (Table 1-2). Metabolism of the phenoxyacetic acids was demonstrated in growth

experiments (*87, 90, 95, 96, 99*), in experiments with resting cells grown on
2,4-D or MCPA (*87–91,97*), or in experiments with cell-free extracts (*98,
99*). The 2,4-D-decomposing bacteria generally degraded 4-CPA, 2-CPA,
and MCPA (*87–91, 97,98*), in agreement with the soil-perfusion results of
Brownbridge (in Refs. *81* and *82*), except for the metabolism of 2-CPA.
However, 2-CPA metabolism by the isolated bacteria was often slow in
comparison with the degradation of 2,4-D, 4-CPA, and MCPA (*89,91,97*).
Phenoxyacetic acid and 2,4,5-T were also commonly oxidized by 2,4-D-
decomposing bacteria (*87,90,91,97*), but the consumption of oxygen during
the metabolism of these substrates was small. In the case of *Arthrobacter*
sp. metabolizing phenoxyacetic acid, the low oxygen uptake was due to
incomplete degradation of the molecule, which was metabolized only to
the corresponding phenol (*97*). The MCPA-decomposing *Achromobacter*
strain of Steenson and Walker (*88,89*) degraded 2,4-D, 2-CPA, 4-CPA,
2,4-dibromophenoxyacetic acid, and 4-bromo-2-chlorophenoxyacetic acid,
but if it was grown on 2,4-D instead of MCPA, it lost the ability to degrade
MCPA. This result agrees with the conclusion of Audus (*79–82*) that
different enzyme systems are responsible for the degradation of 2,4-D and
MCPA.

The oxidation of 2-hydroxy-4-chlorophenoxyacetic acid (2-OH-4-CPA)
and 6-hydroxy-2,4-dichlorophenoxyacetic acid (6-OH-2,4-D) by strains of
Achromobacter that degraded 4-CPA and 2,4-D, respectively (*88,91*), is of
particular interest, since these hydroxy acids were proposed as intermediates
in the bacterial degradation of 4-CPA and 2,4-D (*84*). The significance of
these results and of the oxidation of phenols and catechols that might be
intermediates in the breakdown of 4-CPA, 2,4-D, and MCPA is discussed
in the following section.

Steenson and Walker (*108*) investigated the induction of 2,4-D- and
MCPA-degrading enzymes in *Flavobacterium peregrinum* and *Achromobacter* sp. *Flavobacterium peregrinum* was adapted to metabolize 2,4-D when
grown on 2,4-D or MCPA but it did not decompose MCPA. MCPA was
therefore an inducer but not a substrate of the 2,4-D-degrading enzyme
system. Enzyme induction by compounds that are not substrates of the
enzymes they induce is well known in bacteria (see Ref. *109*). In the *Achromobacter*, 2,4-dichlorophenol and 4-chloro-2-methylphenol were inducers
of both the 2,4-D- and MCPA-degrading enzyme systems. These phenols
are probably early intermediates in the degradation of 2,4-D and MCPA,
respectively, by the bacterium (*89*). Induction of the *Achromobacter*
MCPA- and 2,4-D-degrading enzymes therefore appears to resemble the
induction of the tryptophan-degrading enzymes of *Pseudomonas fluorescens*,

for which kynurenin, an early intermediate in the breakdown of tryptophan, is the inducer (*110*).

3. Degradation Pathways

There appear to be two main pathways for the microbial degradation of phenoxyacetic acids, namely, degradation via a hydroxyphenoxyacetic acid intermediate and degradation via the corresponding phenol. The degradation of phenoxyacetic acids via hydroxyphenoxyacetic acids was first reported by Evans and Smith (*84*). Cultures of a soil pseudomonad growing on 4-CPA accumulated 2-OH-4-CPA and 4-chlorocatechol as

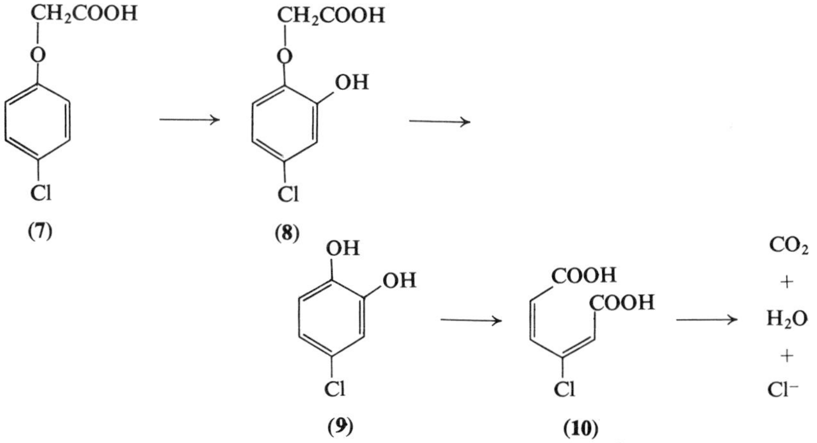

Fig. 1-4. Microbial degradation of 4-CPA (**7**) via 2-OH-4-CPA (**8**), 4-chlorocatechol (**9**), and β-chloromuconic acid (**10**). [After (*83*).]

breakdown products; these metabolites satisfied the criteria of simultaneous adaptation (*111*) when supplied as substrates to cells grown on 4-CPA. A second pseudomonad growing on 2,4-D produced an unidentified phenolic acid which gave similar color reactions to 2-OH-4-CPA. Evans and Smith (*84*) suggested that the phenolic acid metabolite produced from 2,4-D was 6-OH-2,4-D.

The breakdown of 4-CPA was further investigated by Evans and Moss (*86*), who showed the formation of β-chloromuconic acid in pseudomonad cultures. Suspensions of 4-CPA-grown cells also produced β-chloromuconic acid from 4-chlorocatechol. Figure 1-4 shows the pathway that was proposed for 4-CPA breakdown by the bacterium (*83,86*). The 4-CPA-decomposing *Achromobacter* strain of Steenson and Walker (*88*) oxidized 2-OH-4-CPA and 4-chlorocatechol without a lag when grown on 4-CPA, suggesting that the same pathway for 4-CPA breakdown might be operating in this organism.

The suggestion that 2,4-D is degraded via 6-OH-2,4-D has not been confirmed. The phenolic acid metabolite of Evans and Smith (*84*) was apparently not 6-OH-2,4-D (*83,112*). Nevertheless, a 2,4-D-breakdown pathway involving the production of 6-OH-2,4-D as an intermediate has been proposed (*82,91*). According to this pathway, the 6-OH-2,4-D is degraded via 3,5-dichlorocatechol and α-chloromuconic acid. Both of these compounds, as well as 2,4-dichlorophenol, were detected in *Pseudomonas* cultures growing on 2,4-D (*83,85,114*). However, Evans (*83*) suggested that *Pseudomonas* converted 2,4-D to 3,5-dichlorocatechol via 2,4-dichlorophenol (see Fig. 1-6, pathway A) rather than via 6-OH-2,4-D. The *Achromobacter* sp. studied by Bell (*91*), when grown on 2,4-D, oxidized 6-OH-2,4-D without a lag, but it also metabolized both 2,4-dichlorophenol and 3,5-dichlorocatechol. Bell (*91*) was therefore unable to decide on the probable pathway of 2,4-D breakdown in this organism. The breakdown of 2,4-D via 6-OH-2,4-D still requires proof.

Cultures of an unidentified gram-negative organism produced, during growth on MCPA, α-methyl-γ-carboxymethylene-Δ^α-butenolide, 2-methyl-4-chlorophenol (5-chloro-*o*-cresol), and an unidentified phenolic acid that had a molecular weight of 216 and contained one halogen substituent (*102*). Gaunt and Evans (*102*) suggested that the phenolic acid was 6-OH-MCPA. The pathway shown in Fig. 1-5 was proposed for MCPA breakdown by the bacterium. This pathway does not include 4-chloro-2-methylphenol as an intermediate. However, it seems possible that the bacterium might convert MCPA to 5-chloro-3-methylcatechol via either 6-OH-MCPA or 4-chloro-2-methylphenol. The possibility that a phenoxyacetic acid might be degraded by more than one pathway in the same organism has been suggested by Audus (*82*).

Aspergillus niger hydroxylates phenoxyacetic acids without metabolizing the resulting hydroxy acids (*40,103–107*). Phenoxyacetic acid is converted to 2-, 3-, or 4-hydroxyphenoxyacetic acid (*103,106,107*); 4-CPA to 2- or 3-hydroxy-4-chlorophenoxyacetic acid; and 2-CPA to 3-, 4-, 5-, or 6-hydroxy-2-chlorophenoxyacetic acid (*104*). With 2-CPA, the chlorine can be replaced by a hydroxyl group to give 2-hydroxyphenoxyacetic acid (*104*). The fungus hydroxylates 2,4-D and MCPA in the 5 position, but 2,4-D is also metabolized by 4 hydroxylation coupled with a chlorine shift to 2,5-dichloro-4-hydroxyphenoxyacetic acid (*40,105*). This mechanism of 2,4-D metabolism is also found in higher plants.

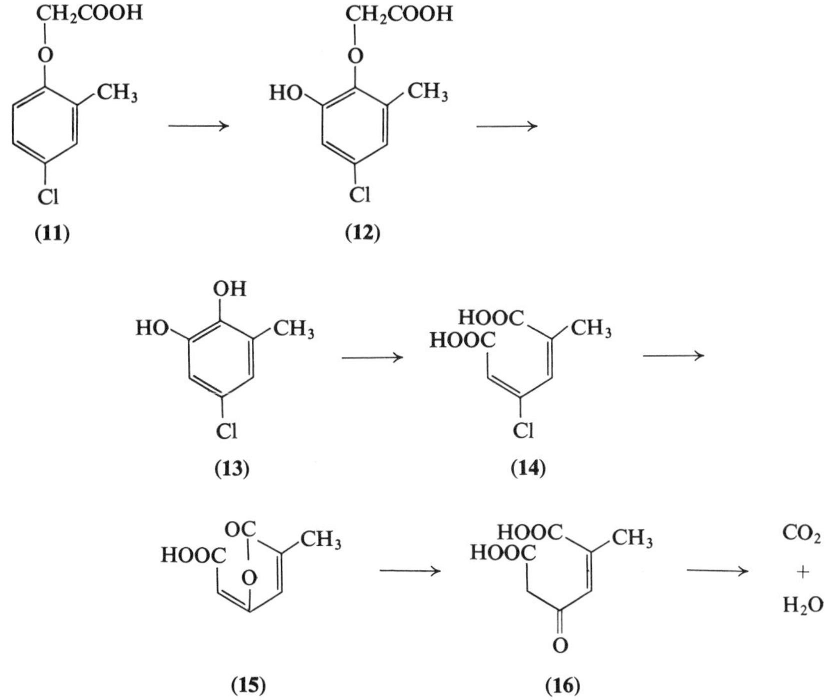

Fig. 1-5. Microbial degradation of MCPA (11) via 6-OH-MCPA (12), 5-chloro-3-methylcatechol (13), α-methyl-γ-chloromuconic acid (14), α-methyl-γ-carboxymethylene-Δ^{α}-butenolide (15), and α-methylmaleylacetic acid (16).

Degradation of phenoxyacetic acids via the corresponding phenols was first proposed by Audus (80). Soil containing an active 2,4-D-decomposing microflora metabolized 2,4-dichlorophenol without a lag, whereas soil not previously treated with 2,4-D decomposed 2,4-dichlorophenol only after a long lag period. According to the sequential induction (simultaneous adaptation) hypothesis of Stanier (111), these results suggested that 2,4-dichlorophenol was an intermediate in 2,4-D degradation by soil microorganisms. Subsequent sequential induction studies with an *Achromobacter* strain suggested the degradation of 2,4-D via 2,4-dichlorophenol and 4-chlorocatechol, of 4-CPA via 4-chlorophenol and 4-chlorocatechol, and of MCPA via 2-methyl-4-chlorophenol (89). The proposed pathways are indicated in Fig. 1-6 (pathways B, C, and D). Audus (82) has summarized other circumstantial evidence suggesting degradation of 2,4-D via 2,4-dichlorophenol. The formation of 2,4-dichlorophenol from 2,4-D by strains of *Pseudomonas*, *Achromobacter*, and *Nocardia* was reported by Evans and his colleagues (*83,85,114*), Bell (*90*), and Symonds (see Ref. *82*), respectively, but none of these workers established that the 2,4-dichlorophenol was a major intermediate in 2,4-D breakdown.

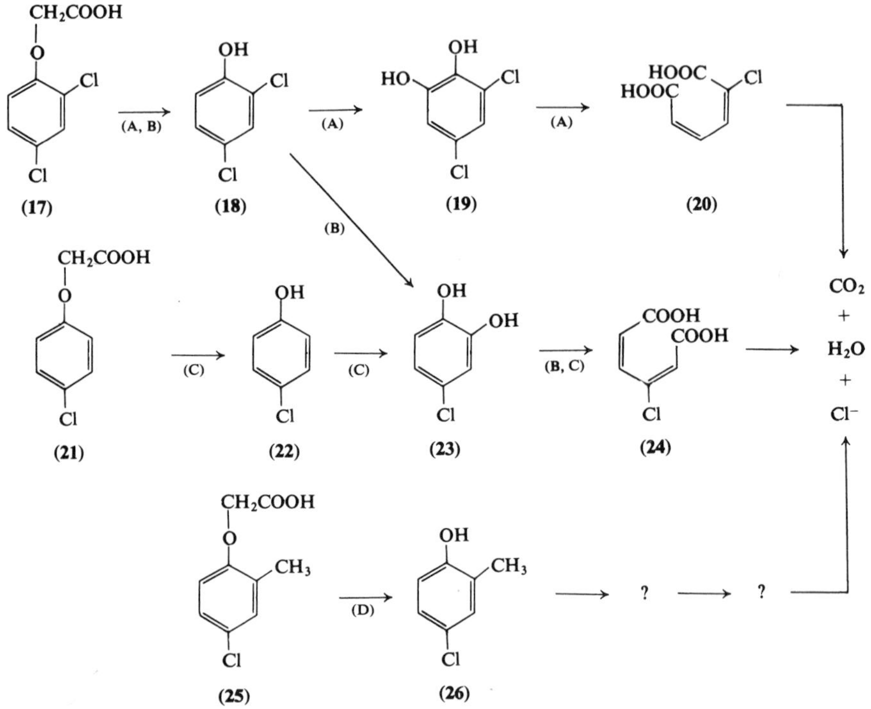

Fig. 1-6. Microbial degradation of phenoxyacetic acids via the corresponding phenols. (A) 2,4-D (**17**) degradation via 2,4-dichlorophenol (**18**), 3,5-dichlorocatechol (**19**), and α-chloromuconic acid (**20**); (B) 2,4-D degradation via 2,4-dichlorophenol, 4-chlorocatechol (**23**), and β-chloromuconic acid (**24**); (C) 4-CPA (**21**) degradation via 4-chlorophenol (**22**), 4-chlorocatechol, and β-chloromuconic acid; and (D) MCPA (**25**) degradation via 2-methyl-4-chlorophenol (**26**). [After (*83,89*).]

Recent studies with an *Arthrobacter* species (*97–99,115*) have confirmed the breakdown of 2,4-D and other phenoxyacetic acids via their corresponding phenols. Resting cells of the bacterium grown on 2,4-D completely degraded 2,4-D, 2-CPA, 4-CPA, and the corresponding chlorophenols, but phenoxyacetic acid and 4-hydroxyphenoxyacetic acid (4-OH-PA) were quantitatively converted to phenol and hydroquinone, respectively, which were not metabolized (97). None of the phenoxyacetic acids was metabolized by cells grown in the absence of 2,4-D. The results with phenoxyactic acid and 4-OH-PA demonstrate that growth of the organism on 2,4-D induced the formation of an enzyme or enzymes that catalyze the conversion of phenoxyacetic acids to their corresponding phenols. The formation of 2,4-dichlorophenol was subsequently demonstrated in cultures growing on 2,4-D (115).

An enzyme preparation isolated from the 2,4-D-grown *Arthrobacter* produced 2,4-dichloro-, 2-, and 4-chlorophenol during the metabolism of 2,4-D, 2-CPA, and 4-CPA, respectively (98). Fractionation of the preparation yielded an NADPH-requiring enzyme that converted the chlorophenols to catechols, 2,4-dichlorophenol being converted to 3,5-dichlorocatechol (116). The breakdown pathway for 2,4-D suggested by Evans (83) was thus confirmed (Fig. 1-6, pathway A). The products of 3,5-dichlorocatechol degradation in the *Arthrobacter* remain to be determined, but α-chloro-muconic acid is a probable product (85). The *Arthrobacter* enzymes also degraded MCPA and an enzyme converting MCPA to 2-methyl-4-chloro-phenol (Fig. 1-6, pathway D) was isolated (98,99).

Bell (91) suggested that 2,4-dichloroanisole (see Fig. 1-1) might be an intermediate in the bacterial conversion of 2,4-D to 2,4-dichlorophenol. *Arthrobacter* cultures growing on 2,4-D produced small amounts of 2,4-dichloroanisole (115), but the molecule was not metabolized at a significant rate by enzyme preparations that actively degraded 2,4-D (98). In addition, 2,4-D-grown *Arthrobacter* cells, that metabolized 4-OH-PA to hydroquinone, failed to form hydroquinone during the metabolism of 4- hydroxy-anisole (115). Similarly, cell extracts of *Arthrobacter* and *Flavobacterium peregrinum*, cultured on MCPA, did not metabolize 2-methyl-4-chloro-anisole (99). These results indicate that the degradation of phenoxyacetic acids to the corresponding phenols by the *Arthrobacter* does not involve the formation of the corresponding anisoles. The first step in the degradation of phenoxyacetic acids in this organism is not decarboxylation of the phenoxyacetic acid side chain.

A mechanistic approach to phenoxyacetate degradation was taken by Helling et al. (118). Phenoxy-^{18}O-acetic acid was metabolized to phenol-^{18}O by resting cells and cell-free extracts of an MCPA-grown *Arthrobacter* sp. (99). The complete conversion and quantitative retention of ^{18}O in the phenol demonstrated that bond cleavage occurred between the aliphatic side chain and the ether–oxygen atom (Fig 1-7). Prior oxidation of the methylene carbon, yielding a hemiacetal or a phenyl ester, was suggested as preceding ether cleavage in the oxygen-requiring breakdown.

Audus (*82*) proposed alternative pathways for the breakdown of 2,4-D, involving the formation of chlorohydroquinone or a monochlorophenol and phenol. These compounds were detected by gas chromatography among the volatile metabolites produced by a *Nocardia* species growing on 2,4-D. The degradation of 2,4-D by these alternative pathways requires confirmation. The production of phytotoxic metabolites of unknown identity during 2,4-D degradation by *Arthrobacter globiformis* was also reported (*117*).

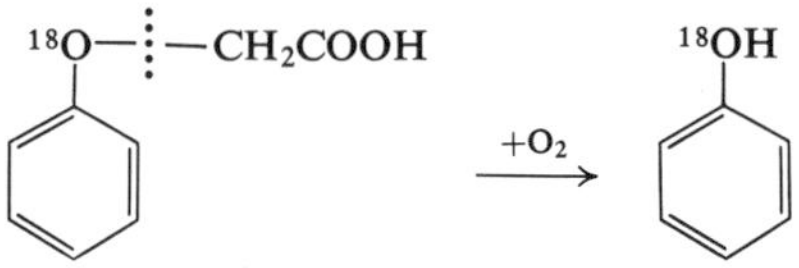

$$^{18}O-\vdots-CH_2COOH \qquad\qquad ^{18}OH$$

$$\xrightarrow{+O_2}$$

Fig. 1-7. Ether–oxygen bond cleavage in phenoxyacetic acid by *Arthrobacter* sp. (*118*).

4. Resistance to Microbial Degradation

In the early soil-perfusion experiments of Audus (*79*), 2,4-D, MCPA, and 2,4,5-T were detoxified in 14, 70, and 270 days, respectively. Such results indicate that phenoxyacetic acids differ greatly in their resistance to attack by the soil microflora.

Extensive studies have been conducted to determine the effect of molecular structure on the breakdown of phenoxyacetic acids in soil (*81,82,119,120*). The following effects of ring substitution on the degradation of the phenoxyacetic acid molecule were reported by Audus (*81,82*):

1. Chlorine substitution in the para position made the molecule much more labile. Thus, 4-CPA, at a concentration of 100 ppm, was 80% detoxified in 12.1 days, compared to 34.5 days for phenoxyacetic acid.

2. Chlorine substitution in the ortho position deactivated the molecule, so that 2-CPA was not degraded in 1 year.

3. Meta substitution also deactivated the molecule, but 10 ppm of 3-chlorophenoxyacetic acid was detoxified in about 60 days.

4. In the di- and trichlorophenoxyacetic acids the activating effect of the 4 substitution largely overcame the deactivating effect of other substituents. In contrast to 2-CPA, 2,4-D was rapidly detoxified (16.0 days), while 2,4,5-T was more easily degraded than 2,5-D. None of the phenoxyacetic acids with a *m*-chlorine in the molecule was rapidly degraded, however.

5. The methyl group was more deactivating than the chloro group. The periods required for 80% detoxication of 100-ppm MCPA and 2,4-

dimethylphenoxyacetic acid were 85.7 and 102.5 days, respectively, compared with 16.0 days for 2,4-D.

A similar pattern of resistance to degradation was observed by Alexander and his collaborators (119,120), who particularly emphasized the high degree of resistance of phenoxyacetic acids with a *m*-chlorine substituent. Such molecules were termed "recalcitrant" (121–123). The recalcitrance of certain side-chain-substituted phenoxyacetic acids, i.e., α-phenoxyalkanoic acids with three or more carbons in the side chain, will be discussed later.

1-3. DEGRADATION OF HIGHER PHENOXYALKANOIC ACIDS

A. Degradation in Plants

Higher phenoxyalkanoic acids in the present context are phenoxyalkanoic acids with a side chain containing more than two carbon atoms. Two groups of herbicides fall in this category, namely, α-phenoxyalkanoic acids and ω-phenoxyalkanoic acids. In the former group, several substituted 2-phenoxypropionic acids are important herbicides (Table 1-1). Their slow degradation in big leaf maple (26), prickly pear (30) and *Galium aparine* (22) has been discussed earlier.

Degradation of the ω-phenoxyalkanoic acids has been the subject of intense investigation, especially by Wain and his colleagues (3,4,124,125), who demonstrated the role of β oxidation in the metabolism of these compounds in plants. This work, and the significance of β oxidation in the selective chemical control of weeds, has been reviewed by Wain (126–129) and Fawcett et al. (130). Linscott (131) has also discussed the β oxidation of phenoxyalkanoic acids in plants.

1. β Oxidation and Growth-Regulating Activity of ω-Phenoxyalkanoic Acids

Synerholm and Zimmerman (132) first obtained evidence that plants metabolized ω-phenoxyalkanoic acids by β oxidation of the side chain. In a study of the growth-regulating activities of the homologous series of 2,4-dichlorophenoxyalkanoic acids from the acetic to the caprylic acid, they found that only the 2,4-dichlorophenoxy acids with an even number of carbon atoms in the side chain were active on tomato. They postulated that only the 2,4-dichlorophenoxyacetic acid was active per se and that the butyric, caproic, and caprylic acids owed their activity to their β oxidation in the plant to the acetic acid homolog. The acids with an odd number of carbon atoms in the side chain would be converted to the half-ester of 2,4-dichlorophenol with carbonic acid. This compound would decompose to CO_2 and 2,4-dichlorophenol, which is inactive as a growth regulator (133). The scheme proposed for the β oxidation of the two goups of 2,4-dichlorophenoxyalkanoic acids is shown in Fig. 1-8.

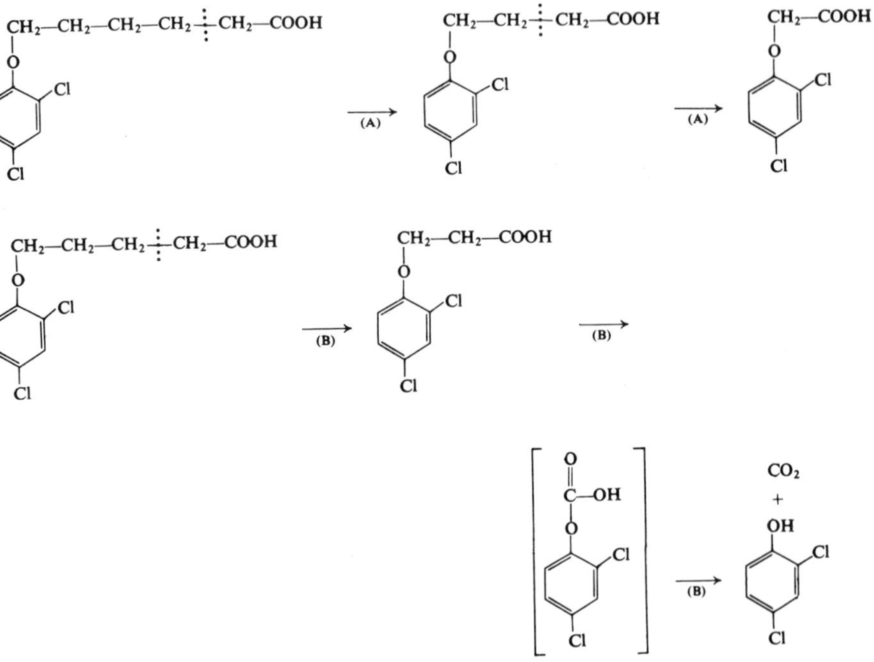

Fig. 1-8. β Oxidation of 2,4-dichlorophenoxyalkanoic acids in plants. (A) Formation of 2,4-D from acids with an even number of carbons in the side chain and (B) formation of 2,4-dichlorophenol from acids with an odd number of carbons in the side chain. [After (132).]

The formation of phenoxyacetic acids from higher ω-phenoxyalkanoic acids with an even number of carbons in the side chain and of phenols from ω-phenoxyalkanoic acids with an odd number of carbons in the side chain was demonstrated by chemical and chromatographic procedures, for example, in flax seedlings metabolizing unsubstituted phenoxyalkanoic acids (124), wheat and pea tissue metabolizing 2,4-dichlorophenoxyalkanoic acids (3), and wheat tissue metabolizing 2,4,5-trichlorophenoxyalkanoic acids (125). However, flax seedlings metabolizing 10-phenoxy-n-decanoic acid (9-phenoxynonane-1-carboxylic acid) unexpectedly produced considerable amounts of phenol (124). Fawcett et al. (124) proposed that the phenoxydecanoic acid side chain was degraded by ω oxidation as well as by β oxidation.

Pea tissue failed to produce 2,5-D and 2,4,5-T when treated with higher homologs with an even number of carbons in the side chain (4,125). Paper ionophoresis and bioassay with wheat coleoptile cylinders showed that 2,5-dichlorophenoxycaproic acid was β-oxidized by the pea only to the butyric acid stage (4). The ability of certain substituents on the phenoxy ring to block β oxidation of the aliphatic acid side chain had a profound influence on the growth-regulating activity of ω-phenoxyalkanoic acids in pea (4,125).

The relationship between growth-regulating activity and β oxidation among ω-phenoxyalkanoic acids was extensively investigated by Wain and his colleagues (3,4,124,125). The most comprehensive study was that of Fawcett et al. (4), who included 18 homologous series of phenoxyalkanoic acids and three test plants in their investigations. The 18 series of phenoxyalkanoic acids had no substituents or different combinations of chlorine and methyl substituents on the phenoxy ring. With all series the pattern of growth-regulating activity on the test plants could be explained in terms of β oxidation of the phenoxyaliphatic acid side chain. The comprehensive study (4) confirmed the results of earlier studies (3,124,125) and indicated additional conclusions.

Four response patterns were observed in wheat cylinder and pea curvature or pea segment tests with the 18 series of phenoxyaliphatic acids (4). These response patterns and the β-oxidation reactions which were proposed to explain them are indicated in Table 1-3. Type 1 and 3 responses are obtained where β oxidation results in the production of the acetic or propionic acid homolog. If only the acetic acid homolog is active as a growth regulator, a type 1 response is observed; if both the acetic and propionic acid homologs are active, a type 3 response results. The wheat cylinder tests gave type 1 responses with all the phenoxy aliphatic acids tested, except the unsubstituted series and the 2-chloro series, which produced type 3 responses. In wheat tests, none of the combinations of substituents on the phenoxy ring prevented β oxidation of the long-chain phenoxyaliphatic acids to the active phenoxyacetic or phenoxypropionic acid.

In pea tests, type 1, 2, and 4 responses were observed, depending on the combination of substituents on the phenoxy ring. In the type 2 and 4

TABLE 1-3

Plant-Growth Responses to Homologous Series of Phenoxyalkanoic
Acids and β-Oxidation Reactions Causing the Responses[a]

Response type	Plant response to homologs[b]	β-Oxidation reactions in plant[b]
1	H C[c] V B[c] P A[c]	H C V B P A[d]
2	H C V B P A[c]	H C V B P A[d]
3	H[c] C[c] V[c] B[c] P[c] A[c]	H C V B P[d] A[d]
4	H[c] C V[c] B P[c] A[c]	H C V B P[d] A[d]

[a] Compiled from Ref. 4.

[b] H, C, V, B, P, and A: heptanoic, caproic, valeric, butyric, propionic and acetic homologs, respectively.

[c] Positive response of test plant; other homologs gave no growth responses.

[d] Active as plant growth regulator per se.

responses, β oxidation of the long-chain phenoxyaliphatic acids appears to be inhibited at the butyric acid or propionic acid stage. If the acetic but not the propionic acid homolog is a growth regulator for pea, a type 2 response results; if both the acetic and propionic homologs are active, then a type 4 response is produced.

The various combinations of substituents on the phenoxy ring produced types 1, 2, and 4 responses in pea tests as follows (4):

Type 1	Type 2	Type 4
3-Chloro-	2,5-Dichloro-	Unsubstituted
4-Chloro-	2,3,4-Trichloro-	2-Chloro-
3,4-Dichloro-	2,4,5-Trichloro-	2,3-Dichloro-
2,4-Dichloro-	2-Chloro-5-methyl-	
3-Chloro-4-methyl-	5-Chloro-2-methyl-	
4-Chloro-2-methyl-	2,4-Dichloro-5-methyl-	
4-Chloro-3-methyl-	2,5-Dichloro-4-methyl-	
	4,5-Dichloro-2-methyl-	

Thus, the homologous series with an *o*-chloro or *o*-methyl substituent group on the phenoxy ring usually produced a type 2 or 4 response, indicating that these substituent groups hindered β oxidation of long-chain phenoxy-aliphatic acids at the butyric or propionic acid stage. However, the blocking effect of the *o*-chloro and *o*-methyl substituents was eliminated by the introduction of a chlorine atom in the para position, provided there was no additional chlorine or methyl substituent in the meta position. Fawcett et al. (*4*) concluded that both steric and electronic effects of the substituent groups were involved in the hindering of β oxidation of the phenoxy-aliphatic acid side chain. Type 1 responses were produced by substituent combinations that did not hinder β oxidation. The unsubstituted phenoxy-aliphatic acids, which had no substituents to hinder β oxidation, unexpectedly showed a type 4 response. However, in this series the activity of the acetic acid homolog was low and it was assumed that too little phenoxy-acetic acid was produced by β oxidation of the caproic and butyric homologs to give a growth response.

The responses of tomato to the various substituted phenoxyaliphatic acids were in most cases similar to those of pea (*4*).

The sequence of reactions involved in the β oxidation of aliphatic acids is indicated in Fig. 1-9. A key intermediate in the breakdown sequence is the β-hydroxyaliphatic acid–coenzyme A thioester. In the hindered β oxidation of phenoxybutyric acids in pea, the oxidation sequence appears

$$R—CH_2—CH_2—CH_2—COOH \xrightarrow[\text{(ATP)}]{+HS–CoA} R—CH_2—CH_2—CH_2—CO—S—CoA \xrightarrow[\text{(FAD)}]{-2H}$$

$$R—CH_2—CH=CH—CO—S—CoA \xrightarrow{+H_2O} R—CH_2—\overset{\text{OH}}{\underset{|}{CH}}—CH_2—CO—S—CoA \xrightarrow[\text{(NAD}^+)]{-2H}$$

$$R—CH_2—CO \vdots CH_2—CO—S—CoA \xrightarrow[\text{(HS–CoA)}]{} R—CH_2—COOH + CH_3—CO—S—CoA$$

Fig. 1-9. β Oxidation of unsubstituted and substituted aliphatic acids. Cofactors: HS–CoA, coenzyme A; ATP, adenosine triphosphate; FAD, flavin adenine dinucleotide; and NAD$^+$, nicotinamide adenine dinucleotide. [After (*131*).]

to be blocked after the formation of the β-hydroxyphenoxybutyric acid derivative. Thus, Fawcett et al. (*4*) obtained evidence that 2,5-dichloro-phenoxybutyric acid was converted in pea to its β-hydroxy derivative, but the β-hydroxy-2,5-dichlorophenoxybutyric acid was not metabolized by pea tissue to 2,5-D. Wheat tissue, on the other hand, carried out this conversion. Both wheat and pea tissue metabolized β-hydroxy-2,4-dichloro-phenoxybutyric acid to 2,4-D.

Recently, gas chromatography has been used to demonstrate the β oxidation of phenoxybutyric acid herbicides in plants, for example, the conversion of 2,4,5-TB to 2,4,5-T in wheat but not in peas (134), MCPB to MCPA in beans (135), and 2,4-DB to 2,4-D in big leaf maple (136), timothy grass, birdsfoot trefoil, and peas (137). In all these studies the conversion was demonstrated where herbicide was applied externally to intact plants, in contrast to many of the earlier chemical studies (3,4,125) where plant segments were used and absorption and translocation of the herbicide played no role. In the 2,4-DB experiments with pea, the plants were grown under sterile conditions to exclude the possibility of β oxidation by micro-organisms on the plant surface (137). The work of Norris and Freed (136) and Fertig et al. (137) demonstrates the application of gas chromatography to quantitative studies of β oxidation.

Unsubstituted phenoxyalkanoic acids undergo ring hydroxylation as well as β oxidation in the tissues of certain plants (4,35). The hydroxylation of the ring may precede (4) or follow (35) the β oxidation of the phenoxy-alkanoic acid side chain.

2. Significance of β Oxidation for Weed Control

The inability of pea and tomato β-oxidizing enzymes to convert certain phenoxyalkanoic acids with an even number of side-chain carbons to the acetic acid homolog suggested to Wain (126,127) a new approach to the selective control of weeds. A long-chain substituted phenoxyalkanoic acid could be used for weed control in a crop if the weeds, but not the crop, could metabolize it by β oxidation to the corresponding phenoxyacetic acid. Several phenoxybutyric acids, such as MCPB, 2,4-DB, and 2,4,5-TB, can be used in this way. For example, MCPB and 2,4-DB are active against the annual nettle and creeping thistle, which can β-oxidize them, but not against celery and clover where β oxidation is apparently hindered (126,127). Other weeds killed by MCPB and 2,4-DB are fumitory, fat hen, and charlock, whereas carrots, parsnips, flax, and alfalfa are relatively resistant to these two herbicides (127). Wain (127) noted that MCPB and 2,4-DB appeared to be better weed killers than 2,4,5-TB.

The resistance of clovers and alfalfa to MCPB, 2,4-DB, and 2,4,5-TB was confirmed by Shaw and Gentner (138), who also showed 2,4,5-TB resistance in rape, flax, soybeans, and sweet clover, which are highly susceptible to 2,4,5-T. The use of 2,4-DB, MCPB, and 2,4,5-TB was sug-gested for weed control in cereals underseeded by certain forage legumes

(*126,127,138*), in pure stands of forage legumes, in forage legume seed-production fields, in flax, in tolerant crops (such as corn or rice) grown in the vicinity of crops (such as cotton and grapes) which are highly susceptible to the phenoxyacetic and α-phenoxypropionic acid herbicides, and in certain other weed-crop situations (*138*). It was emphasized, however, that the susceptibility of plants to phenoxybutyric acid herbicides is dependent not only on β oxidation, but also on penetration of the herbicide into the plant, its translocation in the plant to the loci of activity, and the susceptibility of the plant to the phenoxyacetic acid formed by β oxidation (*126,127, 138*).

3. ω Oxidation

Fawcett et al. (*124*), in their chemical studies of β oxidation, found that 10-phenoxy-*n*-decanoic acid unexpectedly produced large amounts of phenol during its breakdown in flax seedlings. Other phenoxyalkanoic acids with an even number of side-chain carbons produced little or no phenol. It was proposed that the 10-phenoxy-*n*-decanoic acid was broken down by ω oxidation as well as by β oxidation. The proposed ω-oxidation pathway is indicated in Fig. 1-10.

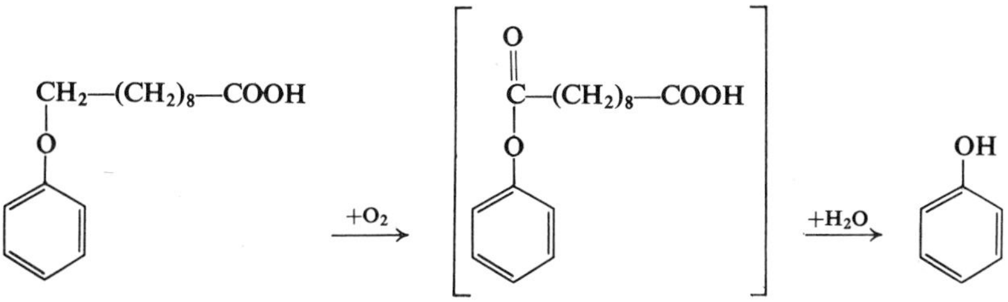

Fig. 1-10. ω Oxidation of 10-phenoxy-*n*-decanoic acid in flax. [After (*124*).]

4. 2,4-DB Degradation in Silage

Linscott and his colleagues (*131,139,140*) studied the degradation of ^{14}C-carboxyl-labeled 2,4-DB in forage plants "ensiled" on a laboratory scale. Loss of radioactivity from the silage indicated the extent of degradation. Silage prepared from alfalfa, birdsfoot trefoil, timothy, orchard grass, or bromegrass lost about 30–60% of the applied radioactivity in 1 to 3 months. The three grass silages decomposed 2,4-D and silvex to about the same extent as 2,4-DB. Most of the ^{14}C loss from the 2,4-DB-treated alfalfa silage occurred within the first 15 days, and considerable losses occurred during the first 8 hours. It was not known whether the plant enzymes or micro-organisms in the silage were responsible for the 2,4-DB degradation, but the rapid breakdown in the early stages of the silage fermentation suggested that the degradation was mainly an aerobic process. However, losses of radioactivity still continued when conditions were almost certainly highly anaerobic. The pathway of degradation of the 2,4-DB was not investigated.

B. Degradation by Microorganisms

Wain (*126,127*), in his early reviews, suggested that soil microorganisms probably β-oxidized ω-phenoxyalkanoic acids in a manner similar to plants. However, the postulated conversion in soil of phenoxybutyric acids to biologically active phenoxyacetic acids was not detrimental to crop plants. The lack of a detrimental effect was ascribed to the low-volume applications of phenoxybutyric acids used in weed control (*126,127*).

It is now known that ω-phenoxyalkanoic acids are β-oxidized by soil microorganisms, including species of *Nocardia* (*141,144*), *Pseudomonas* and *Micrococcus* (*144*), and the fungus *Aspergillus niger* (103). *A. niger* also hydroxylates the phenoxyalkanoic acid ring (*103*). An alternative mechanism for the degradation of ω-phenoxyalkanoic acids, namely, cleavage of the molecule at the ether linkage, was observed in a *Flavobacterium* species (*145,146*).

The mechanisms of degradation of α-phenoxyalkanoic acids are unknown, although certain of these compounds are degraded in soil (*119, 120*). A strain of *Streptomyces viridochromogenes* isolated from soil-detoxified silvex (*101*).

1. β Oxidation

According to the evidence presently available (*141–144*), soil bacteria β-oxidize ω-phenoxyalkanoic acids in the same way as plants (Fig. 1-8). Substituents on the phenoxy ring that hinder β oxidation in plants also tend to hinder β oxidation in microorganisms, for example, an *o*-chloro or *o*-methyl group (*142,144*). In agreement with the plant studies (*4*), the hindrance appeared to be reduced in the case of *Nocardia coeliaca* by the introduction of a 4-chloro group into the 2-chlorophenoxyalkanoic acid molecule (*144*). By contrast, *Nocardia opaca* β-oxidized MCPB with greater difficulty than 2-methylphenoxybutyric acid, and 3,4-dichlorophenoxy-butyric acid with greater difficulty than either 3- or 4-chlorophenoxybutyric acid, indicating a greater hindrance to β oxidation by disubstitution than by monosubstitution (*142*). The introduction of a methyl substituent group on the γ carbon of phenoxybutyric acid or MCPB considerably retarded β oxidation of these compounds by *N. opaca*; however, lengthening the side chain of the methyl-substituted MCPB to give ϵ-(2-methyl-4-chlorophenoxy)-ϵ-methylcaproic acid reduced the retarding effect of the methyl substitution (*143*). Lengthening of the side chain also facilitated the β oxidation of ω-phenoxyalkanoic acids by *N. coeliaca* (*144*). Phenoxyalkanoic acids with 10 or 11 carbons in the side chain appeared to undergo α oxidation as well as β oxidation in *N. coeliaca* (*144*). Thus, in the initial stage of side-chain oxidation they apparently lost one carbon atom instead of two, so that short-chain phenoxy acids that would not be produced by β oxidation alone were detected as metabolic products.

As indicated in Fig. 1-9, β-hydroxyacyl–coenzyme A thioesters are key intermediates in the β oxidation of aliphatic acids. The metabolism of phenoxybutyric acids to their corresponding β-hydroxy derivatives was demonstrated with *Nocardia opaca*, especially where ring substituent groups hindered β oxidation to the phenoxyacetic acids (*141,142*). Blockage of β oxidation in plants also appears to occur at the β-hydroxyphenoxybutyric acid stage.

Gutenmann et al. (*147*), using gas chromatography, showed that β oxidation of 2,4-dichlorophenoxyalkanoic acids occurred in a natural soil. The metabolism of 2,4-DB via 2,4-D was also indicated by the sequential induction technique (*148*). The degradation of higher phenoxyalkanoic acids by the mixed natural soil microflora was thus similar to their degradation by the pure cultures of soil bacteria studied by Webley et al. (*141–143*) and Taylor and Wain (*144*). However, the mixed population was able to further degrade the products of β oxidation, namely, 2,4-D and 2,4-dichlorophenol, so that these compounds did not accumulate in high concentrations. Gutenmann and Lisk (*149*) subsequently obtained evidence that the β oxidation of 2,4-DB in soil proceeded via the expected first intermediate, the unsaturated 2,4-dichlorophenoxycrotonic acid.

2. β Oxidation and Ring Hydroxylation

Aspergillus niger β-oxidized the side chain and hydroxylated the ring of 4-phenoxybutyric and 5-phenoxyvaleric acid to form 4-OH-PA and 3-(4-hydroxyphenoxy)propionic acid, respectively (*103*). These conversions resemble the metabolism of unsubstituted phenoxyalkanoic acids in certain higher plants (*4,35*). The fungus also produced small amounts of 2-hydroxyphenoxyacetic acid and 3-(2-hydroxyphenoxy)propionic acid from the phenoxybutyric and phenoxyvaleric acids, respectively (*103*).

3. Cleavage of the Ether Linkage

MacRae et al. (*145*) demonstrated that a 2,4-DB-decomposing *Flavobacterium* species (*120*) produced 2,4-dichlorophenol, 4-chlorocatechol, and butyric and crotonic acid when grown in the presence of 2,4-DB. These results suggested that the 2,4-DB was cleaved at the ether linkage and the products metabolized as shown in Fig. 1-11. In agreement with the ether cleavage hypothesis, the bacterium produced phenolic material and the expected unsubstituted aliphatic acids when incubated with ω-2,4-dichlorophenoxyalkanoic acids from the propionic to the undecanoic homolog

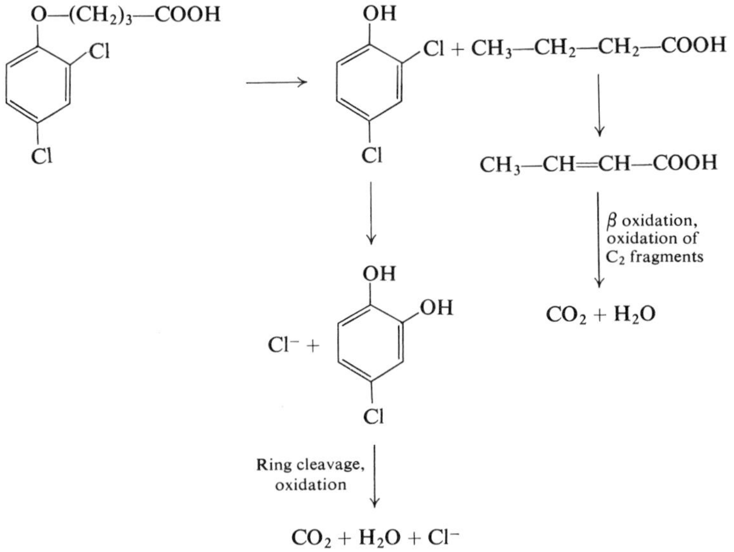

Fig. 1-11. 2,4-DB degradation by *Flavobacterium* sp., involving cleavage of the ether linkage. [After (*145*).]

(*146,150*). The cleavage of 2,4-DB at the ether linkage, unlike β oxidation, would lead to immediate detoxication of the herbicide. This detoxication was shown experimentally when alfalfa seed inoculated with the *Flavobacterium* was grown in 2,4-DB-treated sterilized soil (*151*). However, in nonsterilized soil, the inoculated organism could not establish itself well enough to effect a noticeable detoxication of the 2,4-DB.

4. Ring Cleavage

The results of Alexander and Aleem (*119*) show that the ring structure of several α- and ω-phenoxyalkanoic acids was lost during their degradation in soil. Loss of aromatic structure was indicated by disappearance of the ultraviolet absorption spectra of the compounds. Many or all of the compounds were probably metabolized prior to ring cleavage by the mechanisms outlined previously.

5. Resistance to Microbial Degradation

The effect of ring and side-chain substitution on the β oxidation of phenoxyalkanoic acids by two *Nocardia* species is discussed on p. 38. Alexander and co-workers (*119,120*) investigated the degradation of α- and ω-phenoxyalkanoic acids in soils and soil suspensions. The ω-phenoxypropionic and butyric acids with no meta substituent in the molecule were readily degraded, in many cases more rapidly than the corresponding phenoxyacetic acids. However, degradation of the α-phenoxypropionic, butyric, and valeric acids was retarded in comparison with the corresponding phenoxyacetic and ω-phenoxyalkanoic acids. When the side chain was lengthened to give the α-phenoxycaproic acids, the 4-chloro- and 2,4-dichloro-α-phenoxycaproic acids were readily degraded. In agreement with the observations on phenoxyacetic acid degradation, the meta-substituted α- and ω-phenoxyalkanoic acids were highly resistant to microbial attack, although in one experiment 2,4,5-TB was degraded in 103 days (*120*).

1-4. DEGRADATION OF ESTER, AMIDE, AND NITRILE DERIVATIVES OF PHENOXYALKANOIC ACIDS

A. Degradation in Plants

Most ester, amide, and nitrile derivatives of phenoxyalkanoic acids are probably not active as plant growth regulators per se but require conversion to an active acid as a prerequisite for activity (*128,129*). Degradation of these compounds in plants is therefore, in many cases, an activation mechanism.

1. Esters

Hydrolysis of 2,4-D esters has been reported in barley (*152*) and lemons (*58*) treated with the isopropyl ester, and in corn and beans treated with the butoxyethanol and propylene glycol butyl esters (*153*). Meal from castor beans contained an esterase that hydrolyzed the butyl ester of 2,4-D (*154*), while the octyl ester was hydrolyzed by crude protein preparations or extracts from cucumber, spinach, corn, and pumpkin seeds (*155*). The ability to hydrolyze 2,4-D esters thus appears to be widespread among plants and is presumably an important factor contributing to the success of weed control with ester formulations of 2,4-D.

The formation of the ethyl ester of 2,4-D has been detected by gas chromatography in forage treated with the 2,4-D butyl ester (156). The transformation mechanism is unknown but transesterification and a type of β oxidation were suggested as possible mechanisms (15).

2. Amides

Fawcett et al. (3) obtained evidence that amides of ω-2,4-dichlorophen-oxyalkanoic acids, from the acetic to the heptanoic homolog, were hydro-lyzed by wheat or pea tissue. The resulting acids were β-oxidized to 2,4-D or 2,4-dichlorophenol, depending on the number of carbons in the aliphatic acid side chain. The homologous series of 2,4-dichlorophenoxyalkanoic acid amides thus showed the same alternation of growth-regulating activity in the wheat cylinder, pea curvature, pea segment, and tomato leaf epinasty tests as the free acids.

Wood and Fontaine (43) and Krewson and his colleagues (44–46,157,158) investigated the growth-regulating activity of many amino acid derivatives of phenoxyacetic and α-phenoxypropionic acids. The amino group of the amino acids was linked to the carboxyl group of the phenoxy acids. In studies with the amino acid derivatives of 2,4-D (43), MCPA (44), and 4-CPA (45), it was found that the L- and DL-amino acid derivatives of the phenoxy acids usually had about the same growth-regulating activity as the free parent phenoxy acids, whereas the D-amino acid derivatives were inactive or had little activity. It was postulated that the test plants were able to hydrolyze the derivatives of the natural L-amino acids but not those of the unnatural D-amino acids to yield free phenoxyacetic acids, which were assumed to be necessary for activity (44–46). However, it was subse-quently established (157,158) that certain amino acid derivatives of dichlor-prop and silvex differed in their growth-regulating activity from the parent phenoxypropionic acids. These results suggested that hydrolysis of the amide bond might not be essential for activity,. i.e., that the amino acid derivatives were active per se (157,158). This important suggestion needs further investigation.

3. Nitriles

The work of Fawcett and his colleagues (3,159) indicates that ω-(2,4-dichlorophenoxy)alkane nitriles are degraded in wheat tissue by two different mechanisms. One mechanism involves hydrolysis of the nitrile group to a carboxyl group followed by β oxidation of the resulting 2,4-

dichlorophenoxyalkanoic acid (Fig. 1-12, pathway A). The second mechanism involves the oxidative removal of the nitrile carbon from the side chain (α oxidation) followed by β oxidation of the resulting acid (Fig. 1–12, pathway B). These mechanisms were proposed to explain the formation of both 2,4-D and 2,4-dichlorophenol from all the ω-(2,4-dichlorophenoxy)alkane

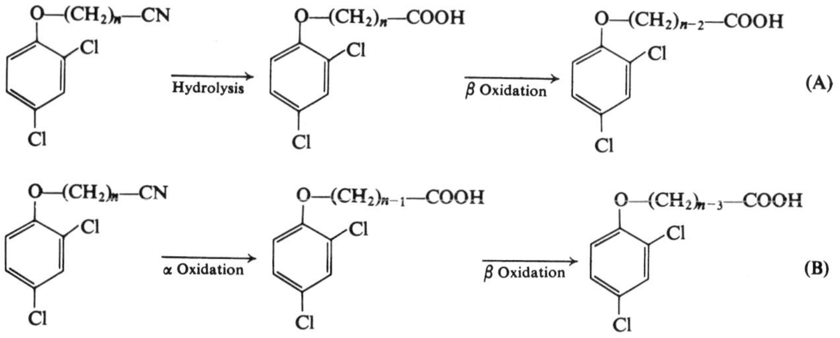

Fig. 1-12. Degradation of ω-(2,4-dichlorophenoxy)alkane nitriles in wheat tissue. Alternative pathways involving (A) hydrolysis followed by β oxidation and (B) α oxidation followed by β oxidation. [After (3).]

nitriles supplied to the wheat tissue, with the exception of the propionitrile. The propionitrile produced no detectable 2,4-D and showed little growth-regulating activity in the wheat cylinder test.

With peas and tomatoes only 2,4-dichlorophenoxyacetonitrile showed growth-regulating activity (3,159). Only this nitrile produced 2,4-D on incubation with pea tissue. None of the nitriles, except possibly the propionitrile, produced 2,4-dichlorophenol. The higher ω-(2,4-dichlorophenoxy)-alkanoic acids and amides all produced either 2,4-D or 2,4-dichlorophenol. Pea tissue therefore was unable to convert the higher ω-(2,4-dichlorophenoxy)alkane nitriles to the corresponding amides or acids, or to α-oxidize them to an acid with a shorter side chain.

B. Microbial Degradation of 2,4-D Esters

Aly and Faust (160) obtained manometric evidence that sewage microorganisms oxidized the alcohol moiety of the isopropyl and butyl esters of 2,4-D. The 2,4-D was not decomposed during the 9-day incubation period. It was assumed that hydrolysis of the ester preceded oxidation of the alcohol moiety.

1-5. DEGRADATION OF SODIUM 2,4-DICHLOROPHENOXY-ETHYL SULFATE

Sodium 2,4-dichlorophenoxyethyl sulfate (sesone) is nonherbicidal if applied to the foliage of plants but becomes highly toxic for susceptible plant species if applied to the soil (8). It shows little toxicity in sterilized soils of pH 5.5 and higher, but in nonsterile soil it is rapidly converted to 2,4-dichlorophenoxyethanol and 2,4-D (161). Figure 1-13 shows the proposed degradation sequence. A strain of *Bacillus cereus* var. *mycoides* that degraded sesone to 2,4-dichlorophenoxyethanol was isolated (161,162).

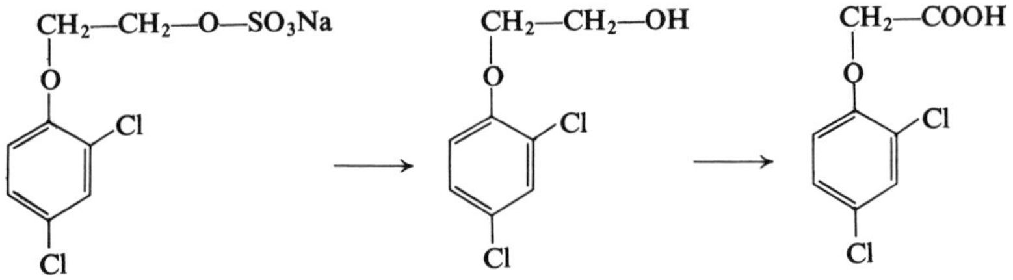

CH_2—CH_2—O—SO_3Na CH_2—CH_2—OH CH_2—COOH

(27)   (28)   (29)

Fig. 1-13. Degradation of sodium 2,4-dichlorophenoxyethyl sulfate (27) in soil to 2,4-dichlorophenoxyethanol (28) and 2,4-D (29). [After (161).]

The formation of 2,4-D, which was also demonstrated by Audus (163), is apparently microbiological, but the responsible organisms were not isolated (161,163). The contribution of 2,4-dichlorophenoxyethanol to the phytotoxicity of sesone-treated soil is controversial (164,165). In soils with a pH of 4.0 or lower, 2,4-dichlorophenoxyethanol is formed nonbiologically from sesone (166).

1-6. SUMMARY AND CONCLUSIONS

Many phenoxyalkanoic acids and their derivatives are degraded by plants and soil microorganisms. The plant and microbial degradation mechanisms are strikingly similar, hydroxylation of the aromatic ring and degradation of the side chain being common to both. The side chains of higher phenoxyalkanoic acids are degraded usually by β oxidation. Conjugation of phenoxyalkanoic acids with metabolites such as glucose and aspartic acid is known only in plants. On the other hand, cleavage of the aromatic ring is documented only for bacteria.

Degradation of phenoxyacetic acid herbicides is a resistance mechanism for many plants. A rapid rate of metabolism is required for resistance; phenoxyacetic acids are degraded slowly by many susceptible plant species. The β oxidation of higher phenoxyalkanoic acids to the propionic or acetic acid homolog is a prerequisite for herbicidal activity. Phenoxyalkanoic acid esters and amides and phenoxyalkane nitriles are also activated by degradation in the plant. Sesone is activated by degradation in soil to 2,4-dichlorophenoxyethanol and 2,4-D.

The resistance of certain phenoxyalkanoic acids to degradation in plants and soil is of interest from both the theoretical and practical points of view. Resistance and susceptibility to degradation have been correlated with patterns of ring substitution, although the basis of the relationship at the molecular level is not yet understood. Many plants are resistant to phenoxybutyric acid herbicides because β oxidation of these compounds is hindered; phenoxybutyric acid herbicides are consequently more selective than the corresponding phenoxyacetic acids. The persistence of phenoxyalkanoic acid herbicides in soil is important for weed control, but degradation is essential to prevent damage to succeeding crops and pollution of the soil and ground water. The widely used phenoxy herbicides, 2,4-D, MCPA, 2,4-DB, and MCPB, are readily degraded in soil, but 2,4,5-T, 2,4,5-TB, and the 2-phenoxypropionic acid herbicides tend to resist degradation. The use of such compounds on a large scale should be approached with caution.

REFERENCES

1. E. K. Woodford and S. A. Evans (eds.), *Weed Control Handbook*, Blackwell, Oxford, 4th ed., 1965, Chap. 2.
2. M. E. Synerholm and P. W. Zimmerman, *Contrib. Boyce Thompson Inst.*, **14**, 91 (1947).
3. C. H. Fawcett, H. F. Taylor, R. L. Wain, and F. Wightman, *Proc. Roy. Soc. (London)*, **B148**, 543 (1958).
4. C. H. Fawcett, R. M. Pascal, M. B. Pybus, H. F. Taylor, R. L. Wain, and F. Wightman, *Proc. Roy. Soc. (London)*, **B150**, 95 (1959).
5. W. G. Templeman, *Ann. Appl. Biol.*, **42**, 162 (1955).
6. G. C. Klingman, *Weed Control: As a Science*, Wiley, New York, 1961, Chap. 8.
7. U.S. Department of Agriculture, *The Pesticide Review 1967*, USDA, Stabil. and Conserv. Serv., Washington, D.C., 1967.
8. L. J. King, J. A. Lambrech, and T. P. Finn, *Contrib. Boyce Thompson Inst.*, **16**, 191 (1951).
9. R. W. Holley, F. P. Boyle, and D. B. Hand, *Arch. Biochem. Biophys.*, **27**, 143 (1950).
10. R. L. Weintraub, J. W. Brown, M. Fields, and J. Rohan, *Am. J. Botany*, **37**, 682 (1950).

11. R. L. Weintraub, J. W. Brown, M. Fields, and J. Rohan, *Plant Physiol.*, **27**, 293 (1952).

12. R. W. Holley, *Arch. Biochem. Biophys.*, **35**, 171 (1952).

13. W. C. Shaw, J. L. Hilton, D. E. Moreland, and L. L. Jansen, *U.S. Dept. Agr.*, **ARS 20-9**, 119 (1960).

14. L. J. Audus, in *Encyclopedia of Plant Physiology*, Vol. 14 (W. Ruhland, ed.), Springer, Berlin, 1961, pp. 1061-1067.

15. J. L. Hilton, L. L. Jansen, and H. M. Hull, *Ann. Rev. Plant Physiol.*, **14**, 353 (1963).

16. V. H. Freed and M. L. Montgomery, *Residue Rev.*, **3**, 1 (1963).

17. R. C. Brian, *Weed Res.*, **4**, 105 (1964).

18. A. S. Crafts, in *The Physiology and Biochemistry of Herbicides* (L. J. Audus, ed.), Academic Press, New York, 1964, Chap. 3.

19. L. C. Luckwill and C. P. Lloyd-Jones, *Ann. Appl. Biol.*, **48**, 613 (1960).

20. L. C. Luckwill and C. P. Lloyd-Jones, *Ann. Appl. Biol.*, **48**, 626 (1960).

21. L. J. Edgerton and M. B. Hoffman, *Science*, **134**, 341 (1961).

22. E. L. Leafe, *Nature*, **193**, 485 (1962).

23. R. L. Weintraub, J. H. Reinhart, and R. A. Scherff, in *A Conference on Radioactive Isotopes in Agriculture*, *A.E.C. Rept. TID-7512*, 1956, pp. 203-208.

24. P. W. Morgan and W. C. Hall, *Weeds*, **11**, 130 (1963).

25. E. Basler, *Weeds*, **12**, 14 (1964).

26. L. A. Norris and V. H. Freed, *Weed Res.*, **6**, 212 (1966).

27. M. J. Canny and K. Markus, *Australian J. Biol. Sci.*, **13**, 486 (1960).

28. M. C. Williams, F. W. Slife, and J. B. Hanson, *Weeds*, **8**, 244 (1960).

29. F. W. Slife, J. L. Key, S. Yamaguchi, and A. S. Crafts, *Weeds*, **10**, 29 (1962).

30. P. N. Chow, O. C. Burnside, T. L. Lavy, and H. W. Knoche, *Weeds*, **14**, 38 (1966).

31. N. G. Marinos, F. H. Chapman, and L. H. May, *Australian J. Biol. Sci.*, **17**, 631 (1964).

32. R. L. Weintraub, J. N. Yeatman, J. A. Lockhart, J. H. Reinhart, and M. Fields, *Arch. Biochem. Biophys.*, **40**, 277 (1952).

33. S. C. Fang, E. G. Jaworski, A. V. Logan, V. H. Freed, and J. S. Butts, *Arch. Biochem. Biophys.*, **32**, 249 (1951).

34. D. I. Chkanikov, N. N. Pavlova, and D. F. Gertsuskii, *Khim. v Sel'skom Khoz.*, **3**, 56 (1965) (in Russian); through *CA*, **63**, 8250c (1965).

35. M. Wilcox, D. E. Moreland, G. C. Klingman, *Physiol. Plantarum*, **16**, 565 (1963).

36. E. W. Thomas, B. C. Loughman, and R. G. Powell, *Nature*, **199**, 73 (1963).

37. E. W. Thomas, B. C. Loughman, and R. G. Powell, *Nature*, **204**, 286 (1964).

38. D. G. Crosby, *J. Agr. Food Chem.*, **12**, 3 (1964).

39. E. W. Thomas, B. C. Loughman, and R. G. Powell, *Nature*, **204**, 884 (1964).

40. J. K. Faulkner and D. Woodcock, *Nature*, **203**, 865 (1964).

41. H. D. Klämbt, *Planta*, **57**, 339 (1961).

42. W. A. Andreae and N. E. Good, *Plant Physiol.*, **32**, 566 (1957).

43. J. W. Wood and T. D. Fontaine, *J. Org. Chem.*, **17**, 891 (1952).

44. C. F. Krewson, C. H. H. Neufeld, T. F. Drake, T. D. Fontaine, J. W. Mitchell, and W. H. Preston, *Weeds*, **3**, 28 (1954).

45. C. F. Krewson, T. F. Drake, C. H. H. Neufeld, T. D. Fontaine, J. W. Mitchell, and W. H. Preston, *J. Agr. Food Chem.*, **4**, 140 (1956).

46. J. F. Carmichael, E. J. Saggese, J. S. Ard, C. F. Krewson, and E. M. Shantz, *J. Agr. Food Chem.*, **12**, 434 (1964).

47. E. G. Jaworski and J. S. Butts, *Arch. Biochem. Biophys.*, **38**, 207 (1952).
48. S. C. Fang and J. S. Butts, *Plant Physiol.*, **29**, 56 (1954).
49. E. G. Jaworski, S. C. Fang, and V. H. Freed, *Plant Physiol.*, **30**, 272 (1955).
50. S. C. Fang, *Weeds*, **6**, 179 (1958).
51. J. S. Butts and S. C. Fang, in *A Conference on Radioactive Isotopes in Agriculture*, *A.E.C. Rept. TID-7512*, 1956, pp. 209–214.
52. M. K. Bach and J. Fellig, in *Plant Growth Regulation, 4th Intern. Conf. Plant Growth Regulation*, Iowa State Univ. Press, Ames, 1961, pp. 273–287.
53. M. K. Bach, *Plant Physiol.*, **36**, 558 (1961).
54. M. K. Bach and J. Fellig, *Plant Physiol.*, **36**, 89 (1961).
55. M. K. Bach and J. Fellig, *Nature*, **189**, 763 (1961).
56. J. R. Corbett and C. S. Miller, *Weeds*, **14**, 34 (1966).
57. W. R. Meagher, *J. Agr. Food Chem.*, **14**, 599 (1966).
58. E. A. Erickson, B. L. Brannaman, and C. W. Coggins, *J. Agr. Food Chem.*, **11**, 437 (1963).
59. R. L. Weintraub, J. H. Reinhart, R. A. Scherff, and L. C. Schisler, *Plant Physiol.*, **29**, 303 (1954).
60. D. L. Linscott and M. K. McCarty, *Weeds*, **10**, 65 (1962).
61. R. C. Fites, F. N. Slife, and J. B. Hanson, *Weeds*, **12**, 180 (1964).
62. E. Basler, C. C. King, A. A. Badiei, and P. W. Santelman, *Proc. Southern Weed Conf.*, **17**, 351 (1964).
63. H. L. Morton, *Weeds*, **14**, 136 (1966).
64. A. A. Badiei, E. Basler, and P. W. Santelman, *Proc. Southern Weed Conf.*, **18**, 603 (1965).
65. F. M. Ashton, *Weeds*, **6**, 257 (1958).
66. L. A. Norris and V. H. Freed, *Weed Res.*, **6**, 203 (1966).
67. P. S. Nutman, H. G. Thornton, and J. H. Quastel, *Nature*, **155**, 498 (1945).
68. H. R. De Rose, *Botan. Gaz.*, **107**, 583 (1946).
69. J. W. Mitchell and P. C. Marth, *Botan. Gaz.*, **107**, 408 (1946).
70. O. H. Kries, *Botan. Gaz.*, **108**, 510 (1947).
71. H. R. De Rose and A. S. Newman, *Proc. Soil Sci. Soc. Am.*, **12**, 222 (1948).
72. J. W. Brown and J. W. Mitchell, *Botan. Gaz.*, **109**, 314 (1948).
73. T. P. Hernandez and G. F. Warren, *Proc. Am. Soc.-Hort. Sci.*, **56**, 287 (1950).
74. A. S. Newman and J. R. Thomas, *Proc. Soil Sci. Soc. Am.*, **14**, 160 (1950).
75. A. S. Newman, J. R. Thomas, and R. L. Walker, *Proc. Soil Sci. Soc. Am.*, **16**, 21 (1952).
76. E. K. Akamine, *Botan. Gaz.*, **112**, 312 (1951).
77. L. J. Audus, *Plant Soil*, **2**, 31 (1949).
78. L. J. Audus, *Nature*, **166**, 356 (1950).
79. L. J. Audus, *Plant Soil*, **3**, 170 (1951).
80. L. J. Audus, *J. Sci. Food Agr.*, **3**, 268 (1952).
81. L. J. Audus, in *Herbicides and the Soil* (E. K. Woodford and G. R. Sagar, eds.), Blackwell, Oxford, 1960, pp. 1–19.
82. L. J. Audus, in *The Physiology and Biochemistry of Herbicides* (L. J. Audus, ed.), Academic Press, New York, 1964, Chap. 5.
83. W. C. Evans, in *Encyclopedia of Plant Physiology*, Vol. 10 (W. Ruhland, ed.), Springer, Berlin, 1958, pp. 474–476.
84. W. C. Evans and B. S. W. Smith, *Biochem. J.*, **57**, xxx (1954).

85. H. N. Fernley and W. C. Evans, *Biochem. J.*, **73**, 22P (1959).
86. W. C. Evans and P. Moss, *Biochem. J.*, **65**, 8P (1957).
87. R. L. Walker and A. S. Newman, *Appl. Microbiol.*, **4**, 201 (1956).
88. T. I. Steenson and N. Walker, *Plant Soil*, **8**, 17 (1956).
89. T. I. Steenson and N. Walker, *J. Gen. Microbiol.*, **16**, 146 (1957).
90. G. R. Bell, *Can. J. Microbiol.*, **3**, 821(1957).
91. G. R. Bell, *Can. J. Microbiol.*, **6**, 325 (1960).
92. C. Stapp and G. Spicher, *Zentr. Bakteriol. Parasitenk. Abt. II*, **108**, 113 (1954).
93. G. Spicher, *Zentr. Bakteriol. Parasitenk. Abt. II*, **108**, 225 (1954).
94. M. H. Rogoff and J. J. Reid, *J. Bacteriol.*, **71**, 303 (1956).
95. H. L. Jensen and H. I. Petersen, *Nature*, **170**, 39 (1952).
96. H. L. Jensen and H. I. Petersen, *Acta Agr. Scand.*, **2**, 215 (1952).
97. M. A. Loos, R. N. Roberts, and M. Alexander, *Can. J. Microbiol.*, **13**, 679 (1967).
98. M. A. Loos, J.-M. Bollag, and M. Alexander, *J. Agr. Food Chem.*, **15**, 858 (1967).
99. J.-M. Bollag, C. S. Helling, and M. Alexander, *Appl. Microbiol.*, **15**, 1393 (1967).
100. O. B. Weeks, *J. Bacteriol.*, **69**, 649 (1955).
101. H. C. Bounds and A. R. Colmer, *Weeds*, **13**, 249 (1965).
102. J. K. Gaunt and W. C. Evans, *Biochem. J.*, **79**, 25P (1961).
103. R. J. W. Byrde and D. Woodcock, *Biochem. J.*, **65**, 682 (1957).
104. J. K. Faulkner and D. Woodcock, *J. Chem. Soc.*, **1961**, 5397.
105. J. K. Faulkner and D. Woodcock, *J. Chem. Soc.*, **1965**, 1187.
106. D. R. Clifford and D. Woodcock, *Nature*, **203**, 763 (1964).
107. S. M. Bocks, J. R. Lindsay-Smith, and R. O. C. Norman, *Nature*, **201**, 398 (1964).
108. T. I. Steenson and N. Walker, *J. Gen. Microbiol.*, **18**, 692 (1958).
109. A. B. Pardee, in *The Bacteria*, Vol. 3 (I. C. Gunsalus and R. Y. Stanier, eds.), Academic Press, New York, 1962, Chap. 12.
110. N. J. Palleroni and R. Y. Stanier, *J. Gen. Microbiol.*, **35**, 319 (1964).
111. R. Y. Stanier, *J. Bacteriol.*, **54**, 339 (1947).
112. J. P. Brown and E. B. McCall, *J. Chem. Soc.*, **1955**, 3681.
113. M. H. Rogoff, *Advan. Appl. Microbiol.*, **3**, 193 (1961).
114. W. C. Evans, J. K. Gaunt, and J. J. Davies, *Proc. Intern. Congr. Biochem.*, *5th, Moscow, 1961*, pp. 306–307.
115. M. A. Loos, R. N. Roberts, and M. Alexander, *Can. J. Microbiol.*, **13**, 691 (1967).
116. J.-M. Bollag, C. S. Helling, and M. Alexander, private communication, 1967.
117. L. J. Audus and K. V. Symonds, *Ann. Appl. Biol.*, **42**, 174 (1955).
118. C. S. Helling, J.-M. Bollag, and J. E. Dawson, *J. Agr. Food Chem.*, **16**, 538 (1968).
119. M. Alexander and M. I. H. Aleem, *J. Agr. Food Chem.*, **9**, 44 (1961).
120. K. Burger, I. C. MacRae, and M. Alexander, *Proc. Soil Sci. Soc. Am.*, **26**, 243 (1962).
121. M. Alexander, *Ann. Rev. Microbiol.*, **18**, 217 (1964).
122. M. Alexander, *Advan. Appl. Microbiol.*, **7**, 35 (1965).
123. M. Alexander, *Proc. Soil Sci. Soc. Am.*, **29**, 1 (1965).
124. C. H. Fawcett, J. M. A. Ingram, and R. L. Wain, *Proc. Roy. Soc. (London)*, **B142**, 60 (1954).
125. R. L. Wain and F. Wightman, *Proc. Roy. Soc. (London)*, **B142**, 525 (1954).
126. R. L. Wain, *Ann. Appl. Biol.*, **42**, 151 (1955).
127. R. L. Wain, *J. Agr. Food Chem.*, **3**, 128 (1955).
128. R. L. Wain, *Advan. Pest Control Res.*, **2**, 263 (1958).

129. R. L. Wain, in *The Physiology and Biochemistry of Herbicides* (L. J. Audus, ed.), Academic Press, New York, 1964, Chap. 16.

130. C. H. Fawcett, H. F. Taylor, R. L. Wain, and F. Wightman, in *The Chemistry and Mode of Action of Plant Growth Substances* (R. L. Wain and F. Wightman, eds.), Butterworth, London, 1956, pp. 187–194.

131. D. L. Linscott, *J. Agr. Food Chem.*, **12**, 7 (1964).

132. M. E. Synerholm and P. W. Zimmerman, *Contrib. Boyce Thompson Inst.*, **14**, 369 (1947).

133. R. L. Wain and H. F. Taylor, *Nature*, **207**, 167 (1965).

134. P. G. Balayannis, M. S. Smith, and R. L. Wain, *Ann. Appl. Biol.*, **55**, 261 (1965).

135. C. A. Bache, D. J. Lisk, and M. A. Loos, *J. Assoc. Offic. Agr. Chemists*, **47**, 348 (1964).

136. L. A. Norris and V. H. Freed, *Weed Res.*, **6**, 283 (1966).

137. S. N. Fertig, M. A. Loos, W. H. Gutenmann, and D. J. Lisk, *Weeds*, **12**, 147 (1964).

138. W. C. Shaw and W. A. Gentner, *Weeds*, **5**, 75 (1957).

139. D. L. Linscott and R. D. Hagin, *Proc. Northeast. Weed Control Conf.*, **17**, 260 (1963).

140. D. L. Linscott, R. D. Hagin, and M. J. Wright, *Crop Sci.*, **5**, 455 (1965).

141. D. M. Webley, R. B. Duff, and V. C. Farmer, *Nature*, **179**, 1130 (1957).

142. D. M. Webley, R. B. Duff, and V. C. Farmer, *J. Gen. Microbiol.*, **18**, 733 (1958).

143. D. M. Webley, R. B. Duff, and V. C. Farmer, *Nature*, **183**, 748 (1959).

144. H. F. Taylor and R. L. Wain, *Proc. Roy. Soc. (London)*, **B156**, 172 (1962).

145. I. C. MacRae, M. Alexander, and A. D. Rovira, *J. Gen. Microbiol.*, **32**, 69 (1963).

146. I. C. MacRae and M. Alexander, *J. Bacteriol.*, **86**, 1231 (1963).

147. W. H. Gutenmann, M. A. Loos, M. Alexander, and D. J. Lisk, *Proc. Soil Sci. Soc. Am.*, **28**, 205 (1964).

148. J. S. Whiteside and M. Alexander, *Weeds*, **8**, 204 (1960).

149. W. H. Gutenmann and D. J. Lisk, *J. Agr. Food Chem.*, **12**, 322 (1964).

150. I. C. MacRae and M. Alexander, *Agron. J.*, **56**, 91 (1964).

151. I. C. MacRae and M. Alexander, *J. Agr. Food Chem.*, **13**, 72 (1965).

152. A. S. Crafts, *Weeds*, **8**, 19 (1960).

153. S. S. Szabo, *Weeds*, **11**, 292 (1963).

154. C. E. Hagen, C. O. Clagett, and E. A. Helgesen, *Science*, **110**, 116 (1949).

155. D. J. Morré and B. J. Rogers, *Weeds*, **8**, 436 (1960).

156. G. Yip and R. E. Ney, *Weeds*, **14**, 167 (1966).

157. C. F. Krewson, T. F. Drake, J. W. Mitchell, and W. H. Preston, *J. Agr. Food Chem.*, **4**, 690 (1956).

158. C. F. Krewson, J. F. Carmichael, T. F. Drake, J. W. Mitchell, and B. C. Smale, *J. Agr. Food Chem.*, **8**, 104 (1960).

159. C. H. Fawcett, R. C. Seeley, H. F. Taylor, R. L. Wain, and F. Wightman, *Nature*, **176**, 1026 (1955).

160. O. M. Aly and S. D. Faust, *J. Agr. Food Chem.*, **12**, 541 (1964).

161. A. J. Vlitos, *Contrib. Boyce Thompson Inst.*, **17**, 127 (1953).

162. A. J. Vlitos, *Contrib. Boyce Thompson Inst.*, **16**, 435 (1952).

163. L. J. Audus, *Nature*, **170**, 886 (1952).

164. A. J. Vlitos and L. J. King, *Nature*, **171**, 523 (1953).

165. L. J. Audus, *Nature*, **171**, 523 (1953).

166. R. B. Carroll, *Contrib. Boyce Thompson Inst.*, **16**, 409 (1952).

CHAPTER 2

s-Triazines

ENRICO KNUESLI, DAGMAR BERRER,
GERARD DUPUIS, AND HERBERT ESSER

PESTICIDES RESEARCH LABORATORIES
J. R. GEIGY S.A.
BASEL, SWITZERLAND

2-1. Introduction: Chemical and Physical Properties 51
2-2. Degradation of Triazine Herbicides by Nonbiological Systems . . 57
    A. Chemical Degradation 57
    B. Degradation by Soil Physicochemical Factors 61
    C. Degradation by Irradiation 62
2-3. Degradation of Triazine Herbicides by Biological Systems . . 62
    A. General Evidence for s-Triazine Degradation 62
    B. Definite Metabolic Degradation Reactions 66
2-4. Conclusions 74
References 74

2-1. INTRODUCTION: CHEMICAL AND PHYSICAL PROPERTIES

The herbicidal activity of the s-triazines was discovered in 1952 by a research group of J. R. Geigy S.A. in Basel, Switzerland (1,2). Subsequent investigations with many experimental compounds in a large field-testing program resulted in the present series of commercial herbicides. Simazine, atrazine, prometryne, and ametryne have gained major recognition due to their outstanding performance with respect to selective herbicidal effects and crop tolerances. The structures, chemical names, original code numbers, common names, and some chemical and physical data on the more important herbicides are listed in Table 2-1.

Several additional s-triazine derivatives have reached the marketing stage or have been announced as experimental compounds. Du Pont (3) in the United States and Geigy (4) in several other countries own patents

TABLE 2-1

Chemical and Physical Properties of Several s-Triazine Herbicides[a]

Structure and chemical denomination	Code number	Common name	Melting point, °C	Solubility, ppm		Vapor pressure, p mm Hg, 293°K	pK	Dipole moment, Debyes
				Water	Organic solvents			
 Cl—triazine with C_2H_5NH and NHC_2H_5 2-chloro-4,6-bis(ethylamino)-s-triazine	G 27692	Simazine	223–225	5	Slightly soluble Chloroform, 900 n-Pentane, 3 Acetic ester, 1200	6.1×10^{-9}	1.65	Solubility too limited
 Cl—triazine with C_2H_5NH and $NH\text{-}i\text{-}C_3H_7$ 2-chloro-4-ethylamino-6-isopropylamino-s-triazine	G 30027	Atrazine	173–175	33^b	Soluble Acetic ester 28,000	3.0×10^{-7}	1.68	4.6_3
 Cl—triazine with $i\text{-}C_3H_7NH$ and $NH\text{-}i\text{-}C_3H_7$ 2-chloro-4,6-bis(isopropylamino)-s-triazine	G 30028	Propazine	212–214	8.6	Slightly soluble	2.9×10^{-8}	1.85	4.5_2

Structure	Designation	Common name	mp (°C)		Solubility			
Cl / (C₂H₅)₂N / NHC₂H₅ — 2-chloro-4-diethylamino-6-ethylamino-*s*-triazine	G 27901	Trietazine	102–104	20	Very soluble	—	1.88	4.7₇
OCH₃ / C₂H₅NH / NH-*i*-C₃H₇ — 2-methoxy-4-ethylamino-6-isopropylamino-*s*-triazine	G 32293	Atratone	94–96	1800	Very soluble	2.9×10^{-6}	4.20[a]	—
OCH₃ / *i*-C₃H₇NH / NH-*i*-C₃H₇ — 2-methoxy-4,6-bis(isopropyl-amino)-*s*-triazine	G 31435	Prome-tone	91–92	750	Very soluble	2.3×10^{-6}	4.3	2.9₄
SCH₃ / CH₃NH / NH-*i*-C₃H₇ — 2-methylthio-4-methylamino-6-isopropylamino-*s*-triazine	G 34360		84–86	580	Very soluble	1.0×10^{-6}	3.08	—

TABLE 2-1–continued

Structure and chemical denomination	Code number	Common name	Melting point, °C	Solubility, ppm		Vapor pressure, p mm Hg, 293°K	pK	Dipole moment, Debyes
				Water	Organic solvents			
SCH$_3$ ... C$_2$H$_5$NH—⬡—NH-i-C$_3$H$_7$ 2-methylthio-4-ethylamino-6-isopropylamino-s-triazine	G 34162	Ametryne	84–86	185	Very soluble	8.4×10^{-7}	3.12	3.1_5
SCH$_3$ ... i-C$_3$H$_7$NH—⬡—NH-i-C$_3$H$_7$ 2-methylthio-4,6-bis(isopropylamino)-s-triazine	G 34161	Prome-tryne	118–120	48	Very soluble	10×10^{-6}	3.05	3.5_4

2-methylthio-4-isopropylamino-6-γ-methoxypropylamino-s-triazine — G 36393, 68–70, 320, Very soluble, —, 3.03, —

2-methylthio-4-ethylamino-6-t-butylamino-s-triazine — GS 14260, 104–105, 58, Very soluble, 9.6×10^{-7}, —, —

[a] J. B. Weber, North Carolina State University, published for *Spectrochimica Acta*. The remaining physical data: Analytical Laboratories, J. R. Geigy S.A., Basel, Switzerland.

[b] According to new determinations (Analytical Laboratories, J. R. Geigy S.A., Basel, Switzerland, 1968).

covering 2-alkylthio-4,6-bisalkoxyalkylamino-s-triazines. An example of these compounds, 2-methylthio-4,6-bis-y-methoxypropylamino-s-triazine, was developed by Monsanto (5). Degussa (6) synthesized 2-azido-4,6-diamino-s-triazines of which Shell proposed 2-azido-4-sec-butylamino-6-ethylamino-s-triazine (Shell WL-9385) for further testing (7). CIBA (8) selected 2-azido-4-isopropylamino-6-methylthio-s-triazine (CIBA 7019) and 2-azido-4-sec-butylamino-6-methylthio-s-triazine (CIBA 8250) for further evaluation from a group of 2-azido-4-amino-6-alkylthio-s-triazines.

Several papers have appeared which provide either a general review of the s-triazine herbicides or deal with special subjects, such as the relation between structure and activity, mode of action, analysis, and absorptive behavior in soil (9–28). The present chapter considers the degradation of s-triazine herbicides. A condensed summary of chemical and physical reactions known to occur in nonbiological systems is presented. A few of these reactions may directly parallel physicochemical alterations occurring in soil or in other systems. Such relations should be of interest to everyone involved in the elucidation of the fate of triazines and may serve as a useful tool for comparative purposes. Then, the degradation of s-triazines in biological systems such as microorganisms, plants, and animals is reviewed.

All present s-triazines, used as general or selective herbicides, are diamino-s-triazines which have a chlorine, methoxy, or methylthio group as a third radical bonded directly to the ring. The two amino groups bear short-chain alkyls or alkoxyalkyls as substituents. Positions 2, 4, and 6 of the s-triazine ring are equivalent (1). For uniformity, the alkylamino groups or radicals which may take their places will be assigned to C atoms 4 and 6 in the following sections. The chlorine, methoxy, and methylthio groups, or radicals which may take their places, will be coordinated to C atom 2.

(1)

In the following pages individual sections will cover reactions involving the groups located in position 2, alterations of the alkylamino groups located in positions 4 and 6, and ring cleavage. The amount of available information differs from compound to compound, depending on their importance and date of introduction. Degradation reactions described for a few s-triazine herbicides in a homologous series can often be used to predict the biological fragmentation pattern in structurally related herbicides.

2-2. DEGRADATION OF TRIAZINE HERBICIDES BY NON-BIOLOGICAL SYSTEMS

A. Chemical Degradation

1. Reactions Affecting the Substituents at C Atom 2

a. CHLOROTRIAZINES

The chlorine atom in 2-chloro-4,6-bisamino-s-triazines is readily displaced by a variety of nucleophiles. These reactions are reviewed in Table 2–2.

TABLE 2-2

Nucleophilic Reactions Affecting the Chlorine Atom of
2-Chloro-4,6-bisamino-s-triazines

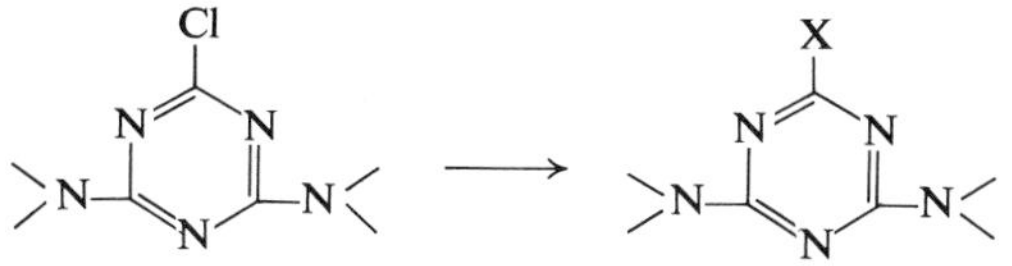

(1)

Attacking agent	Resultant substituent[a]	Ref.
H· or OH⁻	—OH	*29a*
SH⁻	—SH	*29b*
NH₂CSNH₂·HCl/NaOH	—SH	*30*
Alkyl OH, OH⁻	—O-alkyl	*29c*
Alkyl SH, OH⁻	—S-alkyl	*31*
NH₃, alkyl NH₂, (alkyl)₂NH	—NH₂, —NH alkyl, N(alkyl)₂	*29d*
N(CH₃)₃	—[N(CH₃)₃]⁺·Cl⁻	*32*
NH₂NH₂, NH₂NH-alkyl	—NHNH₂, —NHNH-alkyl	*33*
KF	—F	*34*
KCN	—CN	*35*
NaN₃	—N₃	*36*

[a] X in Eq. (1).

Although the products resulting by hydrolysis of 2-chloro-4,6-bisamino-s-triazines (and also of the 2-methoxy- and 2-methylthio-4,6-diamino-s-triazines) are usually named 2-hydroxy-4,6-bisamino-s-triazines, it should be noted that they are present in the form of their tautomeric 2-oxo-4,6-diamino-1,2-dihydro-s-triazines (*37*). This latter structure, evident from infrared spectra, also explains various aspects of their chemical behavior such as the failure to form methoxy derivatives by usual methylating methods. In the corresponding S analogs, however, the thiol form prevails and therefore they are readily methylated to the respective methylthio derivatives. The 2-hydroxy-4,6-bisdiamino-s-triazines are slow-melting compounds of very low solubility in water, but soluble in dilute solutions of mineral acids or alkalis. The corresponding nitrates are less soluble than the chlorohydrates or sulfates.

Treatment of 2-chloro-s-triazine herbicides with polysulfide ions has been proposed as a method for the destruction of unwanted residues in soils (38). The effectiveness of this procedure is controversial, however, under practical conditions (39,40,41).

In view of potential parallelisms in biological systems, special attention is drawn to the quaternary group compounds obtained by reaction with trimethylamine. The quaternary group is extremely reactive. Using these intermediates for further reaction with some of the above-mentioned nucleophilic agents, like alkylthiols, KCN, and NaN_3, the respective end products are obtained more readily than by direct reaction with the 2-chloro-4,6-bisamino-s-triazines (36,42). Triethylamine does not form an analogous quaternary compound under identical conditions (43).

Reference is also made to a reaction (44) which was considered a model for analogous conditions suspected in connection with the detoxification of 2-chloro-4,6-bisamino-s-triazines by corn [Eq. (2)].

$$(2)$$

b. METHOXYTRIAZINES

Acid or alkaline hydrolysis of 2-methoxy-4,6-bisamino-s-triazines leads to the corresponding 2-hydroxy-4,6-bisamino-s-triazines (43). Heat causes isomeration into 2-oxo-1-methyl-1,2-dihydro-*s*-triazines (*45*). After heating prometone at 260°, the following isomeration and dismutation products could be identified* [Eq. (3)].

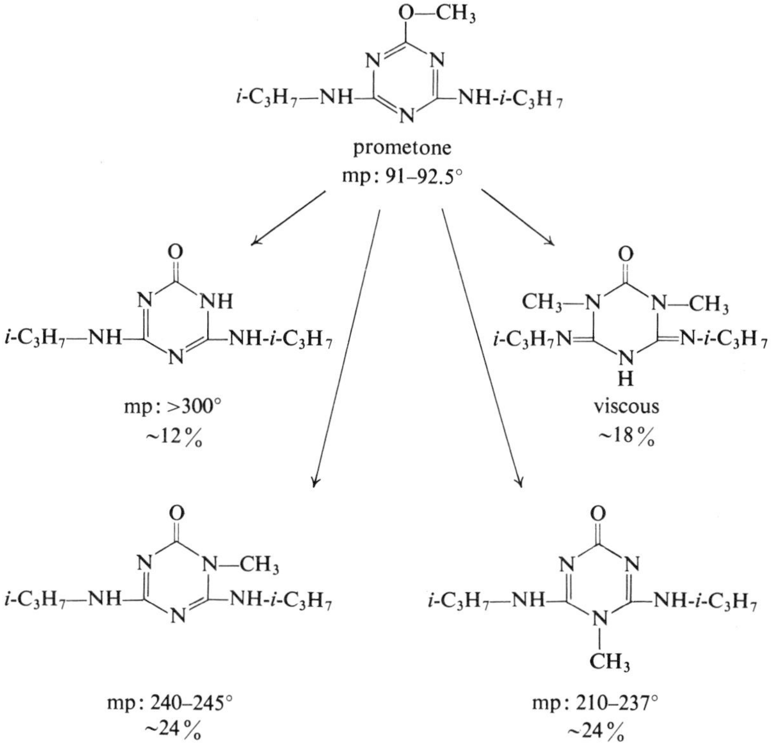

(3)

prometone
mp: 91–92.5°

mp: >300°
~12%

viscous
~18%

mp: 240–245°
~24%

mp: 210–237°
~24%

c. METHYLTHIOTRIAZINES

Acid or alkaline hydrolysis of 2-methylthio-4,6-bisamino-*s*-triazine does not lead to the respective 2-mercapto-4,6-bisamino-*s*-triazines, but again to the 2-hydroxy-4,6-bisamino-*s*-triazines (*46*). 2-Methylthio-4,6-bisamino-*s*-triazines can be oxidized by phthalomonoper-acid, whereby the corresponding sulfoxy and sulfono analogs are obtained (*45*). Of special interest is the hydrolytic behavior of these two compounds when compared with the original methylthio analog. The data in Table 2-3 were determined for prometryne and its derivatives (*47*). It is evident from Table 2-3 that under acid, neutral, and alkaline conditions the sulfone is more rapidly hydrolyzed

* All temperatures referred to in this book are in degrees Celsius unless otherwise noted.

than the sulfoxide, i.e., 6, 50, and 10 times more quickly, respectively. The most impressive observation, however, is the increased rate of hydrolysis of both, when compared with prometryne.

TABLE 2-3

Hydrolytic Behavior of Prometryne and Its Derivatives

	Time required for hydrolysis of:		
Hydrolytic agent, 25°	—CH$_3$S	—CH$_3$SO	—CH$_3$SO$_2$
0.1 N HCl	22 days	96 min	16 min
H$_2$O	About 500 years	150 days	3 days
0.01 N NaOH	About 30 years	20 min	2 min

2. Reactions Affecting the Substituents at C Atoms 4 and 6

a. CHLOROTRIAZINES

The secondary amino groups of 2-chloro-4,6-bisamino-s-triazines do not readily undergo reaction. Acylation with the usual acylating agents normally leads to substitution of the chlorine atom by a hydroxy group. However, under special conditions acylation to 2-chloro-4-acylamido-6-amino-s-triazines is possible (48). Another method for acetylation to 2-chloro-4-acetamido-6-amino-s-triazines makes use of carbomethylene (ketene) (48).

Patents of BASF (49) and Degussa (50) describe N-nitroso derivatives of 2-chloro-4,6-bisamino-s-triazines received by treatment with sodium nitrite.

Treatment of simazine with concentrated nitric acid results in the substitution of the chlorine atom by a hydroxy group. At the same time nitration of one ethylamino group occurs (44). The N-nitroethylamino group readily undergoes nucleophilic replacement reactions.

Patents of Degussa (51,52) report the synthesis of N-trichloromethylthio and N-phosphorylamido derivatives.

b. METHOXY- AND METHYLTHIOTRIAZINES

The basicity of the amino groups of 2-methoxy- and 2-methylthio-4,6-bisamino-s-triazines is greater than that of the corresponding 2-chloro analogs. Substitution on the lateral nitrogen occurs more easily and under conditions which do not significantly interfere with the methoxy or methylthio group. By acylation with the usual acylation agents or carbomethylene,

N-mono- or *N,N'*-bisacylamido-*s*-triazines are obtained (*53*). The *N*-tri-chloromethylthio, *N*-carbamido, *N*-sulfonamido, and *N*-phosphorylamido derivatives are prepared by using analogous methods (*51,52,54*).

3. Cleavage of the Triazine Ring

Cleavage of the triazine ring of 2-chloro-, 2-methoxy-, or 2-methylthio-4,6-bisamino-*s*-triazines by in vitro reactions has not been demonstrated. Reports describing ring cleavage of *s*-triazine derivatives are relatively few if one excludes such drastic conditions as heating with concentrated sulfuric acid, melting with alkali, and heating at very high temperatures (*29e*). The splitting of cyanuric chloride through reaction with dimethylformamide (*55,56*), and the splitting of *s*-triazine itself (*57–59*), cannot be considered as general reaction due to the special chemical character of these two com-pounds, which is very different from that of bisamino-*s*-triazines. Potential mechanisms for ring degradation have been suggested in reactions where unexpected end products were encountered (*60–62*).

B. Degradation by Soil Physicochemical Factors

Information concerning degradation of *s*-triazines by soil factors exclud-ing biological interference is limited. Most work has involved a comparison of nonsterilized soils with sterilized soils to elucidate the role of micro-organisms, rather than the role of sterile soil itself. From an experimental standpoint, the problem of eliminating biological factors without funda-mentally changing the soil is the most critical consideration.

Hydroxyatrazine was reported to be the major product in sterilized soils in studies on the significance of microbial degradation of atrazine by pure cultures and the native soil population in nonsterile soils (*63–66*). Avoiding losses by volatility, a high rate of atrazine deactivation can be obtained in various soils incubated at 95 or 50° for 24 hours, the respective hydroxy derivative being cited as the major product (*41*). Since the pH of the soil ranged between 4.6 and 6.2, a simple acid hydrolysis may have occurred. Localized areas in soils of low pH, resulting from organic matter decom-position, plant root exudates, or microbial exudates may provide the conditions for acid hydrolysis even under normal ambient temperature (*67*). Furthermore, compounds found in plants, such as the *N*-hydroxy-benzoxazinones, may also be present in soil and could lead to a purely chemical degradation. The same possibility exists for various nitrosation and nitration reactions cited in section 2-2,A.2. But these are all assumptions not yet proved experimentally.

C. Degradation by Irradiation

Exposure of simazine and atrazine to ultraviolet light on aluminum planchets at 42° caused a change in the UV absorbance; the color of the compounds turned from white to light tan (*68*). The greatest change occurred with far-UV irradiation. The small quantities used did not permit identification of degradation products. A similar, although qualitatively different, result was reported earlier by the same group (*69*) working with *s*-triazine compounds absorbed on filter paper. The experimental data did not indicate, however, whether reactive interference with the filter paper could be excluded. Similar problems are encountered in studies with soil. The main difficulty is the experimental exclusion of factors such as absorption, volatilization, physicochemical degradation, or degradation by biological systems. When degradation is shown by bioassay, only where interference by these factors is avoided can the result be conclusive.

With this proviso, reference is made to various papers reporting studies on the influence of irradiation (*70–74*).

2-3. DEGRADATION OF TRIAZINE HERBICIDES BY BIOLOGICAL SYSTEMS

A. General Evidence for *s*-Triazine Degradation

The most striking difference between the purely chemical and biochemical types of degradation is the complexity of the biological systems metabolizing these herbicides. In contrast to the fairly defined conditions of chemical degradation experiments, the living organisms represent complex, differentiated structures. In addition they are closely connected with their respective environment by various mutual effects. The consequence of these heterogeneous influences are continuous biochemical and chemical attacks on the applied herbicide. In spite of the difficulty in distinguishing the physicochemical and biochemical alterations, only the degradation attributable to biological systems will be considered in this section. The chemical catalytic action of the soil has been discussed previously. The elucidation of the metabolic fate of *s*-triazines has been attempted under many different conditions, resulting in an immense number of publications. Many authors make only a general statement that metabolism of *s*-triazines has occurred, without reporting a definite metabolite. These publications are summarized in the following section. Thereafter, biochemical degradation studies which have established the structure of metabolites are reviewed in more detail.

The biological system attacking the *s*-triazines is determined in part by the

mode of application of these herbicides. After pre- or postemergent application the degradative action is initiated by the soil alone, or simultaneously
by the plants and the soil. In either case the essential role of the soil and the
pronounced ability of this heterogeneous system to degrade the *s*-triazines
is recognized. It must be stressed that the separate analysis of the physical
chemical, chemical, or biochemical degradative capacity of the soil is prob-
lematic. These problems mainly emerge with the sterilization of the soils (i.e.,
alteration of the structure of soil, efficiency of sterilization, etc.). Results
actually obtained strongly depend on a variety of other factors (i.e., type of
soil, environmental conditions analytical methods, period of experiment,
etc.). For example, a bioassay alone is an insufficient proof of degradation
of *s*-triazines in the soil. Likewise, failure of ring-labeled *s*-triazines to evolve
$^{14}CO_2$ does not mean that degradation has not occurred. At present, the
question on the relative importance of the different factors under field
conditions is still under study. But evidence is accumulating in the case
of the chlorotriazines that chemical hydrolysis is more rapid in soils than
microbial degradation. Further degradation may proceed by the influence
of microorganisms.

1. Degradation by Microorganisms

Information on the herbicidal persistence in soils is a necessary prerequisite for its application. This problem stimulated numerous investigations on the dissipation of *s*-triazines. Early experiments attempted to
determine the respective importance of the different environmental factors.
It was stated that inactivation of triazines was greatest when the conditions
in the soil were optimum for microbial growth (*27,70,75–83*). Laboratory
experiments comparing sterile v. nonsterile conditions also support the
same contention (*72,84*).

Furthermore, the degradative capacity of different soil microorganisms
resulted from growth experiments with isolated fungi and bacteria. Several
species were capable of growing in nutrient media containing triazines as
the sole source of carbon and/or nitrogen. Other investigations followed
the progressive dissipation of triazines by means of bioassays. Chemical
analysis of residual triazine in the nutrient medium demonstrated a direct
correlation between these two analytical techniques (*63,80,85–94*).

Tracer experiments with ^{14}C-labeled triazines confirmed these results,
showing the C moiety of the side chains being used preferably as an energy
source. The incorporation into protein, lipid, and, to a lesser extent, nucleic
acid fractions was observed primarily with ^{14}C fragments originating from
side chains (*84,93,95–97*).

A decrease in phytotoxicity proportional to a decrease in the actual concentration of the *s*-triazine demonstrates that degradation products do not have herbicidal properties. These observations have been confirmed by experiments involving various synthetic degradation products. A single exception is reported for dialkylamino-*s*-triazines, which may be converted to monoalkylamino derivatives possessing higher phytotoxicity to some species than the parent compound. Observations on the behavior of these triazines are presented in the section dealing with dealkylation reactions (*15,20,41,73,78,98,99*).

2. Degradation by Plants

A quantitative consideration of the factors involved in the dissipation of triazines from the soil ultimately must also consider the essential role played by the plants. Therefore, the metabolic fate of *s*-triazines in plants is discussed, but without regard for alterations of the original herbicide concomitantly occurring in the soil.

Early work on plant metabolism of the *s*-triazines was stimulated by the extraordinary efficacy and selectivity observed in a variety of crops. To explain these selective properties, the uptake, translocation, and general metabolism have been investigated in different species by comparing sensitive and resistant plants. The use of *s*-triazines labeled with different isotopes greatly facilitated the elucidation of the complex metabolic degradation schemes. Rapid uptake by the roots and distribution into all parts of the plant were readily observed, thus demonstrating that no correlation existed between uptake and selectivity. The apparent resistance observed in deep-rooted plants was shown not to be related to selective uptake but to be a result of strong adsorption of the *s*-triazines near the soil surface. Another exception was observed in cotton where the *s*-triazines are removed from the transpiration stream and stored inside the lysigenous glands. By means of this unique compartmentalization, the *s*-triazines are prevented from exerting their phytotoxic action (*100–112*).

Suitable methods for chemical fractionation in addition to the early radioautographic techniques have been developed which discriminate between the original *s*-triazine and its degradation products. Separation of the different radioactive fractions into lipophilic (chloroform), hydrophilic (water or water–alcohol mixtures), and residual fractions has been achieved. Unchanged *s*-triazines were found exclusively in the lipophilic fractions, as established by control experiments. The remainder of the radioactivity detected in the hydrophilic and residual fractions has been used as a criterion for metabolism. This type of data has been established for a wide variety of economically important crops such as cereals, vegetables, forage plants, cotton, etc. The influence of various environmental conditions on distribution and metabolic fate have been thoroughly studied, particularly the relationship between *s*-triazine transport and temperature and humidity. A direct dependence on the transpirational stream has been established (*12,113–119*).

Further improvement of the separation methods to include use of partition and ion-exchange chromatography, electrophoresis, etc., revealed that a pattern of metabolites was obtained. The presence of several metabolites in the polar phase, the number of which varies with plant and *s*-triazine type, was demonstrated. The lipophilic chloroform phase was found to contain degradation products in addition to the original *s*-triazines. The total amount of radioactivity retained in the hydrophilic and residual phases, frequently used as an expression of metabolism, is of limited value because it may underestimate the real metabolic capacity of the plants (*24,120–130*).

The results thus far reported have clearly established the ability of plants to metabolize the *s*-triazines. However, the degradation rates observed vary considerably from species to species. The actual capacity of plants to prevent the *s*-triazines from reaching a phytotoxic level seems an essential factor in determining the degree of resistance.

3. Degradation in Animals

General toxicological evaluation of *s*-triazines in animals induced further biochemical investigations. Despite a remarkably low toxicity to mammals, additional information on their metabolic fate was necessary to establish their safety. Therefore, most work has been performed from the residue point of view, demonstrating that the essential organs and the milk of sheep and cattle are free of the parent triazines and the corresponding hydroxy analogs after subchronic feeding of the herbicides (*15,131–134*).

Several investigations have dealt with the general detoxification of the *s*-triazines and their excretion. Both chloro- and methylthio-*s*-triazines were observed in metabolism studies with laboratory and domestic animals. After an oral dosage to rats, only minor amounts of parent propazine and prometryne were excreted in the feces, whereas the urine was free of detectable amounts of these compounds. Several ^{14}C-labeled metabolites other than hydroxypropazine were demonstrated in the urine (*135–137*). In experiments with ^{14}C-labeled simazine, atrazine, prometone, and propazine fed to rats by means of a stomach tube, both urine and feces were of similar importance for the excretion of simazine, whereas the urine was the predominant route for atrazine, prometone, and propazine. Approximately 70 to 90% of the total radioactivity administered was recovered from both excreta within 48 hours after treatment (*138–141*). Chemical analysis, by ion-exchange chromatography, of the radioactive excretion products revealed the presence of several metabolites in the urine and feces (*124,140–142*). In other experiments unlabeled simazine and atrazine were fed to dairy cows for several days. Only minor amounts of the parent compounds (1–2% of the total dosage applied) were found in the urine. Since the analytical method used depended on the presence of an active chlorine atom, no discrimination between the original material and degradation products still retaining their chlorine atom was possible (*131,132*).

B. Definite Metabolic Degradation Reactions

General evidence for the biochemical degradation of the *s*-triazines has been confirmed and metabolic studies have elucidated the structure of metabolites. These chemical prerequisites met, it has been possible to construct a detailed pattern of pathways which are followed in the metabolic degradation of the triazines. The classification used in the subsequent discussions is based on the C-atom position within the *s*-triazine ring and the substituent attached to these carbons (**2**).

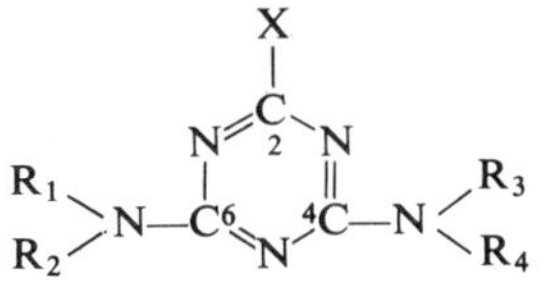

X: Cl, OCH$_3$, SCH$_3$
R$_1$–R$_4$: H or alkyl

(**2**)

1. Reactions Affecting the Substituents at C Atom 2

a. CHLOROTRIAZINES

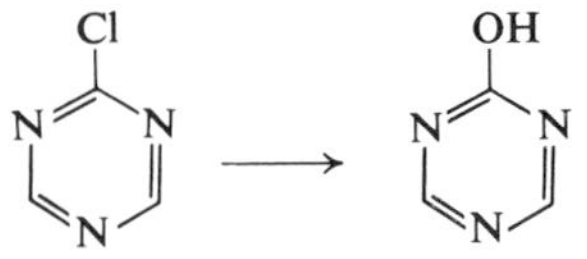

Hydroxytriazines were detected by means of TLC and spectrophotometry in soils treated with ^{14}C-labeled atrazine, simazine, and propazine under both laboratory and field conditions. The concentrations of the respective hydrolysis products are dependent on the soil type used. Repressing micro-bial growth under laboratory conditions did not appreciably affect the rate of hydrolysis. Consequently, the hydrolysis observed was concluded to be chemically catalyzed in nature. Discrimination between chemical and enzymatic hydrolysis is difficult, however, because effective sterilization of the soil without changing its properties is extremely difficult (*41,63,143*). To date, one example is known where a fungus, *Fusarium roseum* (Lk., Synder and Hansen), hydrolyzed a chlorotriazine to its corresponding hydroxy analog. The results, obtained with the aid of TLC, indicated a rapid degradation of atrazine to hydroxyatrazine (*97*).

Proof for the biochemical hydrolysis of the triazines in plants was obtained with in vitro systems. Cell sap, homogenates, and even particulate free extracts from corn rapidly formed the corresponding hydroxy derivatives when incubated with atrazine and simazine (*15,120,144–148*).

Detailed work was stimulated when the resistance of corn, in contrast to susceptible wheat, was attributed to an active principle capable of inactivating the chlorotriazines more rapidly in corn. Its structure was elucidated and shown to be 2,4-dihydroxy-7-methoxy-1,4-benzoxazin-3-one (MBOA), which is originally present in the plant in the form of its 2-glucoside (3) (*149–154*).

(3)

The rate of chemical hydrolysis of chlorotriazines to their corresponding hydroxy derivatives was directly correlated to actual concentrations of MBOA. This was proved, however, to be a generalized assumption, since the same hydroxy compounds were found in plants devoid of MBOA, for example, grain, sorghum, and Johnson grass. Moreover, MBOA was also detected in susceptible plant species. At the present time it is accepted that MBOA hydrolysis is in fact an important mechanism but nevertheless only one out of several possible mechanisms (*127,155–158*).

Intensive research since 1962 on the in vivo degradation of triazines in plants has resulted in an increasing number of publications all demonstrating the formation of hydroxytriazines. Independent of the magnitude of sensitivity to triazines, a wide variety of plant species (including cereals, vegetables, etc.) have demonstrated this hydrolytic capacity in varying degrees when treated with ^{14}C-labeled simazine, atrazine, ipazine, and propazine (*24,116,123–127,147,155,157,159,160*).

An interesting result was obtained with a recessive corn mutant having an MBOA content in the same low range as that found in wheat. Compared to the normal line, the hydrolytic capacity of this mutant was only moderately reduced, but it was considerably higher than that of wheat. The resistance of this mutant was essentially the same as that observed in the normal line (*156*).

The detection of hydroxy derivatives in the course of triazine degradation by animals was reported. With the aid of an ion-exchange chromatographic procedure especially developed for the separation of triazine metabolites, the presence of hydroxyatrazine was established in the urine and feces of rats fed ^{14}C-ring-labeled atrazine (*124*). Similarly, small amounts of the corresponding free hydroxy compounds were observed when the fate of propazine was followed in rats (*137*). In contrast, hydroxyatrazine and hydroxysimazine were detected only in the feces of rats treated with the corresponding chlorotriazines (*142*).

When ^{14}C-labeled hydroxy derivatives of atrazine and simazine themselves were fed to rats, a rapid excretion was again observed. The predominant amount was detected in the feces almost exclusively in the form of intact hydroxy compounds. Several other metabolites were determined in addition to the hydroxy derivatives in the urine. From these results it was concluded that the hydroxy compounds are only slightly resorbed in contrast to their corresponding parent compounds (*142,161*).

b. METHOXYTRIAZINES

At present only limited results concerning biochemical hydrolysis of the methoxytriazines in in vitro experiments with plants are known. The reason for only moderate interest in these *s*-triazines can be accounted for by the fact that the methoxytriazines are used essentially for nonselective weed control. It has been demonstrated, however, in corn extracts that MBOA system catalyzes less than 20% hydrolysis with methoxy compounds as compared to 100% hydrolysis of the chloro compounds under the same experimental conditions (*15,26,162*).

c. METHYLTHIOTRIAZINES

$$CH_3-S \longrightarrow CH_3-S{\rightarrow}O \longrightarrow CH_3-SO \longrightarrow OH$$

Although the MBOA system was shown to be inactive on the methylthio-triazines (*24,26,162*), the corresponding hydroxypropazine was detected in different plant species (cotton, carrots, soybeans, broad beans, etc.) treated with ^{14}C-ring-labeled prometryne and ametryne (*24,25,124,128,160*). Additional information resulted from experiments with peas cultivated in nutrient solution containing —$S^{14}CH_3$-labeled prometryne. A pronounced evolution of $^{14}CO_2$ was observed (*25*).

Sulfoxide and sulfone derivatives were claimed to be hypothetical intermediates during the removal of the entire methylthio group (*17*). Experimental proof was obtained with broad beans stem-injected with ^{14}C-ring-labeled prometryne and analyzed by TLC and special hydrolytic procedures (*21,25*).

Experiments have been conducted to compare directly the metabolic fate of chloro- and methylthiotriazines in mammals. The pattern of excreted metabolites in rats obtained after prometryne–^{14}C treatment was found similar to that already reported for propazine. The common hydroxy derivative was detected in an extractable form in both excreta. Recovery from the feces was remarkably increased after acidic incubation, indicating that hydroxypropazine may exist originally in the form of a conjugate or is liberated from some other chemical combination (*124,135,137*).

$$CH_3-S \longrightarrow SH \longrightarrow S{-}S$$

An unusual degradation sequence was reported to occur in rats and rabbits treated with unlabeled prometryne. Two urinary metabolites were identified as the free mercapto derivative and its corresponding disulfide concomitantly *N*-dealkylated at the C atom 4 (*163*).

2. Reactions Affecting the Substituents at C Atoms 4 and 6

a. MICROORGANISMS

Indirect evidence for the oxidative removal of the α-alkyl side chains was obtained in experiments with isolated fungi and bacteria. Evolution of labeled CO_2 was demonstrated when microorganisms were cultured in nutrient solution containing side-chain-labeled triazines (63,93,96,97). Knowledge of this type of reaction was substantially expanded by work utilizing the soil fungus *Aspergillus fumigatus Fres.* When cultured in the presence of ^{36}Cl- and ^{14}C-labeled simazine, two metabolites were extracted and separated by means of column chromatography. The structure of one of them was identified as the 2-chloro-4-amino-6-ethylamino-s-triazine by TLC, IR, NMR, and mass spectroscopy. The second metabolite contained the unchanged chlorine atom attached to the intact s-triazine ring, but the two ethyl groups were absent. The final structure of this metabolite remains unresolved (93,95,165). Evidence was accumulated in the preceding experiments suggesting partial deamination following the dealkylation reactions. Ammelide (2,4-dihydroxy-6-amino-s-triazine) was identified by TLC comparison with authentic material (165). Thus far this special type of degradation has been observed with fungi only.

b. PLANTS

When evaluating the performance of tertiary amino-chlorotriazine derivatives, a pronounced lag phase with respect to herbicidal action was observed. Under experimental conditions with pine seedlings, the phytotoxic action of ipazine (2-chloro-4-diethylamino-6-isopropylamino-s-triazine) did not appear until 80 days after application. A similar result was established under field conditions with oats and chlorazine (2-chloro-4,6-tetraethylamino-s-triazine). Both phenomena were interpreted as a result of a monodealkylation of the respective N-diethyl derivatives yielding the more toxic products: ipazine → atrazine; chlorazine → trietazine → simazine (98,99). Similar experimental proof for the oxidative degradation of the side chains has been furnished in a variety of plants. Appreciable amounts of $^{14}CO_2$ were liberated from corn, cotton, and soybeans when grown in solutions containing side-chain-labeled simazine (*155*). A remarkably high rate of *N*-dealkylation was demonstrated in corn treated with side-chain-labeled atrazine; up to 70% of the radioactivity totally taken up was evolved in the form of $^{14}CO_2$ (*26*).

N-dealkylated metabolites have been identified in experiments with pea plants cultured in the presence of either ring-labeled atrazine or prometryne. In the case of prometryne, the metabolite that was isolated had completely lost one of its isopropyl groups, whereas the rest of the molecule remained intact (*26*). The structure of one of the two possible *N*-dealkylated metabolites from atrazine was elucidated by means of TLC, gas chromatography, and IR spectroscopy and shown to be 2-chloro-4-amino-6-isopropylamino-*s*-triazine. Consequently it was concluded that this type of reaction was responsible for the moderate susceptibility of pea plants to atrazine. In contrast to hydrolysis, this dealkylation reaction does not represent a complete detoxification mechanism because the dealkylated metabolites show an intermediate phytotoxicity to this plant (*166–168*). Examples of complete dealkylation of *s*-triazines in plants were provided in experiments with *Coix lacrima jobi* L. and *Imperata cylindrica* L. When cultivated in the presence of simazine, six metabolites were extracted with 80% ethanol, following a chloroform extraction. Ion-exchange chromatography was used for the separation of hydroxy compounds. In addition to hydroxy-simazine four metabolites were identified with the following synthetic reference substances : (a) 2-hydroxy-4-amino-6-ethylamino-*s*-triazine; (b) 2-hydroxy-4,6-bisamino-*s*-triazine (ammeline) (*159*); and (c) the chloro analogs corresponding to (a) and (b) which were separated by means 'of alox-column chromatography (*169*).

c. ANIMALS

Investigations in animals demonstrated that the *N*-dealkylation is a biochemical degradation mechanism generally valid for all biological systems so far examined. Conclusive evidence was obtained with rats fed side-chain-labeled atrazine, simazine, and propazine. Approximately 50–75% of the total radioactivity applied was recovered in the form of $^{14}CO_2$ (*141*). Dealkylated metabolites were identified in the urine of rats and rabbits treated with chloromethoxy-, and methylmercapto-non-labeled triazines. In all cases it was reported that the substituents at C atom 2 were intact, whereas one or both of the two alkyl groups were removed. Both 2-chloro- and 2-methoxy-4,6-bisamino-*s*-triazines were extracted from urine of rats in sufficient amounts to be crystallized and analyzed (*163, 164*).

Another metabolic degradation sequence has been described in rats and rabbits treated with unlabeled triazines. α-Amino acids were found as end products of ω oxidation of one of the N-alkyl side chains. In the structures of urinary metabolites reported, the original chloro and methoxy substituents remained unchanged, but the alkyl of the second amino group was completely removed. This ω oxidation was found not to be operative with methylthiotriazines (*163,164*).

3. Cleavage of the Triazine Ring

In addition to hydrolytic and dealkylation reactions, cleavage of the heterocyclic ring has found comparable interest in the evaluation of the degradation of triazines. All investigations have been performed with ^{14}C-ring-labeled triazines because the conveniently detectable $^{14}CO_2$ is a conclusive proof for the complete oxidation of the heterocycle.

a. MICROORGANISMS

In isolated microbial systems $^{14}CO_2$ evolution was demonstrated only when side-chain-labeled triazines were used in the nutrient media (*93,96,97*). A small but significant release of $^{14}CO_2$ was reported in experiments where unspecified microorganisms were cultured either in solution or in different types of soil in the presence of ring-labeled chlorotriazines.

The capacity of these systems to liberate $^{14}CO_2$ and the amount of $^{14}CO_2$ actually released depended strongly on the respective experimental conditions, i.e., soil type, temperature, humidity, additional energy sources for microbial growth, etc. Therefore, these factors may account for the different data occasionally reported for the same triazine (*84,126,170,171*). Also, the length of the observation period seems important when attempting to obtain a clear picture of a given soil's degradative capacity. Results from long-term experiments with simazine in different soil types indicated that an initial period of marked $^{14}CO_2$ evolution (approximately 2.5% of the total treatment applied to the soil, within 5 weeks) was followed by a lag phase (up to 15 weeks). Then, a second period of $^{14}CO_2$ evolution started, which came to an end after 30 weeks. Depending on the soil type, the cumulative amount of $^{14}CO_2$ varied from 6 to 17% (*172*). It is apparent from all investigations reported that the liberation of CO_2 as a consequence of complete ring cleavage is not a main route of triazine degradation in soil since no correlation could be observed between herbicide dissipation and CO_2 evolution.

b. PLANTS

Cleavage of chloro-*s*-triazines with subsequent $^{14}CO_2$ evolution has also been investigated in a series of crops including corn, sorghum, oats, soybeans, cotton, etc. Generally, a moderate liberation of $^{14}CO_2$ up to 2.5% of the absorbed radioactivity, within 1 week after application, was observed with simazine, atrazine, and propazine (*24,26,84,113,120,173,174*). To date one exception is known with atrazine in corn where no $^{14}CO_2$ evolution was detected under a variety of experimental conditions (*109*). It should be stressed that the final results reported here are also dependent on the particular experimental conditions. Two factors in particular exert an important influence, namely, illumination and the CO_2 content of the flushing gas used to aerate the closed metabolic apparatus. The release of $^{14}CO_2$ under illumination and darkness conditions has been compared in corn cultured in nutrient solution in the presence of labeled simazine. A large increase in $^{14}CO_2$ evolution, from approximately 9 to 63% of that taken up by the plant, was observed within 68 hours when the plants were kept in total darkness (*121,122*). In the case of labeled propazine in sorghum, the removal of atmospheric CO_2 from the flush gas resulted in a complete interruption of the $^{14}CO_2$ evolution (*173,174*).

As mentioned previously, cotton plants seem to exhibit atypical behavior due to their particular morphologic features. When treated with labeled ipazine, no $^{14}CO_2$ evolution was detected (*126*). Comparable results were obtained with a methylthiotriazine. Experiments with prometryne in cotton failed to demonstrate $^{14}CO_2$ liberation, thus confirming that the capacity of cotton to metabolize *s*-triazines is limited with respect to both the rate and the pathways used (i.e., hydrolysis and *N* dealkylation) (*128*).

Additional information concerning the degradation of methylthio-triazines was obtained in experiments with prometryne in carrots, peas, and broad beans. Despite a rapid degradation of prometryne in carrots, no $^{14}CO_2$ liberation was observed. Failure to detect $^{14}CO_2$ after prometryne application to corn was also reported (*24*). In contrast, a slow release of $^{14}CO_2$ was observed in experiments with peas cultured in nutrient solution. In stem-injected broad beans a relatively high percentage (approximately 6% within 13 days) of the injected radioactivity was recovered as $^{14}CO_2$ (*26*).

Further investigations with hydroxyatrazine and cyanuric acid (a prospective metabolite) have yielded interesting results. Oats were capable for degrading the hydroxy analog as rapidly as corn degrades the parent chloro compound when compared on a $^{14}CO_2$-evolution basis (*24*). Almost complete degradation of uniformly labeled cyanuric acid was observed in experiments with corn where a large amount of radioactivity taken up by corn plants was recovered as $^{14}CO_2$ (80% within 6 days) (26).

Gysin and Knuesli (15) proposed a scheme for further degradation of the triazine heterocycle. After hydrolytic removal of the C atom 2 as CO_2, a fragment with a biguanide structure remains which is readily susceptible to further hydrolysis. Evidence was obtained in an experiment where the fate of propazine was followed in corn. The similarity of two metabolites with the postulated biguanide and biuret was determined by paper chromatography (24).

2-4. CONCLUSIONS

This chapter summarizes a large number of investigations concerned with the degradation of triazine herbicides. The enthusiasm of the many research workers has led to numerous interesting and illuminating findings. However, it may also be said that many questions remain unanswered.

Three major degradative pathways are evident: hydrolysis at C atom 2, N-dealkylation at C atoms 4 and 6, and splitting of the triazine ring. These examples show once again how living matter rids itself of foreign substances by differentiated chemical reactivity. The limits are defined, however, by the great variety of sensitive plants.

It may be concluded that in the face of complex biological systems the thorough study of small, well-defined sectors provides the highest probability for obtaining conclusive results and for approaching the final goal of a general understanding.

REFERENCES

1. A. Gast, E. Knuesli, and H. Gysin, *Experientia*, **11**, 107 (1955).
2. A. Gast, E. Knuesli, and H. Gysin, *Experientia*, **12**, 146 (1956).
3. Du Pont de Nemours, U.S. Pats. 3,185,561 (1957); 3,267,099 (1965).
4. J. R. Geigy, S.A., Swiss Pat. 409,516, Fr. Pat. 1,239,782 (1958).
5. Anon., *Chem. Eng. News*, **41**, 33 (1963).
6. Degussa, Ger. Pat. 1,187,241 (1958).
7. G. E. Barnsley and P. A. Gabbott, *Proc. Brit. Weed Control Conf. 8th*, **2**, 372 (1966).
8. CIBA, Swiss Pat. BE656,233, NE6,413,689 (1963)
9. L. J. Audus, *The Physiology and Biochemistry of Herbicides*, Academic Press, New York, 1964.
10. A. S. Crafts, *The Chemistry and Mode of Action of Herbicides*, Wiley (Interscience), New York, 1961.
11. R. Delley, K. Friedrich, B. Karlhuber, G. Székely, and K. Stammbach, *Z. Anal. Chem.*, **228**, 23 (1967).

12. V. H. Freed and M. L. Montgomery, *Residue Rev.*, **3**, 1 (1963).
13. H. Gysin and E. Knuesli, *Verhandl. Intern. Pflanzenschutz-Kongr. 4, Hamburg, 1957*, **1**. 549 (1959).
14. H. Gysin, *Weeds*, **8**, 541 (1960).
15. H. Gysin and E. Knuesli, *Advan. Pest Control Res.*, **3**, 289 (1960).
16. H. Gysin and E. Knuesli, *Proc. Brit. Weed Control Conf.*, 1960, p. 1.
17. H. Gysin, *Chem. Ind. (London)*, **1962**, 1393.
18. C. I. Harris, D. D. Kaufman, T. J. Sheets, R. G. Nash, and P. C. Kearney, *Advan. Pest Control Res.* (1968), in press.
19. P. C. Kearney, *Advan. Chem. Ser.*, **60**, 250 (1966).
20. E. Knuesli, *Phytiat-Phytopharm.*, **7**, 81 (1958).
21. E. Knuesli, *Proc. Brit. Weed Control Conf., 7th*, 1964, p. 287.
22. E. Knuesli, *Analytical Methods for Pesticides, Plant Growth Regulators and Food Additives*, Vol. 4 (G. Zweig, ed), Academic Press, New York, 1964, pp. 13, 27, 33, 171, 179, 187, 213.
23. E. Knuesli, *XVIth Intern. Symp. Crop Protection, Ghent*, 1964.
24. M. L. Montgomery and V. H. Freed, *J. Agr. Food Chem.*, **12**, 11 (1964).
25. P. W. Mueller, *Proc. 463rd Meeting Biochem. Soc., Aberystwyth, Colloq. Biochem. Herb.*, 1966, p. 1P.
26. P. W. Mueller and P. H. Payot, *Proc. IAEA Symp. Isotopes Weed Res., Vienna, 1965*, 1966, p. 61.
27. T. J. Sheets, C. I. Harris, D. D. Kaufman, and P. C. Kearney, *Proc. Northeast. Weed Control Conf.*, **18**, 20 (1964).
28. K. Stammbach, H. Kilchher, K. Friedrich, M. Larsen, and G. Székely, *Weed Res.*, **4**, 64 (1964).
29. (a) E. M. Smolin and L. Rapoport, *Chemistry of Heterocyclic Compounds*, Vol. 13, Wiley (Interscience), New York, 1959, p. 293; (b) p. 301; (c) p. 285; (d) p. 351; (e) pp. 44, 45, 53, 77, 78, 102, 162, 163, 206, 221, 328, 399, 401, 407.
30. J. R. Geigy, S.A., Swiss Pat. 393,344; U.S. Pat. 3,145,208 (1961).
31. J. R. Geigy, S.A., Swiss Pat., 396,021 (1961).
32. W. Kloetzer, *Monatsh.*, **93**, 1055 (1962).
33. CIBA, Swiss Pat. 395,116 (1960).
34. J. R. Geigy, S.A., Swiss Pat. 376,926; U.S. Pat. 3,122,541 (1959).
35. J. R. Geigy, S.A., Swiss Pat. 389,633 (1960).
36. Degussa, Ger. Pat. 1,172,684 (1962).
37. O. Alt, unpublished data, Anal. Lab., J. R. Geigy, S.A., Basel, 1957.
38. P. Castelfranco and B. Deutsch, *Weeds*, **10**, 244 (1962).
39. A. Gast, unpublished data, Res. Lab., J. R. Geigy, S.A., Basel, 1962.
40. I. J. Zemanek, *Rostlinna Vyroba*, **10** (9), 959 (1964).
41 C. I. Harris, *J. Agr. Food Chem.*, **15**, 157 (1967).
42. J. R. Geigy, S.A., Swiss Pat. 407,138 (1962).
43. E. Knuesli and D. Berrer, unpublished data, Res. Lab., J. R. Geigy, S.A., Basel, 1956–1961.
44. E. Knuesli, unpublished data, Res. Lab., J. R. Geigy, S.A., Basel, 1959–1961.
45. D. Berrer, unpublished data, Res. Lab., J. R. Geigy, S.A., Basel, 1962–1964.
46. E. Knuesli and D. Berrer, unpublished data, Res. Lab., J. R. Geigy, S.A., Basel, 1959–1963.
47. R. Delley, unpublished data, Anal. Lab., J. R. Geigy, S.A., Basel, 1963–1964.

48. J. R. Geigy, S.A., Swiss Pats. 380,733; 393,829; U.S. Pats. 3,195,998; 3,224,712 (1960).
49. BASF, DAS 1,184,148 (1963).
50. Degussa, BE 663,328, DAS (1964).
51. Degussa, BE 665,127, DAS (1964).
52. Degussa, DAS 1,138,978 (1959).
53. J. R. Geigy, S.A., Swiss Pats. 394,703; 381,699; U.S. Pats. 3,218,148; 3,236,846 (1958).
54. Degussa, BE 639,397, DAS (1963).
55. H. Gold, Bayer, Ger. Pat. 1,108,209 (1958).
56. H. Gold, *Angew Chem..*, **72**, 956 (1960).
57. C. Grundmann, *Angew. Chem.*, **75**, 39 (1963).
58. A. Kreutzberger, *Angew. Chem.*, **77**, 1086 (1965).
59. A. Kreutzberger, *Arch. Pharm.*, **299**, 897a, 984b (1966).
60. A. Hantsch, *Ber.*, **61B**, 1776 (1928).
61. B. S. Joshi, R. Srinivasan, R. V. Talavdekar, and K. Venkataraman, *Tetrahedron*, **11**, 133 (1960).
62. D. R. Osborne and R. Levine, *J. Org. Chem.*, **28**, 2933 (1939).
63. H. D. Skipper, M.S. thesis, Oregon State Univ., Corvallis, 1966.
64. H. D. Skipper, C. M. Gilmour, and W. R. Furtick, unpublished data, 1967.
65. D. E. Armstrong, Ph.D. thesis, Univ. Wisconsin, Madison, 1966.
66. D. E. Armstrong, G. Chesters, and R. F. Harris, *Proc. Soil Sci. Soc.*, **31**, 61 (1967).
67. C. D. Ercegovich, unpublished data, Geigy Chem. Co., Ardsley, N.Y., 1965.
68. L. S. Jordan, J. D. Mann, and B. E. Day, *Weeds*, **13**, 43 (1965).
69. L. S. Jordan, B. E. Day, and W. A. Clerx, *Weeds*, **12**, 5 (1964).
70. O. R. Dewey, *Proc. 2nd Brit. Weed Control Conf.*, **5**, 91 (1960).
71. T. J. Sheets and L. L. Danielson, *U.S. Dept. Agr.*, ARS 20-9, 170 (1960).
72. O. C. Burnside, E. L. Schmidt, and R. Behrens, *Weeds*, **9**, 477 (1961).
73. A. Gast, *Proc. 19th Ann. Symp. Crop Protection*, Ghent, 1962.
74. R. D. Comes and F. L. Timmons, *Weeds*, **13**, 81 (1965).
75. P. Burschel, *Weed Res.*, **1**, 131 (1961).
76. F. E. B. Roadhouse and L. A. Birk, *Can. J. Plant Sci.*, **41**, 252 (1961).
77. G. A. Buchanan and E. G. Rodgers, *Southern Weed Control Conf. Res Progr. Rept.*, 1963, p. 393.
78. T. J. Sheets and W. C. Shaw, *Weeds*, **11**, 15 (1963).
79. L. A. Birk and F. E. B. Roadhouse, *Can. J. Plant Sci.*, **44**, 21 (1964).
80. W. B. Duke, M.S. thesis, Oregon State Univ., Corvallis, 1964.
81. R. E. Talbert and O. H. Fletchall, *Weeds*, **12**, 33 (1964).
82. H. C. Sikka and D. E. Davis, *Weeds*, **14**, 289 (1966).
83. O. Agundis and R. Behrens, *Abstr. Weed Soc. Am.*, 1966, p. 70.
84. M. T. H. Ragab and J. P. McCollum, *Weeds*, **9**, 72 (1961).
85. J. Guillemat, *Compt. Rend.*, **250**, 1343 (1960).
86. J. Guillemat, M. Charpentier, P. Tardieux, and J. Pochon, *Ann. Epiphyties*, **11**, 261 (1960).
87. J. Pochon, P. Tardieux, and M. Charpentier, *Compt. Rend.* **250**, 1555 (1960).
88. J. J. Reid, *Proc. Northeast. Weed Control Conf.*, **14**, 19 (1960).
89. M. Charpentier and J. Pochon, *Ann. Inst. Pasteur*, **102**, 501 (1962).
90. J. B. Bryant, Ph.D. thesis, Pennsylvania State Univ., University Park, 1963.

91. J. V. Gramlich, R. W. Couch, H. C. Sikka, D. E. Davis, and H. H. Funderburk, Jr., *Proc. Southern Weed Conference*, 17, 356 (1964).

92. G. Pantos, P. Gyurko, T. Takacs, and L. Varga, *Acta Agron.*, 13, 21 (1964).

93. D. D. Kaufman, P. C. Kearney, and T. J. Sheets, *J. Agr. Food Chem.*, 13, 238 (1965).

94. S. K. Uhlig, *Wiss. Z. Tech. Univ. Dresden*, 15, 639 (1966).

95. D. D. Kaufman, P. C. Kearney, and T. J. Sheets, *Science*, 142, 405 (1963).

96. D. D. Kaufman and P. C. Kearney, *Abstr. Weed Soc. Am.*, 1964, p. 12

97. R. W. Couch, J. V. Gramlich, D. E. Davis, and H. H. Funderburk, Jr., *Proc. Southern Weed Conf.*, 18, 623 (1965).

98. T. J. Sheets, A. S. Crafts, and H. R. Drever, *J. Agr. Food Chem.*, 10, 458 (1962).

99. T. T. Kozlowski, *Nature*, 205, 104 (1965).

100. C. L. Foy, *Abstr. Weed Soc. Am.* 1961, p. 41.

101. C. L. Foy, *Plant Physiol. Suppl.*, 37, 25 (1962).

102. H. H. Funderburk, Jr. and J. M. Lawrence, *Weeds Res.*, 3, 304 (1963).

103. H. H. Funderburk, Jr. and J. M. Lawrence, *Weeds*, 11, 217 (1963).

104. P. K. Biswas, *Weeds*, 12, 31 (1964).

105. C. L. Foy, *Weeds*, 12, 103 (1964).

106. F. W. Freeman, D. P. White, and M. J. Bukovac, *Forest Sci.*, 10, 330 (1964).

107. H. Minshall, *Weed Soc. Am. Abstr.*, 1964, p. 80.

108. J. L. P. van Oorschot, *XVIth Intern. Symp. Crop Protection, Ghent*, 1964.

109. D. E. Davis, J. V. Gramlich, and H. H. Funderburk, Jr., *Weeds*, 13, 252 (1965).

110. J. L. P. van Oorschot, *Weed Res.*, 5, 84 (1965).

111. L. M. Wax and R. Behrens, *Weeds*, 13, 107 (1965).

112. R. H. Shimabukuro and A. J. Linck, *Weeds*, 15, 175 (1967).

113. D. E. Davis, H. H. Funderburk, Jr., and N. G. Sansing, *Proc. Southern Weed Conf.*, 12, 172 (1959).

114. D. E. Davis, H. H. Funderburk, Jr., and N. G. Sansing, *Weeds*, 7, 300 (1959).

115. T. J. Sheets, *Weeds*, 9, 1 (1961).

116. D. R. Roberts, D. E. Davis, and H. H. Funderburk, Jr., *Weed Soc. Am. Abstr.*, 1964, p. 71.

117. P. V. Saburova and A. A. Petunova, *Dokl. Akad. Nauk USSR*, 160, 1215 (1965).

118. C. A. Leonard, L. A. Lider, and R. K. Glenn, *Weed Res.*, 6, 37 (1966).

119. S. K. Uhlig, Thesis, Tech. Univ., Dresden, 1966.

120. C. L. Foy and P. Castelfranco, *Plant Physiol. Suppl.*, 35, xxviii (1960).

121. V. H. Freed, M. Montgomery, and M. Kief, *Proc. Northeast. Weed Control Conf.*, 15, 6 (1961).

122. M. Montgomery and V. H. Freed, *Weeds*, 9, 231 (1961).

123. P. H. Plaisted and D. P. Ryskiewich, *Plant Physiol. Suppl.*, 37, xxv (1962).

124. P. H. Plaisted and M. L. Thornton, *Contrib. Boyce Thompson Inst.*, 22, 399 (1964).

125. P. H. Plaisted, D. Ryskiewich, and C. Ercegovich, *Plant Physiol. Suppl.*, 39, 68 (1964).

126. R. H. Hamilton and D. E. Moreland, *Weeds*, 11, 213 (1963).

127. N. S. Negi, H. H. Funderburk, Jr., and D. E. Davis, *Weeds*, 12, 53 (1964).

128. D. C. Whitenberg, *Weeds*, 13, 68 (1965).

129. P. K. Biswas and D. D. Hemphill, *Nature*, 207, 215 (1965).

130. H. W. Hilton, *Residue Rev.*, 15, 1 (1966).

131. L. E. St. John, Jr., D. G. Wagner, and D. J. Lisk, *J. Dairy Sci.*, 47, 1267 (1964).

132. L. E. St. John, Jr., J. W. Ammering, D. G. Wagner, R. G. Warner, and D. J. Lisk, *J. Dairy Sci.* 48, 502 (1965).

78   E. KNUESLI, D. BERRER, G. DUPUIS, AND H. ESSER

133. A. M. Mattson, J. Solga, and J. Schneller, Geigy Res. Anal. Dept., internal report, June 30, 1965.
134. A. M. Mattson, J. Solga, and J. Schneller, Geigy Res. Anal. Dept., internal reports, June 30, 1965, June 27, 1966.
135. A. M. Mattson, J. Solga, R. L. Beaudoin, and J. Schneller, Geigy Res. Lab. Anal. Dept., internal report, August 6, 1963.
136. B. Q. Richman, J. H. Kay, and J. C. Calandra, Rept. Ind. Bio-Test Lab., Inc., Sept. 29, 1964.
137. D. P. Ryskiewich, Geigy Res., *Tech. Bull.*, Febr. 11, 1965.
138. J. S. Bowman, Rept. Hazleton Lab., April 29, 1960.
139. J. S. Bowman, Rept. Hazleton Lab., July 21, 1960.
140. J. E. Bakke, J. D. Robbins, and V. J. Feil, *J. Agr. Food Chem.*, 15, 628 (1967).
141. J. E. Bakke and J. D. Robbins, *Am. Chem. Soc. 153rd Meet. Abstr.*, 1967, p. A49.
142. D. P. Ryskiewich, Geigy Res., *Tech. Bull.*, April 3, 1964.
143. C. I. Harris, *Weed Res.*, 5, 275 (1965).
144. W. Roth, *Compt. Rend.*, 245, 942 (1957).
145. W. Roth, Ph.D. thesis, Univ. Strasbourg, 1958.
146. M. Montgomery and V. H. Freed, *Res. Progr. Rept. Western Weed Control Conf.*, 1960, p. 71.
147. R. H. Hamilton and D. E. Moreland, *Science*, 135, 373 (1962).
148. P. Castelfranco, C. L. Foy, and D. B. Deutsch, *Weeds*, 9, 580 (1961).
149. O. Wahlroos and A. I. Virtanen, *Acta Chem. Scand.*, 13, 1906 (1959).
150. P. K. Hietala and A. I. Virtanen, *Acta Chem. Scand.*, 14, 502 (1960).
151. E. Honkanen and A. I. Virtanen, *Acta Chem. Scand.*, 14, 504 (1960).
152. A. I. Virtanen and P. K. Hietala, *Acta Chem. Scand.*, 14, 499 (1960).
153. W. Roth and E. Knuesli, *Experientia*, 17, 312 (1961).
154. P. Castelfranco and M. S. Brown, *Weeds*, 10, 131 (1962).
155. H. H. Funderburk, Jr. and D. E. Davis, *Weeds*, 11, 101 (1963).
156. R. H. Hamilton, *Weeds*, 12, 27 (1964).
157. R. H. Hamilton, *J. Agr. Food Chem.*, 12, 14 (1964).
158. R. D. Palmer and C. O. Crogan, *Weeds*, 13, 219 (1965).
159. J. Hurter, *Experientia* 22, 741 (1966).
160. R. C. Barba, Ph.D. thesis, Univ. Hawaii, Honolulu, 1967.
161. J. Donoso and J. J. Peterson, Rept. Woodard Res. Corp., October 11, 1963.
162. P. W. Mueller, unpublished data, J. R. Geigy, S.A., Basel, 1961.
163. C. Boehme and F. Baer, *Food Cosmet. Toxicol.*, 5, 23 (1967).
164. C. Boehme, Ph.D. thesis, Tech. Univ., Berlin, 1965.
165. P. C. Kearney, D. D. Kaufman, and T. J. Sheets, *J. Agr. Food Chem.*, 13, 369 (1965).
166. R. H. Shimabukuro, *Am. Chem. Soc. 152nd Meet. Abstr.*, 1966, p. A34.
167. R. H. Shimabukuro, R. E. Kadunce, and D. S. Frear, *J. Agr. Food Chem.*, 14, 392 (1966).
168. R. H. Shimabukuro, *J. Agr. Food Chem.*, 15, 557 (1967).
169. J. Hurter, *6th Intern. Congr. Plant Protection, Vienna*, 1967, p. 398.
170. I. C. McRae and M. Alexander, *J. Agr. Food Chem.*, 13, 72 (1965).
171. L. L. McCormick and A. E. Hiltbold, *Weeds*, 14, 77 (1966).
172. A. Suess, private communication, 1967.
173. C. L. Foy, *Proc. 14th Calif. Weed Conf.*, 1962, p. 82.
174. C. L. Foy, unpublished data, Botany Dept., Univ. California, Davis, 1965.

CHAPTER 3

The Substituted Ureas

HANS GEISSBUHLER

AGROCHEMICAL DIVISION CIBA LTD.
BASEL, SWITZERLAND

3-1. Introduction   79
3-2. Soil and Plant Factors Affecting Degradation.   .   .   .   83
    A. Soil–Herbicide Interactions Affecting Degradation   .   .   .   83
    B. Movement of Urea Herbicides within Plants   .   .   .   85
    C. Mode of Action in Plants   87
3-3. Degradation   89
    A. Degradation in Soils   89
    B. Metabolism in Plants   95
    C. Degradation in Animals   101
3-4. Biochemical and Enzymatic Mechanisms Involved in Degradation   .   104
    A. N Dealkylation   104
    B. Additional Pathways   106
    C. Conclusions   107
References   108

3-1. INTRODUCTION

The discovery of the herbicidal properties of phenyl-substituted ureas by Thompson et al. in 1946 (1) and by E. I. du Pont de Nemours & Co. in 1949 (2,3) has stirred the imagination of numerous synthetic chemists on both sides of the Atlantic. From statements made in the literature, it seems certain that literally thousands of urea derivatives have found their way from chemical laboratories to greenhouses for careful scrutiny by the biologists (4,5). From this effort have emerged thus far about a dozen different compounds which are marketed commercially. Whereas the first phenyl-ureas developed were chlorine-substituted dimethylderivatives with a high order of inherent phytotoxicity, in more recent compounds ring structures, ring substituents, and alkyl moieties have become increasingly complex. These structural adaptations, although not introducing a higher order of

79

TABLE 3-1

Chemical and Physical Properties

Structural formula	Chemical designation	Common name	Mol. weight; sol. H_2O, ppm	mp (melting range, °C); vp (vapor pressure, mm Hg)
	3-Phenyl-1,1-dimethylurea	Fenuron	164.2 3850 (25°)	mp: 133–134
	3-(p-Chlorophenyl)-1,1-dimethylurea	Monuron	198.7 230 (25°)	mp:176–177 vp: 5×10^{-7} (25°C)
	3-(3,4-Dichlorophenyl)-1,1-dimethylurea	Diuron	233.1 42 (25°)	mp: 158–159 vp: 0.31×10^{-5} (50°C)
	3-(m-Trifluoromethylphenyl)-1,1-dimethylurea	Fluometuron	232.1 90 (25°)	mp: 163–164.5 vp: 5×10^{-7} (20°C)

Name	Common name	Properties	mp
3-[4-(p-Chlorophenoxy)-phenyl]-1,1-dimethylurea	Chloroxuron	290.7, 3.7 (20°)	mp: 151–152
3-Cyclooctyl-1,1-dimethylurea	Cycluron	198.2, 1200 (20°)	mp: 138
3-(Hexahydro-4,7-methanoindan-5-yl)-1,1-dimethylurea	Norea	222.3, 150	mp: 168–169
3-(3,4-Dichlorophenyl)-1-butyl-1-methylurea	Neburon	275.2, 4.8 (24°)	mp: 102–103
3-(p-Chlorophenyl)-1-methyl-1-(1-methyl-2-propynyl)urea	Buturon	236.7, 30 (20°)	mp: 145–146
3-Phenyl-1-(2-methylcyclohexyl)urea	Siduron	232.3, 18 (25°)	mp: 133–138

TABLE 3-1 –*continued*

Structural formula	Chemical designation	Common name	Mol. weight; sol. H_2O, ppm	mp (melting range, °C); vp (vapor pressure, mm Hg)
	3-(*p*-Chlorophenyl)-1-methoxy-1-methylurea	Monolinuron	214.6 930 (20°)	vp: 1.5×10^{-4} (24°C)
	3-(*p*-Bromophenyl)-1-methoxy-1-methylurea	Metobromuron	259.1 330 (20°)	mp: 95–96 vp: 3×10^{-6} (20°C)
	3-(3,4-Dichlorophenyl)-1-methoxy-1-methylurea	Linuron	249.0 75 (25°) (du Pont) 220 (20°) (Hoechst)	mp: 93–94 vp: 1.5×10^{-5} (24°C)
	3-(3-Chloro-4-bromophenyl)-1-methoxy-1-methylurea	Chlorbromuron[a]	293.6 50	mp: 94–96 vp: 4×10^{-7} (20°C)

[a] Suggested common name.

phytotoxicity, have led to more subtle differences among the molecules in regard to their behavior in soil and plant environments. It is therefore not surprising that parallel to the development of new derivatives, there has been a shift from soil-sterilant use of this group of substances to selective agricultural pre- and postemergent herbicides.

The potent and selective inhibitory effect of substituted ureas on photosynthesis in green plants and algae has stimulated biochemists to investigate this type of compound as a useful tool for elucidating certain fundamental aspects of electron-transfer mechanisms (6). On the practical side, some performance and persistence problems in the field have provoked a host of biological and physical soil-behavior experiments (7). In addition, isotopically labeled ureas have been included in many gross autoradiographic studies dealing with the movement of herbicides in plants (8,9).

In contrast to all these activities, soil, plant, and animal degradation experiments at the biochemical level have been slow in coming. As the present chapter will demonstrate, our knowledge of the pathways of degradation and transformation of ureas is still fragmentary. Practically nothing is known about the particular types of enzymes and enzymatic mechanisms involved. Instead of presenting a well-balanced picture of urea herbicide degradation, the author has been obliged to summarize the fragments and to add some thoughts and speculations on lines of biochemical research which might profitably be investigated in the future.

A large number of substituted ureas have been examined for herbicidal activity. The chemical and physical properties of several important ureas are shown in Table 3-1.

3-2. SOIL AND PLANT FACTORS AFFECTING DEGRADATION

A. Soil-Herbicide Interactions Affecting Degradation

Examination of the herbicidal activity of soil-applied urea compounds under a variety of field conditions immediately demonstrated that certain soil properties and soil environmental factors had a prominent effect not only on their performance but also on their persistence (10,11,12). These initial observations have led to a large number of soil-behavior experiments, mostly of the bioassay type, which have recently been reviewed in detail by Sheets (7). Several of the studies suggest that adsorption of the urea herbicides to certain soil constituents (organic particles, various types of clay

colloids) is an important factor not only in controlling their removal from
soil layers by leaching but also in regulating the rates of their degradation
by microorganisms. Soil adsorption and desorption equilibria determine the
concentration of each particular compound in the soil solution and thus its
availability to microbial decomposition. Adsorption appears to be lowest in
sandy soils, intermediate in clay loams, and highest in organic soils with a
high humus content (4,13–24). In addition, there are significant differences
among the various ureas with regard to their degree of adsorption in a
particular soil. This is demonstrated in Fig. 3-1, which compares the
empirical Freundlich adsorption isotherms of fluometuron, metobromuron,

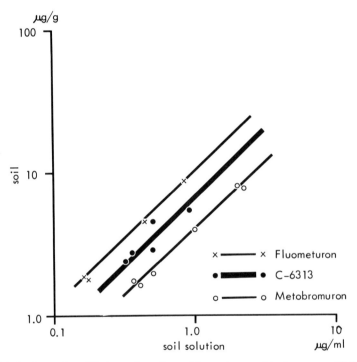

Fig. 3-1. Isothermal equilibrium adsorption of fluometuron, chlorbromuron (C-6313),
and metobromuron on a Swiss humus soil. Data presented in terms of empirical Freundlich relationship ($x/m = KC^n$), whereby the concentrations of herbicide fixed on the soil
(x/m) have been plotted against the concentration in soil solution (C) on a log × log scale.
Admitting the concentration of each herbicide in the soil solution to be 1.0 $\mu g/ml$, the
concentrations of compound fixed on the soil ($\mu g/g$) are about the following: fluometuron
= 10, chlorbromuron = 6, metobromuron = 4 [Reproduced from Ref. (25) by permission
of CIBA Ltd.]

and chlorbromuron as determined for a Swiss humus soil. Although no direct comparison of the adsorptive properties of all commercial ureas is available at this time, there are sufficient data to demonstrate that among the chlorinated phenyldialkyl derivatives, adsorption increases according to the following sequence: fenuron < monuron < diuron < neburon < chloroxuron (*17–19,20,22,26*). Indications are that alkylalkoxy derivatives, such as monolinuron and linuron, are slightly more adsorbed than their corresponding dialkyl analogs and that replacement of chlorine by bromine or trifluoromethyl ring substituents increases adsorption (*22,25*).

Since availability in the soil solution is inversely related to adsorption, it is to be expected that, in a particular soil, the more strongly adsorbed herbicides are less rapidly decomposed by microorganisms. In support of this assumption, fenuron was inactivated most rapidly and diuron least rapidly in a large number of California soils, whereas the rate of monuron inactivation was intermediate (*16*). Similarly, when examined with the same soil and under the same environmental conditions, monuron was found to be more persistent than fenuron (*27*), but less persistent than neburon (*28,29*); linuron was degraded less rapidly than monolinuron (*30*); and metobromuron disappeared at a faster rate than fluometuron (*31*). However, when comparing different soils, it must be remembered that adsorption is highest in the organic type which, at the same time, is most favorable for microbial growth and thus most efficient for biochemical degradation. This phenomenon may mask or offset the rates of microbial degradation which would be predicted on the basis of adsorptive behavior only (*7*).

B. Movement of Urea Herbicides within Plants

Both the site and the rate of degradation of urea herbicides in plants are intimately connected with the capacity of these plants to take up the compounds from the environment and to translocate them into various organs and tissues. The movement of substituted ureas has mainly been investigated with the aid of biological and gross autoradiographic methods (*32–43*). In a few scattered instances, these techniques have been supplemented by parallel quantitative measurements (*30,40,83,86*).

There is general agreement that all ureas so far examined are easily taken up from nutrient and soil solutions by root systems and most of them are rapidly translocated into stems and leaves by the transpiration stream. It is therefore not surprising that factors which lower the rate of transpiration, such as high external water vapor pressure or closure of foliar stomata, also decrease the amounts of herbicide translocated to aerial parts (*33,40,42*). When the compounds are applied to hypocotyls or basal stem sections, uptake appears to be more restricted and translocation proceeds in the apical direction only (*43,44*).

Of particular importance in connection with plant degradation studies is

CHLOROXURON   METOBROMURON   FLUOMETURON
2.5ppm herbicide (equal specific activity)

Fig. 3-2. Comparative uptake by roots and translocation to aerial parts of ^{14}C-labeled chloroxuron, metobromuron, and fluometuron in French dwarf bean seedlings, cultured in nutrient solution supplied with 2.5 ppm (and equal concentrations of radioactivity) of each herbicide. Plants kept in herbicide solution for 24 hours and then cultured in regular nutrient solution for an additional 24 hours. Top: mounted plants. Bottom: radioautographs of same plants. [Adapted from Ref. (*44*).]

the fact that different urea herbicides exhibit different mobilities in plant systems. This is demonstrated in Fig. 3-2, which compares uptake and translocation by bean plants of chloroxuron, fluometuron, and metobromuron when supplied to nutrient cultures in equal concentrations (essentially equimolar) and specific radioactivities. Whereas the movement of chloroxuron to aerial parts was found to be restricted under the short-term conditions applied, both fluometuron and metobromuron were rapidly translocated into leaves. However, the two latter compounds differed strikingly with regard to their distribution pattern within the leaves. In contrast to metobromuron, which was mainly confined to tracheal veins, fluometuron had almost completely moved out into the mesophyll tissues. Such differences in the mobility of herbicides are bound to affect their exposure to different cellular environments and consequently to different enzyme systems.

When applied to leaf surfaces, the substituted ureas are able to penetrate cuticular and epidermal layers to varying degrees and this entry apparently may be enhanced by the addition of suitable surfactants (45–47). Subsequently, a fraction of the compounds not only reaches the photosynthesizing mesophyll cells but also the tracheal veins by which it is moved in a peripheral direction. However, there is little or no entry into the phloem system and therefore practically no translocation into stem, neighboring leaves, flowers, or fruits by the assimilate stream. Even in organs of high phloem and seemingly low xylem activity, such as soybean cotyledons, symplastic movement of diuron has been observed to be practically nonexistent (43). Suggestions that certain surfactants may induce phloem or "downward" movement (48) have not been substantiated by actual measurements.

C. Mode of Action in Plants

The mode of action determining the phytotoxic effects of urea herbicides is intimately connected with their degradation or transformation; these processes regulate the number of unchanged molecules actually reaching the active sites and the time during which they have a chance to exhibit their lethal or inhibitory effects. A brief review of the present status of urea herbicide mode of action will therefore be included in this chapter.

The potent inhibitory effect of substituted ureas on the photosynthetic mechanism of green whole plants, plant parts, isolated chloroplasts, and algae was recognized soon after the discovery of their herbicidal properties. Thus Wessels and van der Veen in 1956 (49) observed that leaves or parts thereof lose their ability to assimilate carbon dioxide when treated with monuron. Extending their studies to a number of related compounds, the same authors were able to demonstrate that these substances inhibit the Hill reaction, i.e., the evolution of oxygen in the presence of living chloroplasts and a suitable hydrogen acceptor. Inhibition of the Hill reaction by low concentrations of ureas was subsequently confirmed with a variety of different chloroplast preparations and hydrogen acceptors (50–54). In addition, inhibitory effects of the compounds on other phenomena connected with photosynthetic energy conversions, such as light reemission and electron-spin resonance (55,56), were observed. These phenomena are beyond the scope of this chapter.

At present, the photosynthetic mechanism of green plants is visualized to include two light reactions, which are schematically presented in Fig. 3-3.

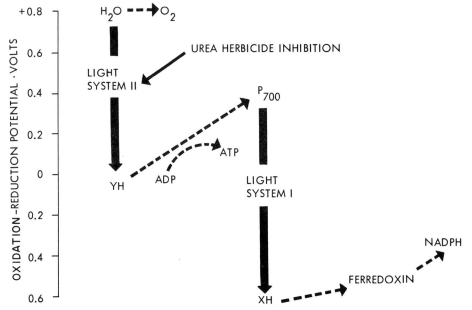

Fig. 3-3. Potential diagram of electron-transfer chain in photosynthesis involving two light reactions (solid arrows). The dashed arrows indicate exergonic dark reactions. Light reaction I accomplishes the reduction of the lowest potential reactant X and oxidizes a reactant of intermediate potential P_{700}. Light reaction II sensitizes the reduction of the intermediate Y while oxidizing water to oxygen. Urea herbicides inhibit electron transfer in light reaction II. ADP, adenosine diphosphate; ATP, adenosine triphosphate; NADPH, reduced nicotinamide adenine dinucleotide phosphate. [Adapted from Ref. (57).]

The net result of this sequence of light reactions is the evolution of oxygen and the formation of adenosine triphosphate (ATP) and reduced nicotinamide adenine dinucleotide phosphate (NADPH). ATP and NADPH are subsequently used for the reduction of carbon dioxide.

The substituted ureas were found to have no inhibitory effect on the photoreduction of hydrogen-adapted *Scenedesmus* cultures (*58*). Since in these cultures the oxygen-liberating pathway was eliminated by using hydrogen instead of water, the site of action of urea herbicides can be located with reasonable certainty to that part of the photosynthetic mechanism which is connected with the process of oxygen evolution. Unfortunately, we are practically ignorant concerning the enzymatic events associated with this process and thus the particular enzyme inhibited by ureas (*59*). Sweetser (*60*) and Homann and Gaffron (*61*) observed that flavin mono-nucleotide (FMN) reversed the inhibitory effects of monuron and that the herbicide formed a complex with FMN in the presence of light. These data no more than suggest the possible involvement of a flavin-containing substance in oxygen evolution and its inhibition by urea herbicides. At this stage it is too early to decide whether such a mechanism would kill plants by buildup of a phytotoxic compound (*62*) or by starvation.

By measuring the rate and the extent of recovery of photosynthetic activity in whole plants and plant parts upon their exposure to urea herbi-cides, van Oorschot (*63–65*) and Swanson et al. (*66*) demonstrated that such measurements may give valuable information on the ability of these plants to degrade or otherwise detoxify the compounds applied.

3-3. DEGRADATION

A. Degradation in Soils

From the many soil experiments which have been carried out during the last fifteen years, the following processes have emerged as being potentially involved in inactivating soil-applied urea herbicides (*7*):

1. Removal through leaching by rainfall and irrigation water, adsorption to soil particles, volatilization, and uptake by plants

2. Degradation by photochemical, chemical, and biochemical mechan-isms

The significance and relative importance of inactivation by removal processes is beyond the scope of this chapter and has been dealt with in recent reviews and articles (*7,67*). With regard to degradation mechanisms, photochemical decomposition, which is of practical importance to urea compounds (*68–70*), will be discussed in Chapter 12. Although no systematic studies have been carried out, urea herbicides appear to be sufficiently stable under normal temperature and soil conditions to resist hydrolytic break-

90   HANS GEISSBUHLER

down or oxidation by purely chemical means (71). This section will therefore be concerned exclusively with biochemical degradation processes which may be attributed to microbial activity.

A number of early investigations demonstrated that conditions favoring growth of microorganisms, such as high temperature, high moisture content, and the presence of organic matter, hasten the inactivation of urea herbicides applied to soils (11,33,72). Further proof for microbial activity as an instrumental factor in the degradation of urea compounds was

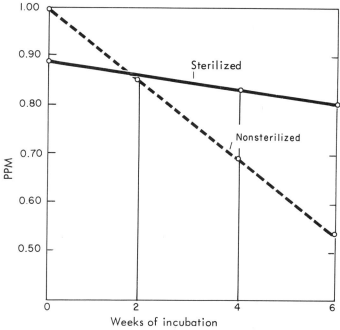

Fig. 3-4. Rate of disappearance of diuron in chloropicrin-sterilized and nonsterilized Cecil loamy sand. Compound applied at the rate of 1 ppm based on weight of air-dry soil. Soil samples watered and then stored at 80°F and 60% relative humidity. Concentrations of herbicide determined by bioassay using oat seedlings as indicator plants. [Redrawn with permission from Ref. (71), p. 100.]

obtained by comparing the rates of disappearance of herbicidal activity in nonsterilized soil samples and in samples sterilized chemically or by auto-claving (17,30,71,73). A typical example of such an experiment with diuron is shown in Fig. 3-4.

Hill et al. (71) were the first to search systematically for soil organisms capable of decomposing ureas and were indeed able to isolate from a

Brookston silty clay loam a bacterium of the *Pseudomonas* group which could utilize monuron as a sole source of carbon. When measuring its respiration by the Warburg technique, the authors demonstrated that, after the compound was added to the buffered medium, total oxygen uptake increased with increasing concentration of herbicide. A further bacterium of the *Pseudomonas* type was found to be able to rapidly oxidize monuron, provided the medium was supplemented with an appropriate growth factor such as yeast extract. Extending the same approach to other groups of microorganisms, Hill and McGahen (74) observed that other bacteria such as *Xanthomonas, Sarcina,* and *Bacillus* spp. and fungi, such as a *Penicillium* and *Aspergillus* spp., all of which are common soil inhabitants, were able to utilize monuron as a carbon source in agar media. Although more than 10 years have passed since these experiments, there have apparently been no successful attempts to prepare from such active organisms cell-free systems or enzyme preparations capable of oxidizing or otherwise degrading urea herbicides.

The availability of several isotopically labeled phenylureas afforded a more systematic approach to possible pathways of microbial degradation. Hill et al. (71) added methyl-^{14}C-monuron to a clay loam and followed the evolution of $^{14}CO_2$. Labeled CO_2 was given off at a low but almost constant rate for about 70 days, after which $^{14}CO_2$ evolution decreased. After 90 days approximately 10% of the originally applied radioactivity was recovered as carbon dioxide. These experiments indicated that microorganisms are able to remove and oxidize the methyl moiety. Using the same type of experiment, Börner (30) observed a much higher rate of $^{14}CO_2$ evolution following addition of carbonyl-^{14}C–linuron to a loamy soil. After a short lag period, labeled carbon dioxide was given off at a constant rate for 60 days, after which evolution of $^{14}CO_2$ again decreased. Upon termination of the experiment, i.e., 130 days after application, more than 90% of the radioactivity originally applied had been evolved as carbon dioxide. Börner suggested that linuron is broken down to 3,4-dichloroaniline, methoxy-methylamine, and carbon dioxide. Although he was able to recover a small percentage of 3,4-dichloroaniline when applying high dosages of linuron to soil samples, he was unable to identify the aliphatic amine.

In a search for possible intermediates, Geissbühler et al. (73) exposed carbonyl-^{14}C–chloroxuron to liquid cultures of mixed soil bacteria and succeeded in isolating metabolites from the culture medium and in identifying them as 3-(4-chlorophenoxy)phenyl-1-methylurea and 3-(4-chloro-phenoxy)phenylurea. Evolution of a small percentage of labeled carbon dioxide suggested formation of some 4-chloro-4'-amino-diphenylether.

The following pathway, including stepwise demethylation and deamination–decarboxylation was therefore proposed for chloroxuron:

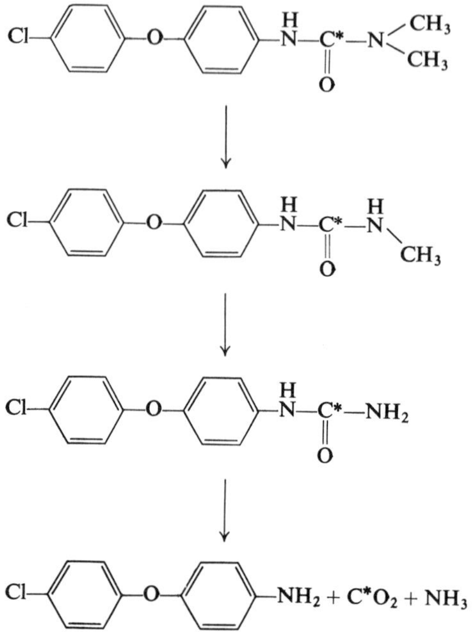

An entirely analogous soil degradation pathway was demonstrated for diuron by Dalton et al. (75) after they had investigated soil samples from herbicide-treated cotton fields and identified the following metabolites: 3-(3,4-dichlorophenyl)-1-methylurea, 3,4-dichlorophenylurea, and 3,4-dichloroaniline. Stepwise demethylation and subsequent hydrolysis were therefore proposed to proceed as follows:

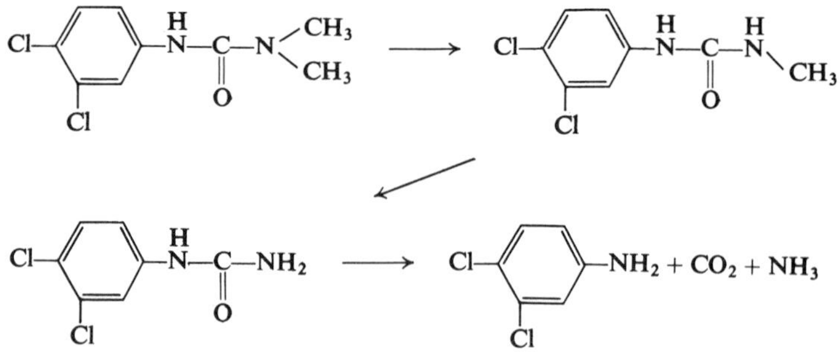

There are preliminary indications that monuron (*83*) and fluometuron (*76*) follow the same pathway of soil microbial degradation. For practical purposes it is important to know that stepwise demethylation and hydrolysis gradually decrease the herbicidal activity and therefore represent detoxification processes. Compared to the parent compounds, the monomethyl derivatives are normally less phytotoxic and the demethyl and aniline compounds are inactive (*73,75*).

As regards the further breakdown of the anilines, Dalton et al. (*75*) suggested an orderly degradation to carbon dioxide, ammonia, and halogen, without, however, demonstrating any of the intermediates, including the state of oxidation of the halogen. That the anilines may indeed be rapidly decomposed was shown by Börner (*30*), who added 4-chloroaniline and 3,4-dichloroaniline to samples of clay loam and observed about 90 to 70% losses, respectively, within a period of 8 days. Unfortunately again no intermediates were identified in these experiments. One of the initial steps of aniline conversion is suggested by the work of Bartha and Pramer (*77*), who, upon addition of large quantities of 3'4-dichloro-propionanilide (DCPA) to soil, surprisingly observed its partial transformation to 3,3',4,4'-tetrachloroazobenzene with 3,4-dichloroaniline as an intermediate.

However, analysis of numerous samples of soils which had been exposed to urea herbicides for various time intervals under field conditions did not reveal the presence of any azo derivatives (*111*).

The kinetics of disappearance of urea herbicides from soils have not yet been clearly defined. The degradation curves of monuron presented by Hill et al. (*71*) were interpreted by Audus (*78*) to follow the "enrichment type," i.e., showing a definite initial lag phase during which the bacteria are adapted enzymatically to cope with the foreign substrate to which they are exposed. The $^{14}CO_2$-evolution curve obtained by Börner (*30*) upon addition of carbonyl-^{14}C–linuron to wet clay loam, which showed a lag period of less than 10 days, might support such a mechanism. However, it is difficult to

see how a mixed soil bacterial population would be enzymatically adapted
or built up within a few days when exposed to such minute quantities of
herbicide. Physical factors, such as slow dissolution of the compound or
gradual establishment of soil solution equilibrium conditions, would also
be expected to cause a certain initial lag period. The present author therefore
favors the suggestion of Sheets (7) that certain microorganisms may utilize
the phenylureas, but not preferentially or selectively to other energy sources.

Soil degradation curves of urea herbicides obtained by chemical analysis
(30,71) must be interpreted with care, since the total analytical method

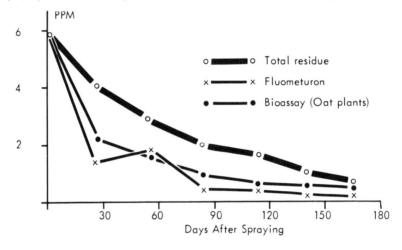

Fig. 3-5. Rate of disappearance of fluometuron in the 0–5-cm layer of a plant-free Swiss
clay loam under field conditions. Soil composition: 18% clay, 12% silt, 67% sand, < 1%
humus; pH 5.7. Herbicide applied at the rate of 4 kg a.i./ha. Total trifluoromethylaniline-
containing residue determined chemically by subjecting the soil sample to alkaline
hydrolysis, steam distillation–extraction, and colorimetric measurement (79). Structurally
unchanged fluometuron measured after exhaustive soil extraction with acetone and
separation of the herbicide from its potential metabolites on a Florisil column. Bioassay
carried out with oat seedlings. [Reprinted by permission from Ref. (31).]

normally applied is based upon the alkaline hydrolysis of the parent compound to the corresponding aniline (79). It thus not only measures the
original herbicide, but also any metabolites which still contain the aniline
structure. For kinetic studies, procedures are therefore required which will
determine the quantities of structurally unchanged herbicide. The application
of such a method, as compared to the standard procedure for determining
the rate of degradation of fluometuron in a Swiss clay loam, is shown in

Fig. 3-5. The curves clearly demonstrate that unchanged fluometuron disappears considerably faster than the total of all trifluoromethylaniline-containing residues.

It seems that not only microorganisms but also plants might be a factor in contributing urea herbicide metabolites to the soil environment. Nutrient solutions which had been used for supplying isotopically labeled herbicides to plants were found by a number of investigators to contain appreciable quantities of metabolites in addition to the structurally unchanged parent compound (73,83,84). Presumably these metabolites, many of which were of unidentified nature, were released from the plant roots to the culture medium. The significance and quantitative aspects of this leaching of metabolites from plant roots into the soil solution under field conditions apparently have not yet been evaluated.

B. Metabolism in Plants

1. Complex Formation

The first study on urea herbicide metabolism in plants was carried out by Fang et al. (39), who applied carbonyl-^{14}C–monuron to bean leaves. Using paper chromatography, they observed the time-dependent formation of a monuron complex which, upon acid hydrolysis, yielded the unchanged herbicide. Within a period of 12 days, about 20% of the original quantity was converted to the complexed form, which was later suggested to be of low molecular weight protein or peptide nature (80). That a certain quantity of urea herbicides taken up by plants may actually be bound to protein fractions has recently been confirmed by Nashed and Ilnicki (81), who applied unlabeled linuron to the roots of corn seedlings and analyzed them according to the methods developed by Katz (82). After the plant material had been extracted with acetone, appreciable amounts of additional herbicide were released from root and shoot residues by submitting them to alkaline digestion or treatment with a proteolytic enzyme such as ficin.

Evidence for the formation of conjugates was also obtained by Voss and Geissbühler (44) when investigating the metabolism of trifluoromethyl-^{14}C–fluometuron in cotton and corn and of ring-^{14}C–metobromuron in potatoes and corn. However, present results indicate that in contrast to the behavior of monuron and linuron as indicated above, some of these conjugates are of low molecular weight and do not necessarily involve the unchanged herbicides but rather certain of their metabolites (76).

The light-dependent formation of a monuron–flavine mononucleotide complex, as observed by Sweetser (60) in Chlorella and under in vitro conditions, also represents a potential complexing reaction which apparently inactivates the herbicide. However, the involvement of a complex formation as a pathway of herbicide inactivation in plants has not yet been demonstrated.

2. Dealkylation

Following their experiments with carbonyl-^{14}C–chloroxuron on soil bacterial cultures, Geissbühler et al. (73) extended their studies to several

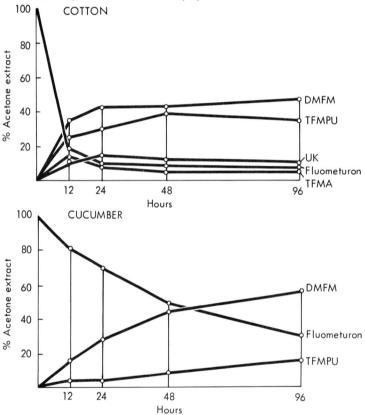

Fig. 3-6. Amounts of ^{14}C–fluometuron and its radioactive metabolites as a function of time in cotton and cucumber leaves. Plants cultured in nutrient solution supplied with 1 ppm of trifluoromethyl-^{14}C–fluometuron. Plant material extracted with acetone and fluometuron and metabolites separated by thin-layer chromatography. DMFM, 3-(3-trifluoromethyl-phenyl)-1-methylurea; TFMPU, 3-trifluoromethylphenylurea; TFMA, 3-trifluoromethylaniline; UK, unknown metabolite. [Redrawn with permission from Ref. (86).]

crop and weed species which had been grown in nutrient solution containing the labeled herbicide. The same metabolites which had been isolated from bacterial culture media were also observed in roots and aerial parts of all plant species investigated. The pathway of demethylation of chloroxuron as shown in scheme (1) of the preceding section was consequently proposed to be valid also for plants. More recently several investigations with isotopically labeled monuron, diuron, and fluometuron have been carried

TABLE 3-2

Demethylation and Hydrolysis of Urea Herbicides after Application of Labeled Compounds to Different Plant Species

^{14}C-Labeled herbicide	Plant species	Mode of application	Exposure time	Recongnized metabolites[a]	Ref.
Monuron	Cotton	{ Nutrient	5 days	U, M, D ≥ A	83
Ring-^{14}C	Soybean	{ solution		U > M, D, (A)	83
	Cotton	⌠ Leaf disks		U < M, D ≥ A	85
	Plantain	⎪ incubated	< 8 hours	U, M, D ≥ A	85
	Soybean	⎪ with		U, M ≥ D ≥ A	85
	Corn	⌡ solution		U ≥ M > D, (A)	85
Diuron					
Carbonyl-^{14}C	Oat	⌠		U < M > D	83
	Soybean	⎪ Nutrient	5 days	U ≤ M > D	83
	Corn	⎨ solution		U > M ≥ D	83
	Cotton	⌡		U < M ≤ D	83
	Cotton	⌠ Leaf disks		U > M > D	85
	Plantain	⎪ incubated	< 8 hours	U < M, D	85
	Soybean	⎪ with		D > M, (D)	85
	Corn	⌡ solution		D ≥ M, (D)	85
Diuron					
Ring-^{14}C	Corn	Nutrient sol.	0–6 days	U ≥ M, D ≥ A	84
Methyl-^{14}C	Corn	Leaves	0–6 days	U, unknowns	84
Carbonyl-^{14}C					
Fluometuron					
Trifluoromethyl-	Cotton	{ Nutrient	0–4 days	U ≤ M, D ≥ A	86
^{14}C	Cucumber	{ solution		U < M > D, (A)	86
	Cotton	{ Nutrient	9–17 days	U ≤ M < D ≥ A	44
	Corn	{ solution		U > M, D, (A)	44

[a] Relative amounts of metabolites as measured upon termination of the experiments: U, structurally unchanged herbicide = R—NH—CO—N(CH$_3$)$_2$; M, monomethylated derivative = R—NH—CO—NHCH$_3$; D, demethylated derivative = R—NH—CO—NH$_2$; A, corresponding aniline = R—NH$_2$; ( ), metabolite searched for, but not observed.

out on a variety of plants or plant parts using different modes of herbicide application. A summary of these studies is presented in Table 3-2. The table demonstrates that stepwise N dealkylation or at least part of this pathway was observed with all plant species and all compounds investigated and thus represents a common degradation mechanism for urea herbicides.

Table 3-2 also shows that apparently there are significant differences

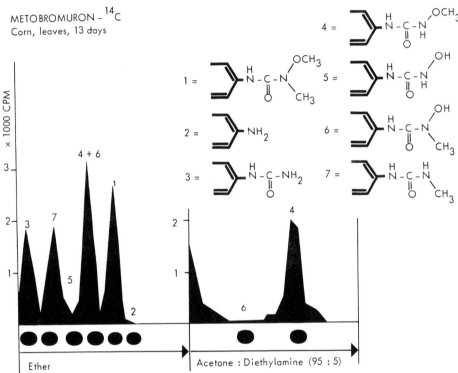

METOBROMURON - ^{14}C
Corn, leaves, 13 days

Fig. 3-7. Thin-layer chromatographic separation of ^{14}C–metobromuron and its organic solvent-soluble radioactive metabolites from corn leaves. Corn seedlings cultured in nutrient solution supplied with 2 ppm of ring-labeled ^{14}C–metobromuron. Plant material extracted with acetonitrile and extract further cleaned by partitioning steps. Ethereal solution applied to silica gel plates. Left: initial separation. Right: Separation of metabolite 4 from compound 6. Hydroxylamine intermediates 5 and 6 are not detectable. [Reproduced from Ref. (76) by permission of CIBA Limited.]

among different plant species with regard to their rates of urea herbicide dealkylation, whereby cotton seems to be particularly efficient in breaking down this type of compound. On the other hand, corn appears to be the most inefficient of the plants investigated. A typical example of the formation of demethylated metabolites with time in cotton and cucumber leaves is presented in Fig. 3-6. That differential rates of degradation of urea compounds may actually determine resistance or susceptibility of plants toward the herbicides is indicated by the work of Smith and Sheets (83), who observed much faster degradation of monuron and diuron in resistant cotton than in susceptible plants such as soybean, oat, and corn. Similar differences in rates of degradation were observed by Rogers and Funderburk (86) for fluometuron, when comparing tolerant cotton and susceptible cucumber, and by Geissbühler et al. (73) for chloroxuron, upon comparison of a resistant and a sensitive weed species.

Information on dealkylation of methylmethoxyphenylureas (linuron, monolinuron, metobromuron, chlorbromuron) is rather limited at this time. Nashed and Ilnicki (81) supplied linuron to the roots of corn, soybean, and crabgrass seedlings. Extraction with acetone and thin-layer chromatography demonstrated that 3-(3,4-dichlorophenyl)-1-methoxyurea was the major metabolite in all three species. None of the other possible demethylated or demethoxylated derivatives were observed. In a more extended study with ring-labeled ^{14}C–metobromuron supplied to potatoes and corn seedlings by nutrient solution, Geissbühler et al. (44,76) subjected extracts of root and leaf tissues to various partitioning, column, and thin-layer chromatographic procedures (see Fig. 3-7) and identified the following metabolites by IR spectroscopy: 3-(4-bromophenyl)-1-methoxyurea, 3-(4-bromophenyl)-1-methylurea, and 4-bromophenylurea. The pathway of metobromuron dealkylation–dealkoxylation may therefore tentatively be proposed as follows:

(4)

The exact pathway of demethoxylation or O demethylation, which was assumed to involve the corresponding hydroxylamine derivatives as intermediates, has not yet been elucidated.

3. Aniline Formation and Additional Pathways

The further hydrolysis of demethylated ureas to the corresponding anilines appears to be more restricted in plants than in soils. In all recent experiments with ring- or substituent-labeled ureas (monuron, diuron, fluometuron), the corresponding free anilines were not detected at all or were present at much lower levels than the mono- and demethylated derivatives (see Table 3-2 and Figs. 3-6 and 3-7). Apparently, these results could also be explained by further rapid transformations of the anilines, such as by conjugation or oxidation, which would prevent accumulation of more abundant quantities in plant tissues. One possibility of aniline transformation is suggested by Onley et al. (84), who applied ring-^{14}C–diuron in nutrient solution to corn seedlings. In addition to small quantities of 3,4-dichloroaniline, they isolated by gas chromatography and identified by IR and mass spectra 3,4-dichloronitrobenzene and thus proposed the following oxidation of the aniline:

$$\text{(5)}$$

Unfortunately the authors were not in a position to decide if nitrobenzene formation represented a chemical or enzymatic oxidative process in plants, the buildup of an artifact during extraction, or a combination of these processes.

In most of the metabolism experiments involving ^{14}C-labeled ureas, which lasted for several days to several weeks, increasing amounts of radioactivity taken up by plants (percentages ranging from about 10 to 60%) were not accounted for by known metabolites. On the basis of partitioning and chromatographic behaviour, these unknown compounds normally appear to represent relatively water-soluble metabolites. It may therefore be expected that additional important pathways and transformations are active in plants which so far have escaped discovery. Ring substitution and ring rupture or dehalogenation have not been reported so far and the complexes and conjugates which are apparently formed remain ill-defined.

4. Site of Urea Herbicide Degradation

From the results of a number of investigations, it may be concluded that leaves, roots, and even stems of plants are potentially capable of N-demethylating urea herbicides. Swanson and Swanson (85) incubated leaf disks of cotton, plantain, soybean, and corn with aqueous solutions of ^{14}C-labeled monuron and diuron. Leaves from all species except corn were able completely or partially to demethylate the herbicides. Geissbühler (87) cultured isolated roots of *Vicia sativa* under sterile conditions in a nutrient solution supplied with ^{14}C–chloroxuron and recovered abundant amounts of mono- and demethylated metabolites from the culture medium and the root tissues. Excised aerial parts of broad and French bean plants cultured under the same conditions took up only small amounts of herbicide and were consequently less active in degradation. The presence of metabolites in stems of these excised bean tops indicated that even stem tissue had a limited ability to degrade chloroxuron, assuming that basal movement of the breakdown products from leaves did not occur.

Under actual growth conditions in the field, the site of urea herbicide degradation would thus appear to depend on the plant species involved and especially on the mobility of the particular herbicide within the plant. Compounds which are rapidly translocated to aerial parts, such as monuron and monolinuron, would be expected to be mainly metabolized in the leaves, whereas for less mobile compounds, such as chloroxuron, degradation in root tissue may be more important.

C. Degradation in Animals

Until very recently no published reports on animal metabolism of urea herbicides were available, although it may be safely assumed that some confidential data have been submitted by commercial companies to governmental authorities for licensing and registration purposes. Bray et al. (88), investigating the animal degradation of arylureas, had already demonstrated in 1949 that the ureido group was biologically rather stable and that ring hydroxylation in ortho positions was a prominent pathway with these compounds. In addition, hydrolysis of such compounds as 3- and 4-tolylurea to the corresponding toluidines was found to be very slight.

In 1965 in two papers Ernst and Böhme (89,90) reported on their extended animal degradation experiments with monuron, monolinuron, diuron, and linuron. The unlabeled herbicides were fed to male albino rats and the urines of these animals were then analyzed for breakdown and transformation products by various partitioning steps and column and thin-layer chromatographic procedures. In addition, the major metabolites were said to have been identified by IR spectroscopy and melting point determinations. With all four compounds investigated, no structurally unchanged herbicide was eliminated in the urine, yet the majority of the recognized urinary metabolites still retained the ureido structure —NH—CO—N⟨. Analogous to results obtained in soil and plant experiments, the demethylation and demethoxylation pathways were also observed in animals. However, the intermediate monomethylated or methoxylated derivatives were present only in traces, whereas the completely demethylated compounds were major metabolites. Dealkylation was much more prominent with the dimethyl compounds monuron and diuron than with their methylmethoxy analogs. In addition to N demethylation and N demethoxylation, Ernst and Böhme demonstrated ring hydroxylation for all four herbicides. The 4-monochlorinated compounds monuron and monolinuron were found to be hydroxylated in ortho and to a smaller extent ın meta positions. The composite demethylation–hydroxylation pathway was consequently summarized as follows:

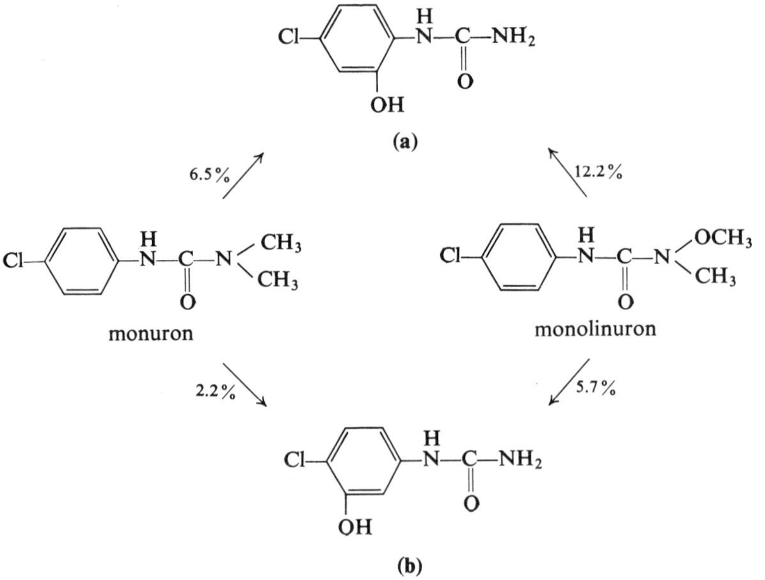

(a)

6.5%   12.2%

monuron   monolinuron   (6)

2.2%   5.7%

(b)

(a) 3-(2-hydroxy-4-chlorophenyl)urea
(b) 3-(3-hydroxy-4-chlorophenyl)urea

Diuron and linuron were observed to be hydroxylated in both possible ortho positions, whereby hydroxylation adjacent to the *m*-chlorine substituent apparently for steric reasons was considerably less extensive.

Dealkylation–hydroxylation of the disubstituted ureas was consequently proposed as follows:

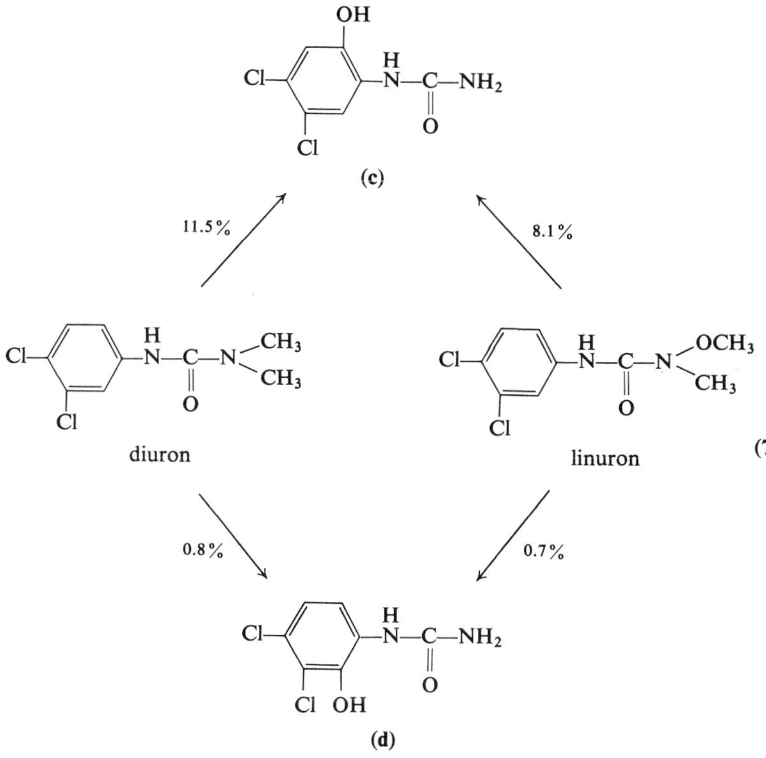

(c)

11.5%   8.1%

diuron   linuron   (7)

0.8%   0.7%

(d)

(c) 3-(2-hydroxy-4,5-dichlorophenyl)urea
(d) 3-(2-hydroxy-3,4-dichlorophenyl)urea

In contrast to the straight dealkylation pathway, which was more prominent with the dialkyl compounds, hydroxylation was found to be more dominant with monolinuron than with monuron. However, no such difference in the percentage of hydroxylated metabolites eliminated was observed between diuron and linuron.

By using enzyme preparations for analysis, Ernst and Böhme (*89,90*) demonstrated that all phenolic metabolites eliminated in the urine were mainly present as glucuronides or ethereal sulfates. As with plants, further hydrolysis of the ureas to their corresponding anilines apparently was not a major pathway in rats since only traces of these metabolites or their hydroxylated derivatives were isolated from urine.

N Demethylation of diuron in animals was confirmed by Hodge et al. (*112*),who analyzed dog urine for transformation products. The metabolites were removed by solvent extraction techniques, separated by thin-layer chromatography, and identified by UV and IR spectroscopy. The completely demethylated urea was again the predominant metabolite, but small amounts of 3-(3,4-dichlorophenyl)-1-methylurea, 3,4-dichloroaniline, 3,4-dichlorophenol, and unmetabolized diuron were also observed.

A recent preliminary report by Boyd and Fogleman (*91*) on the distribution, elimination, and metabolism of trifluoromethyl-^{14}C–fluometuron in female albino rats essentially confirmed the findings of Ernst and Böhme. Thin-layer chromatographic separation of undigested and enzymatically digested urine samples indicated the presence of demethylated and demethylated–hydroxylated metabolites with only traces of trifluoromethylaniline.

The total quantity of recognized metabolites isolated from rat urine by Ernst and Böhme (*89,90*) upon feeding monuron, monolinuron, diuron, and linuron represented about 20–25 % of the amounts of herbicide administered. Therefore, major portions of these quantities still remain to be accounted for.

3-4. BIOCHEMICAL AND ENZYMATIC MECHANISMS INVOLVED IN DEGRADATION

A. *N* Dealkylation

The structure of dialkyl- and alkylalkoxyphenylureas might suggest that the classical urease-type reaction would cleave these compounds directly to their corresponding anilines, carbon dioxide and dialkyl- or alkylalkoxyamine, respectively. Although urease is widely distributed in microorganisms and plants, the enzyme apparently exhibits an absolute specificity for urea. Sumner and Somers (*92*) examined many potential substrates, including substituted ureas and related compounds, but reported no hydrolysis of these substances by urease.

The surprisingly high rate of formation of labeled carbon dioxide observed by Börner (30) upon addition of carbonyl-^{14}C–linuron to soil might indeed suggest direct hydrolysis by a soil microbial enzyme system of undetermined nature; however, such a pathway has not yet been substantiated by isolation of the corresponding metabolites.

In contrast to the lack of information on direct cleavage of the ureido grouping, the process of stepwise enzymatic N demethylation has now been demonstrated for several compounds in soil, plant, and animal systems and therefore represents a major pathway in urea herbicide degradation.

The N demethylation of substituted ureas resembles the N dealkylation as observed for alkylated amines (93,94), amides (95,96), and carbamates (97,98). This common oxidative, enzymatic reaction has been most extensively investigated with mammalian liver microsomal systems and in general requires oxygen and reduced NADPH (94,99).

Apparently the velocity of this reaction depends upon the type of the nonalkyl nitrogen substituents. Thus amides are less rapidly dealkylated than ionizable amines (96). Unfortunately, no systematic kinetic studies on urea-type compounds as compared to amines, amides, and carbamates are available at this time. Hodgson and Casida (97) examined dealkylation of a large number of carbamates in vitro with an enzyme system derived from rat liver microsomes and included monuron and diuron in their ancillary group of noncarbamates. These authors observed that the ureas were less readily dealkylated than the carbamates and they concluded that the former compounds, which are particularly insoluble in water, might not be easily available to the enzymes. On the other hand, high lipid solubility has been demonstrated to be a significant factor in permitting the dealkylation of alkylated amines (100). Apparently additional properties or structural features of urea compounds, which are as yet undetermined, might be more important than their water solubility in controlling their rates of dealkylation.

It is generally thought that N-demethylation reactions proceed through the intermediate formation of an N-hydroxymethyl intermediate (96,99):

$$-N{\overset{\displaystyle CH_3}{\underset{\displaystyle CH_3}{\big<}}} \longrightarrow -N{\overset{\displaystyle CH_2OH}{\underset{\displaystyle CH_3}{\big<}}} \longrightarrow -N{\overset{\displaystyle H}{\underset{\displaystyle CH_3}{\big<}}} \tag{8}$$

In the case of amines, the resulting N-hydroxymethylamine is extremely unstable and breaks down to the dealkylated amine and formaldehyde as a short-lived intermediate in situ. The intermediates appear to be more stable in the case of amides and carbamates, since evidence for their existence as compounds of sufficient stability for isolation has been obtained with alkyl-ated phenylacetamides (*96*), phosphoramides (*101*), phosphoric acid crotonamides (*102*), *N,N*-dimethylcarbamates (*97*), ind *N*-methylcarb-amates (*98*).

With *N,N*-dimethyldiphenylacetamide it has been demonstrated in rat experiments that the hydroxymethyl intermediate is sufficiently stable to be in part "trapped" by the glucuronyltransferase system and converted to a stable *O*-glucuronide (*96*). Recently, evidence has been presented that the hydroxymethyl intermediates of the *N*-alkylated phosphoric acid croton-amide insecticides dicrotophos and monocrotophos are subjected to a simi-lar conjugation or "trapping" mechanism in plants (*103,104*).

So far, no intermediates in the *N* dealkylation or conjugates thereof have been reported for urea herbicides. The above enzymatic mechanisms have been described in some detail, since it is conceivable that they also apply wholly or in part to the class of compounds considered in this chapter.

We are equally ignorant on the kinetics and intermediate pathways of *N* demethoxylation as demonstrated for linuron and monolinuron in animals (*89,90*) and for metobromuron in plants (*76*). Although the cor-responding hydroxylamines were examined as possible intermediates in both investigations, their presence has so far not been substantiated. It might be difficult to detect such intermediates, since arylhydroxylamines have been demonstrated to be rapidly reduced to the corresponding amines in animal systems (*105*).

B. Additional Pathways

The second major pathway which has been postulated for urea herbicides is ring hydroxylation. Since the normally preferred para position is either substituted or sterically covered, as for example in fluometuron, ring substitution seems to occur mainly in the ortho position. Although the reaction has thus far been demonstrated only in animals, it may be specu-lated that it also occurs in microorganisms and in plants. Microbial ring hydroxylations have been extensively observed and they normally appear to precede cleavage of the aromatic nucleus, giving rise to aliphatic com-pounds such as succinate or acetate, with muconic acid as a possible inter-mediate (*106*).

Like the process of *N* dealkylation, ring hydroxylations of foreign com-pounds have been most extensively investigated with mammalian liver microsomal systems. The mechanism again requires oxygen and NADPH, whereby the molecular oxygen apparently is directly incorporated into the hydroxyl group without intermediate water formation (*107*). Although the reaction is considered to involve a "mixed-function" oxidase (*108*), its details are not yet completely elucidated (*99*).

As mentioned earlier, Ernst and Böhme (*89,90*) have demonstrated that, in rat urine, the hydroxylated metabolites are mainly eliminated as glucuronides and ethereal sulfates. Since plants possess glucosyltransferase systems, which are similar to the animal glucuronyltransferase systems (*109*), it is to be expected that hydroxylated metabolites, if they occur, might be conjugated in plants.

The cleavage of the ureido grouping of *N*-dealkylated ureas has not yet been sufficiently demonstrated to discuss the details of its mechanism. The reaction might involve formation of the very unstable carbamic acid derivative as an intermediate which would then spontaneously give rise to carbon dioxide and the corresponding aniline. Further oxidations of the aniline which are conceivable are ring hydroxylation and *N*-oxide and quinoid formation (*99,110*). On the other hand, it is also possible that either the demethylated urea or the aniline is transformed to the more recently discovered *N* conjugates (*99,113*).

C. Conclusions

The present author realizes that the various pathways and mechanisms discussed and speculated on above will not necessarily be involved in urea herbicide transformations and that, indeed, additional as yet undiscovered processes may be expected to contribute their share. However, it has been the purpose of this brief excursion into biochemical and enzymatic problems to stimulate the thoughts of as many researchers as possible so that, hopefully, they will devote their energies and imaginations to the fascinating discoveries still to be made in the degradation of urea herbicides in soils, plants, and animals. Table 3-3 attempts to summarize the present status of biochemical transformations of this class of compounds and to demonstrate the numerous gaps which still exist in our knowledge on the processes involved. In addition, efforts are required to purify and isolate enzyme preparations or systems from microorganisms, plants, and animals which will allow detailed examination of the kinetics of the various reactions and of the relationships between enzymatic activity and chemical structure of the compounds.

From a practical point of view, this type of work will help to develop more efficient herbicides which create increasingly fewer contamination problems for the total environment.

TABLE 3-3

Present Status of Biochemical Pathways and Enzymatic Mechanisms
Involved in the Transformation of Urea Herbicides by Microorganisms,
Plants, and Animals

Pathway or mechanisms	Present status
N Dealkylation	Verified in soils, plants, animals
Hydroxyalkyl intermediates	Postulated by in vitro experiments
Conjugation of intermediates	Assumed
N Dealkoxylation	Demonstrated in plants and animals
Hydroxylamine intermediates	Assumed
Ring hydroxylation	Demonstrated in animals
	Assumed in microorganisms (and plants)
Conjugation of hydroxymetabolites	Demonstrated in animals
	Assumed in plants
Hydrolysis (Cleavage of urea grouping)	Postulated by detection of anilines
Aniline oxidations	
Hydroxylation	Assumed
N-Oxide formation and further oxidations	Partly postulated from plant experiments
Quinoid formation	Assumed
N-Conjugation	Assumed
Ring cleavage	Assumed for microorganisms
Complex formation	
Complexing with peptide or protein structures	Postulated from plant experiments

REFERENCES

1. H. E. Thompson, C. P. Swanson, and A. G. Norman, *Botan. Gaz.*, **107**, 476 (1946).
2. H. E. Cupery, N. E. Searle, and C. W. Todd, Fr. Pat. 1,034,658 (to E. I. du Pont de Nemours and Co.) 1950.
3. H. C. Bucha and C. W. Todd, *Science*, **114**, 453 (1951).
4. A. L. Abel, *Chem. Ind.* (*London*), **1957**, 1106.
5. A. Fischer, *Mededel. Landbouwhogeschool, Gent*, **29**, 719 (1964).
6. H. Gaffron, in *Plant Physiology*, Vol. Ib, (F. C. Steward, ed.), Academic Press, New York, 1959, pp. 3–277.
7. T. J. Sheets, *J. Agr. Food Chem.*, **12**, 30 (1964).
8. A. S. Crafts, in *The Physiology and Biochemistry of Herbicides* (L. J. Audus, ed.), Academic Press, New York, 1964, pp. 75–110.
9. A. S. Crafts, in *Isotopes in Weed Research*, IAEA, Vienna, 1966, pp. 3–7.

10. S. S. Sharp, M. C. Swingle, G. L. McCall, M. B. Weed, and L. E. Cowart, *Agr. Chem.*, **8**(9), 56 (1953).
11. A. J. Loustalot, T. J. Muzik, and H. J. Cruzado, *Agr. Chem.*, **8**(11), 52 (1953).
12. S. Dallyn, *Proc. Northeast. Weed Control Conf.*, **8**, 13 (1954).
13. H. R. Sherburne and V. H. Freed, *J. Agr. Food Chem.*, **2**, 937 (1954).
14. H. R. Sherburne, V. H. Freed, and S. C. Fang, *Weeds*, **4**, 50 (1956).
15. R. P. Upchurch, *Weeds*, **6**, 161 (1958).
16. T. J. Sheets, *Weeds*, **6**, 413 (1958).
17. T. J. Sheets and A. S. Crafts, *Weeds*, **5**, 93 (1957).
18. Q. H. Yuen and H. W. Hilton, *J. Agr. Food Chem.*, **10**, 386 (1962).
19. H. W. Hilton and Q. H. Yuen, *J. Agr. Food Chem.*, **11**, 230 (1963).
20. H. Geissbühler, C. Haselbach, and H, Aebi, *Weed Res.*, **3**, 140 (1963).
21. C. I. Harris and G. F. Warren, *Weeds*, **12**, 120 (1964).
22. R. J. Hance, *Weed Res.*, **5**, 98, (1965).
23. R. J. Hance, *Weed Res.*, **5**, 108 (1965).
24. F. Arndt, *Z. Pflanzenkrankh. Pflanzenschutz*, **67**, 25 (1960).
25. H. Geissbühler and H. Schredt, CIBA Ltd., unpublished data, 1966.
26. C. W. Coggins and A. S. Crafts, *Weeds*, **7**, 349 (1959).
27. A. S. Crafts and H. R. Drever, *Weeds*, **8**, 12 (1960).
28. C. A. Shadbolt and F. L. Whiting, *Calif. Agr.*, **15**(11), 10 (1961).
29. P. A. Frank, *Weeds*, **14**, 219 (1966).
30. H. Börner, *Z. Pflanzenkrankh. Pflanzenschutz*, **72**, 516 (1965).
31. H. Geissbühler, H. Schredt, and L. Ebner, CIBA Ltd. Rept, March 1967.
32. W. H. Minshall, *Can. J. Botan.*, **32**, 785 (1954).
33. T. J. Muzik, H. J. Cruzado, and A. J. Loustalot, *Botan. Gaz.*, **116**, 65 (1954).
34. J. R. Haun and J. H. Peterson, *Weeds*, **3**, 177 (1954).
35. A. S. Crafts and S. Yamaguchi, *Hilgardia*, **27**, 421 (1958).
36. A. S. Crafts and S. Yamaguchi, *Am. J. Botan.*, **47**, 248 (1960).
37. A. S. Crafts, *Plant Physiol.*, **34**, 613 (1959).
38. A. S. Crafts, *Intern. J. Appl. Radiation Isotopes*, **13**, 407 (1962).
39. S. C. Fang, V. H. Freed, R. H. Johnson, and D. R. Coffee, *J. Agr. Food Chem.*, **3**, 400 (1955).
40. H. Geissbühler, C. Haselbach, H. Aebi, and L. Ebner, *Weed Res.*, **3**, 181 (1963).
41. H. Börner, *Z. Pflanzenkrankh. Pflanzenschutz*, **72**, 449 (1965).
42. H. Börner, *Z. Pflanzenkrankh. Pflanzenschutz*, Sonderheft II, 41 (1964).
43. D. E. Bayer and S. Yamaguchi, *Weeds*, **13**, 232 (1965).
44. G. Voss and H. Geissbühler, *Proc. Brit. Weed Control Conf. 8th*, **1**, 266 (1966).
45. G. D. Hill, I. J. Belasco, and H. L. Ploeg, *Weeds*, **13**, 103 (1965).
46. D. E. Bayer and H. R. Drever, *Weeds*, **13**, 222 (1965).
47. C. G. McWhorter, *Weeds*, **11**, 265 (1963).
48. H. Chandler, *Proc. Calif. Weed Conf.*, **15**, 99 (1963).
49. J. S. C. Wessels and R. van der Veen, *Biochim. Biophys. Acta*, **19**, 548 (1956).
50. N. I. Bishop, *Biochim. Biophys. Acta*, **27**, 205 (1958).
51. A. T. Jagendorf, *Brookhaven Symp. Biol.*, **11**, 236 (1958).
52. A. R. Cooke, *Weeds*, **4**, 397 (1956).
53. G. Gingras and C. Lemasson, *Biochim. Biophys. Acta*, **69**, 438 (1963).
54. G. Gingras and C. Lemasson, *Biochim. Biophys. Acta*, **109**, 67 (1965).
55. P. B. Sweetser, C. W. Todd, and R. T. Hersh, *Biochim. Biophys. Acta*, **51**, 509 (1961).

56. R. W. Treharne, T. E. Brown, and L. P. Vernon, *Biochim. Biophys. Acta*, **75**, 324 (1963).
57. C. C. Black and L. Myers, *Weeds*, **14**, 331 (1966).
58. N. I. Bishop, *Ann. Rev. Plant Physiol.*, **17**, 185 (1966).
59. A. San Pietro and C. C. Black, *Ann. Rev. Plant Physiol.*, **16**, 155 (1965).
60. P. B. Sweetser, *Biochim. Biophys. Acta*, **66**, 78 (1963).
61. P. Homann and H. Gaffron, *Science*, **141**, 905 (1963).
62. P. B. Sweetser and C. W. Todd, *Biochim. Biophys. Acta*, **51**, 504 (1961).
63. J. L. P. van Oorschot and M. Belksma, *Weed Res.*, **1**, 245 (1961).
64. J. L. P. van Oorschot, *Meded. Landbouwhogeschool, Gent*, **29**, 683 (1964).
65. J. L. P. van Oorschot, *Weed Res.*, **5**, 84 (1965).
66. C. R. Swanson, G. G. Still, and H. R. Swanson, *Weed Soc. Am. Abstr.*, 1967, pp. 60, 61.
67. G. S. Hartley, in *The Physiology and Biochemistry of Herbicides* (L. J. Audus, ed.), Academic Press, New York, 1964, pp. 111–161.
68. L. W. Weldon and F. L. Timmons, *Weeds*, **9**, 111 (1961).
69. R. D. Comes and F. L. Timmons, *Weeds*, **13**, 81 (1965).
70. L. S. Jordan, J. D. Mann, and B. Day, *Weeds*, **13**, 43 (1965).
71. G. D. Hill, J. W. McGahen, H. M. Baker, D. W. Finnerty, and C. W. Bingeman, *Agron. J.*, **47**, 93 (1955).
72. R. E. Ogle and G. F. Warren, *Weeds*, **3**, 257 (1954).
73. H. Geissbühler, C. Haselbach, H. Aebi, and L. Ebner, *Weed Res.*, **3**, 277 (1963).
74. G. D. Hill and J. W. McGahen, *Proc. Southern Weed Control Conf.*, **8**, 284 (1955).
75. R. L. Dalton, A. W. Evans, and R. C. Rhodes, *Weeds*, **14**, 31 (1966).
76. H. Geissbühler, G. Voss, and D. Gross, CIBA Ltd., unpublished data, 1967.
77. R. Bartha and D. Pramer, *Science*, **156**, 1617 (1967).
78. L. J. Audus, in *The Physiology and Biochemistry of Herbicides* (L. J. Audus, ed.), Academic Press, New York, 1964, pp. 163–206.
79. R. L. Dalton and H. L. Pease, *J. Assoc. Offic. Agr. Chemists*, **45**, 377 (1962).
80. V. H. Freed, M. Montgomery, and M. Kief, *Proc. Northeast. Weed Control Conf.*, **15**, 6 (1961).
81. R. B. Nashed and R. D. Ilnicki, Rutgers the State University, New Brunswick, N.J., private communication, 1967.
82. S. E. Katz, *J. Assoc Offic. Anal. Chemists*, **50**, 911 (1967).
83. J. W. Smith and T. J. Sheets, *J. Agr. Food Chem.*, **15**, 577 (1967).
84. J. H. Onley, G. Yip, and M. H. Aldridge, *J. Agr. Food Chem.*, **16**, 426 (1968).
85. C. R. Swanson and H. R. Swanson, *Weed Sci.*, **16**, 137 (1968).
86. R. L. Rogers and H. H. Funderburk, *J. Agr. Food Chem.*, **16**, 434 (1968).
87. H. Geissbühler, *Mededel. Landbouwhogeschool, Gent*, **29**, 704 (1964).
88. H. G. Bray, H. J. Lake, and W. V. Thorpe, *Biochem. J.*, **44**, 136 (1949).
89. W. Ernst and C. Böhme, *Food Cosmet. Toxicol.*, **3**, 789 (1965).
90. C. Böhme and E. Ernst, *Food Cosmet. Toxicol.*, **3**, 797 (1965).
91. V. F. Boyd and R. W. Fogleman, American Chemical Society, 153rd Meeting, Miami, April 196.
92. J. B. Sumner and G. F. Somers, *Chemistry and Methods of Enzymes*, Academic Press, New York, 3rd ed., 1953.
93. J. Axelrod, *J. Pharmacol. Exptl. Therap.*, **117**, 322 (1956).
94. B. B. Brodie, J. R. Gillette, and B. N. LaDu, *Ann. Rev. Biochem.*, **27**, 427 (1958).

95. R. E. McMahon, *Biochem. Pharmacol.*, **12**, 1225 (1963).

96. R. E. McMahon and H. R. Sullivan, *Biochem. Pharmacol.*, **14**, 1085 (1965).

97. E. Hodgson and J. E. Casida, *Biochem. Pharmacol.*, **8**, 179 (1961).

98. H. W. Dorough and J. E. Casida, *J. Agr. Food Chem.*, **12**, 294 (1964).

99. L. Shuster, *Ann. Rev. Biochem.*, **33**, 571 (1964).

100. L. E. Gaudette and B. B. Brodie, *Biochem. Pharmacol.*, **2**, 89 (1959).

101. D. F. Heath, *Organophosphorus Poisons*, Pergamon Press, New York, 1961, pp. 227–235.

102. R. E. Menzer and J. E. Casida, *J. Agr. Food Chem.*, **13**, 102 (1965).

103. D. L. Bull and D. A. Lindquist, *J. Agr. Food Chem.*, **12**, 310 (1964).

104. D. A. Lindquist and D. L. Bull, *J. Agr. Food Chem.*, **15**, 267 (1967).

105. C. T. Williams, *Detoxification Mechanisms*, Chapman and Hall, London, 1949.

106. M. H. Rogoff, *Advan. Appl. Microbiol.*, **3**, 113 (1961).

107. H. S. Posner, Ch. Mitoma, S. Rothberg, and S. Udenfriend, *Arch. Biochem. Biophys.*, **94**, 280 (1961).

108. H. S. Mason, *Science*, **125**, 1185 (1957).

109. J. B. Pridham, *Ann. Rev. Plant Physiol.*, **16**, 13 (1965).

110. M. Kiese and H. Uehleke, *Naturwiss.*, **48**, 379 (1961).

111. J. A. Guth and V. F. Boyd, CIBA Ltd., unpublished data, 1967.

112. H. C. Hodge, W. L. Downs, B. S. Panner, D. W. Smith, E. A. Maynard, J. W. Clayton, and R. C. Rhodes, *Food Cosmet. Toxicol.*, **5**, 513 (1967).

113. G. G. Still, *Science*, **159**, 992 (1968).

CHAPTER 4

Methyl- and Phenylcarbamates

RICHARD A. HERRETT

UNION CARBIDE CORPORATION
CLAYTON, NORTH CAROLINA

4-1. Introduction 113
    A. Chemistry and Nomenclature 117
    B. History 119
    C. Physical Properties 120
4-2. Pathways of Degradation 121
    A. Hydrolysis 121
    B. Hydroxylation 124
    C. N Dealkylation 128
    D. Sulfur Oxidation 130
    E. Conjugate Formation 131
4-3. Degradation in Plants 132
4-4. Degradation in Soils 134
4-5. Enzymatic Studies 136
    A. Inhibitors and Synergists 138
4-6. Metabolism and Selective Phytotoxicity 139
4-7. Summary 140
References 142

4-1. INTRODUCTION

There is within the carbamates perhaps the broadest spectrum of biological activity of any class of organic compounds. The range of pesticidal activity includes herbicides, fungicides, insecticides, nematocides, miticides, and molluscicides(1); however, biological activity is not limited to pesticides, as many drugs and medicinals are also carbamates.

Herbicidal carbamates are becoming increasingly important for several reasons. They are of low mammalian toxicity, have a relatively short residual life in the soil, and are readily degraded by nontarget organisms (2). Knowledge of pathways of degradation is essential for safe and effective utilization of these materials.

113

TABLE 4-1

Structure, Physical Properties, and Biological Activity of Various
Carbamates and Related Compounds

Chemical class	Common name or designation	Water solubility, ppmw	Melting point, °C	Biological activity
Phenylcarbamates				
IPC structure	IPC	250	87	Herbicide
CIPC structure	CIPC	88	39	Herbicide
Barban structure	Barban	10	75	Herbicide
Swep structure	Swep	—	—	Herbicide
Methylcarbamates				
Terbutol structure	Terbutol	7	200	Herbicide
UC 22463 structure	UC 22463	170	52	Herbicide

TABLE 4-1–*continued*

Chemical class	Common name or designation	Water solubility, ppmw	Melting point, °C	Biological activity
	Carbaryl	40	142	Insecticide
	Zectran	—	—	Insecticide
	Banol	—	—	Insecticide
	Mesurol	—	—	Insecticide
	Temik	6000	113	Insecticide

TABLE 4-1–*continued*

Chemical class	Common name or designation,	Water solubility, ppmw	Melting point, °C	Biological activity
Amides				
	Diphenamid	260	133	Herbicide
	Propanil	500	87	Herbicide
	Bidrin	—	—	Insecticide
Phenylurea				
	Diuron	42	158	Herbicide

The purpose of this chapter is to review the current information concerning the degradation of herbicidal carbamates in plants and soils. As the degradation of herbicidal carbamates is a relatively new area, there is little published information. Therefore, biotransformations of insecticidal carbamates, herbicides which are chemically similar to carbamates, and naturally occurring compounds, will also be considered to illustrate potential degradation pathways. A summary of the pesticidal compounds included in this discussion and their biological activity is presented in Table 4-1.

A. Chemistry and Nomenclature

There is inconsistency in the herbicide literature regarding the nomenclature of carbamates. Chemicals of apparently similar structures are
called variously carbamates, carbanilates, and sometimes urethanes.
Perhaps a rather elementary discussion of the chemistry of carbamates may
provide a clear understanding for this discussion of degradative pathways.
Carbamic acid (1), the parent acid of carbamates, is an unstable compound
(indicated by brackets) which decomposes spontaneously to CO_2 and
ammonia.

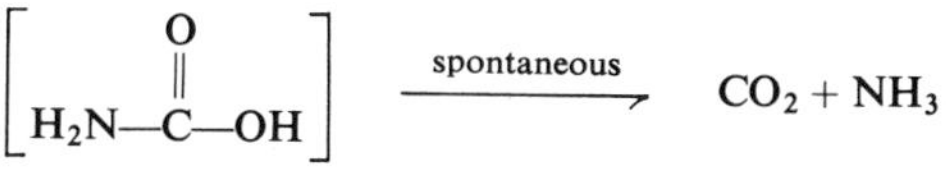

$$\left[\begin{matrix} & O \\ & \parallel \\ H_2N\!-\!\!&C\!-\!OH \end{matrix} \right] \xrightarrow{\text{spontaneous}} CO_2 + NH_3 \qquad (1)$$

(1)

carbamic acid

Derivates of carbamic acid are formed from either or both the amine or
carboxylic acid groups.

1. N-Derivatives

Substitution of an amino proton of carbamic acid with a phenyl group
gives carbanilic acid (2), which is also an unstable compound and decomposes spontaneously to CO_2 and aniline (3).

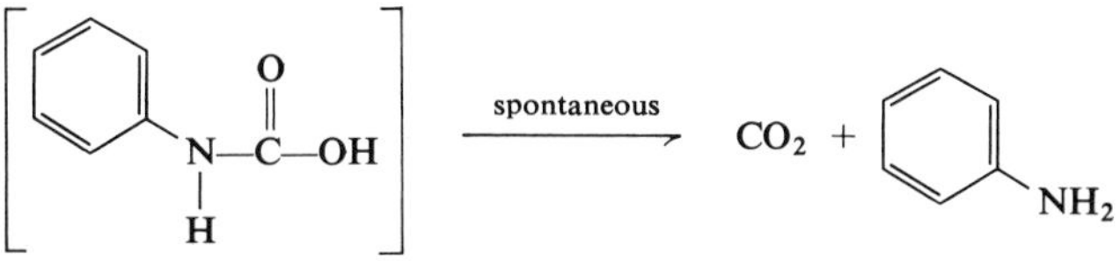

carbanilic acid   aniline

(2)   (3)

N-phenyl esters, as derivatives of aniline, are sometimes referred to as
carbanilates, although the term phenylcarbamates has generally been
accepted by those working with herbicides and will be used in this discussion.

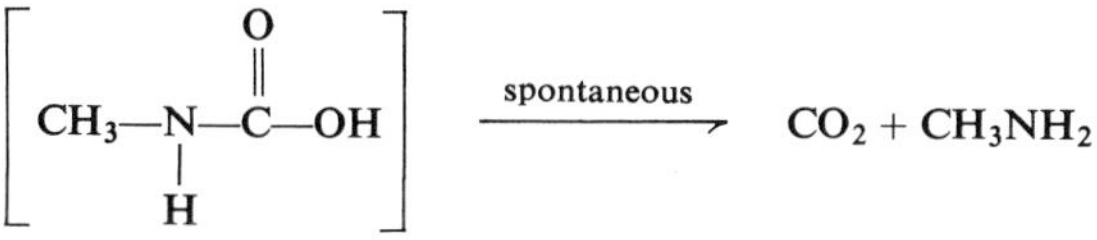

$$\left[\begin{matrix} & & O \\ & & \parallel \\ CH_3\!-\!&N\!-\!\!&C\!-\!OH \\ & \mid & \\ & H & \end{matrix} \right] \xrightarrow{\text{spontaneous}} CO_2 + CH_3NH_2 \qquad (3)$$

methylcarbamic acid   methylamine

(4)   (5)

Substitution of an amino proton of carbamic acid with an alkyl group (e.g., methyl) gives an alkylcarbamic acid (**4**). Methylcarbamic acids are also unstable and decompose to CO_2 and methylamine (**5**). Methyl derivatives of carbamic acid esters are called methylcarbamates.

2. Ester Derivatives

Esters are formed from carbamic acid or a substituted carbamic acid and an alcohol, phenol, enol, or oxime. When the alcohol is ethanol, the resulting ester is ethyl carbamate (**6**). This is often referred to by its trivial name, urethane. The *N*-phenyl derivative of the ethanol ester (**7**) is sometimes called phenylurethane.

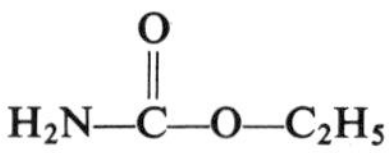

ethyl carbamate ethyl carbanilate (ethyl phenylcarbamate)
(urethane)   (phenylurethane)
(**6**)   (**7**)

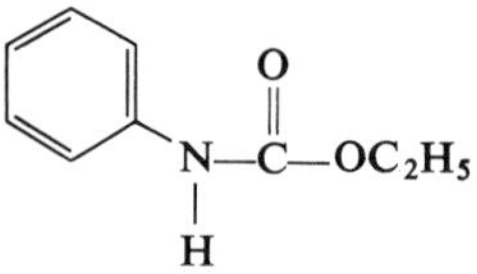

The *N* substituent is appended to carbamate to form one word (phenylcarbamate). The term describing the alcohol moiety is separated (phenyl carbamate) as in (**8**). The use of an *N* (e.g., isopropyl *N*-phenylcarbamate) is unnecessary.

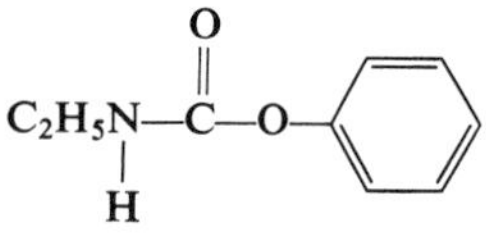

phenyl ethylcarbamate
(**8**)

The fundamental linkage in both phenyl- and methylcarbamates, the carbamoyl group (**9**), is the recurring linkage in proteins. Attachment of a

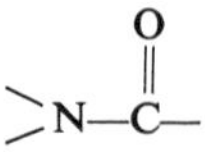

(**9**)

phenyl group to a carbamoyl nitrogen gives a phenylamide (10), which is a structure common to several herbicides.

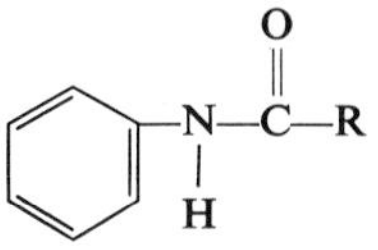

(10)

When R is alkyl, alkoxy, or alkylamino, the corresponding compounds are acylanilides, phenylcarbamates, and phenylureas, respectively. When a proton is attached to the nitrogen, it is referred to as an imino hydrogen. Within the chemically similar phenylamides, there is a wide range of biological activity (2) and pathways of metabolic degradation.

B. History

The plant-growth-regulating properties of phenylcarbamates were discovered in 1929 when Friesen (3) observed that ethyl carbanilate (phenyl-urethane) (7) inhibited the root growth of certain grasses.

It was not until the discovery of IPC (isopropyl N-phenylcarbamate) (4) in 1945 that phenylcarbamates were used for commercial weed control. The success of that discovery led to the development of other phenylcarba-mates such as CIPC [isopropyl N-(3-chlorophenyl)carbamate] and barban (4-chloro-2-butynyl m-chlorocarbanilate), which are widely used herbicides. To date, there are no known examples of commercial phenylcarbamate insecticides, although recently a new series of experimental insecticides was described (5) which contain both a phenyl- and a methylcarbamate in one molecule.

Methylcarbamates are related to the naturally occurring carbamate alkaloid, physostigmine (11), which was isolated from Calabar bean, *Physostigma venenosum* (Balfour), in 1864 (1,6). Because of its pronounced cholinergic action, physostigmine has been used for many years to treat glaucoma and myasthenia gravis in humans.

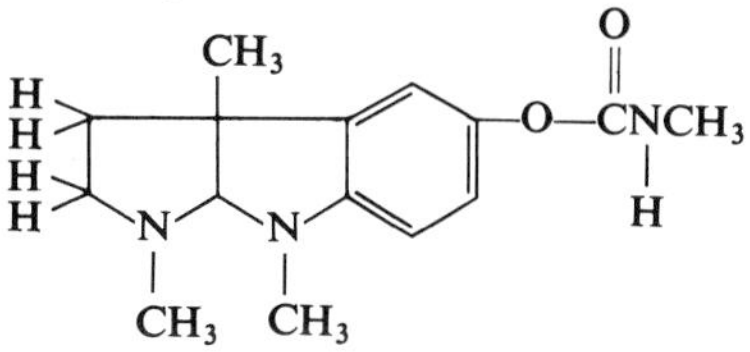

physostigmine

(11)

Studies in the field of medicinal chemistry resulted in the synthesis of methylaminophenylmethyl- and dimethylcarbamates, their hydrochlorides, and quaternary ammonium salts, such as prostigmine (12).

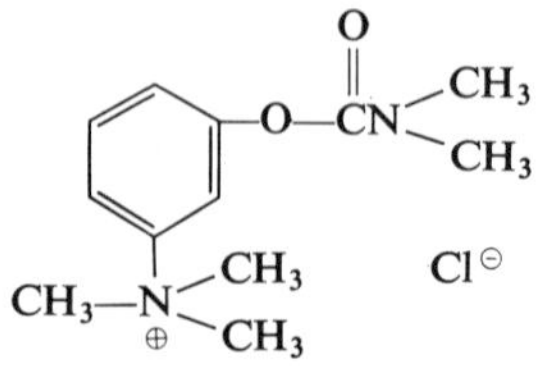

prostigmine

(12)

Many of these derivatives were active anticholinergic substances; however, because of polarity, quaternary ammonium salts were unable to penetrate the insect lipoidal nerve sheath and hence were inactive as insecticides (6,7).

Gysin (8) and Metcalf and co-workers (7) were the first to describe the insecticidal properties of methylcarbamates. Their research and subsequent chemical synthesis which it stimulated has produced several methylcarb- amates which have attained considerable importance as commercial in- secticides (see Table 4-1 for examples).

Plant-growth-regulating properties of methylcarbamates derived from aromatic alcohols were first described in 1957 (9). One of these types, the methylcarbamate derivative of 2,6-di-*t*-butyl 4-methylphenol, terbutol, is a highly specific herbicide for the control of crabgrass in turf (10,11).

The herbicidal activity of various substituted benzyl methylcarbamates, specifically UC 22463 (3,4-dichlorobenzyl methylcarbamate) was recently discovered (12). UC 22463 has demonstrated broad-spectrum activity against both broadleaf and grassy annual weeds in a wide variety of tolerant crops (13).

In contrast to the insecticidal methylcarbamates, terbutol (11) and UC 22463 (76) are poor anticholinergic substances. The lack of activity of UC 22463 is in agreement with the recent observations of Metcalf and Fukuto (13a), who attribute the absence of cholinergic activity of benzyl methylcarbamate to the fact that it is a carbamate derived from an aliphatic alcohol. Such aliphatic alcohols are poor leaving groups and result in slow carbamylation of cholinesterase.

C. Physical Properties

The herbicidal phenyl- and methylcarbamates are generally relatively low-melting solids with the exception of terbutol (Table 4-1). Water solubility of these carbamates is generally low. These physical characteristics are of importance in the dissipation of the chemicals through volatility and leaching and will be considered in more detail in the subsequent discussion.

4-2. PATHWAYS OF DEGRADATION

Before discussing degradation in plants and soils, it may be of value to consider the several potential pathways of biotransformation. Where possible, examples will be taken from the herbicide literature; however, related materials will also be used to illustrate these schemes. Although reactions are discussed individually, this does not imply that a compound is degraded by a single mechanism. Indeed, it is likely that a compound is subjected to several different reactions simultaneously.

A. Hydrolysis

1. Ester Hydrolysis

Since the carbamates are esters, a very likely degradative reaction is hydrolysis. Simple ester hydrolysis results in the formation of the parent acid (unstable) and isopropanol, as illustrated with CIPC.

(4)

The unstable m-chlorophenylcarbamic acid spontaneously decomposes to m-chloroaniline and CO_2. This reaction is catalyzed by esteratic enzymes or aqueous base (14,15).

Mechanistic studies suggest two possible attacks (*14*). One is initiated by a nucleophilic attack (hydroxyl ion) on the carbonyl carbon followed by the cleavage of a carbamate-ion intermediate.

$$R-O-\overset{\overset{\displaystyle O}{\|}}{C}-NR_2' + OH^{\ominus} \underset{k_{-1}}{\overset{k_1}{\rightleftharpoons}} \left[R-O-\overset{\overset{\displaystyle O^{\ominus}}{|}}{\underset{\underset{\displaystyle OH}{|}}{C}}-NR_2' \right] \qquad (5)$$

$$\left[R-O-\overset{\overset{\displaystyle O^{\ominus}}{|}}{\underset{\underset{\displaystyle OH}{|}}{C}}-NR_2' \right] \overset{k_2}{\longrightarrow} ROH + R_2'NCOO^{\ominus} \qquad (6)$$

$$R_2'NCOO^{\ominus} + H_2O \longrightarrow R_2'NH + HCO_3^{\ominus} \qquad (7)$$

In this reaction k_1 is probably rate determining, as the polarity of the carbonyl group appears critical. Increased electrophilicity of the RO group results in increased polarization of the carbonyl group, thus facilitating hydroxyl ion attack. This mechanism appears to be of importance primarily for *N,N*-disubstituted aromatic and *N*-substituted aliphatic carbamates (*14*).

A second mechanism which appears to be of major importance for *N*-unsubstituted and *N*-monosubstituted carbamates involves elimination of the imino hydrogen followed by the formation of an isocyanate intermediate.

$$R-O-\overset{\overset{\displaystyle O}{\|}}{\underset{\underset{\displaystyle H}{|}}{C}}-NR' + OH^{\ominus} \underset{k_{-1}}{\overset{k_1}{\rightleftharpoons}} \left[R-O-\overset{\overset{\displaystyle O^{\ominus}}{|}}{C}=NR' \right] + H_2O \qquad (8)$$

$$\left[R-O-\overset{\overset{\displaystyle O^{\ominus}}{|}}{C}=NR' \right] \overset{k_2}{\longrightarrow} RO^{\ominus} + R'N=C=O \qquad (9)$$

$$R'N=C=O + H_2O \longrightarrow R'-NH-COOH \qquad (10)$$

$$R'NH-COOH \longrightarrow R'NH_2 + CO_2 \qquad (11)$$

In this mechanism, k_2 is the rate-determining step $(7,14)$ and is a function of the ability of the $RO^{\ominus}$ to act as a leaving group.

Kolbezen et al. (7) observed a direct correlation between stability in base and activity against cholinesterase. In the series $C_6H_5OCONHR$, where R was $CH_3 \longrightarrow > C_2H_5 \longrightarrow > C_6H_5CH_2 \longrightarrow > C_6H_5 \longrightarrow$, decreasing stability in base and decreasing anticholinesterase activity going from $CH_3 \longrightarrow$ to $C_6H_5 \longrightarrow$ was found.

Recently, Fukuto et al. (16) proposed an alternative mechanism which is kinetically indistinguishable from the mechanism involving an isocyanate intermediate [reactions (8–11)].

$$\qquad (12)$$

$$\qquad (13)$$

This alternative mechanism involving a water molecule in the transition state has an advantage in that the carbamate does not become a charged ion. The transition molecule then rearranges to methylcarbamic acid which decomposes spontaneously to CO_2 and methylamine [reaction (3)]. In both mechanisms the imino hydrogen is the point of attack. Removal of this proton is a function of its basicity and not the nucleophilicity of the attacking base (16).

The stability of insecticidal methylcarbamates in aqueous base has been studied in an attempt to derive a correlation with activity against the target enzyme, cholinesterase $(1,7,14)$. No similar attempts to relate the stability of phenylcarbamates in basic solutions to herbicidal activity have been made. Perhaps the lack of knowledge concerning the target enzyme in plants has been a contributing factor. Recently, Kearney (17) has attempted to relate certain physical chemical properties such as the polarizability (basicity) of the imino hydrogen and susceptibility to enzymatic attack. This will be discussed in the subsequent section.

2. Amide Hydrolysis

An alternative point of attack is the carbonyl–carbon nitrogen bond. For CIPC this type of attack would proceed as follows:

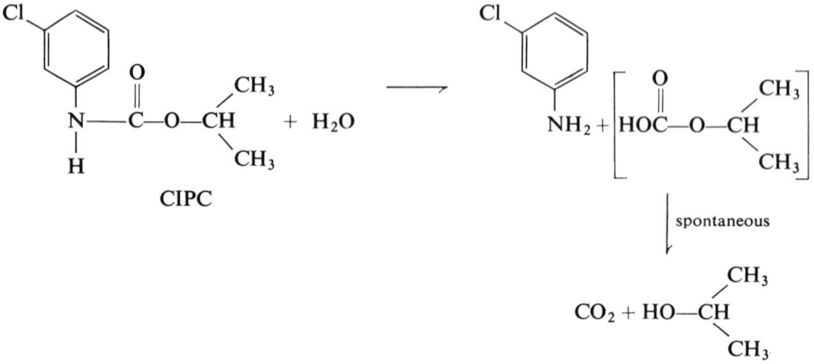

In this instance the carbonate would decompose to CO_2 and isopropyl alcohol. This type of attack would be characteristic of an amidase enzyme. Based on analysis of end products from CIPC, it would be impossible to distinguish between esterase and amidase activity (*18*).

B. Hydroxylation

Hydroxylation reactions play a significant role in the biotransformation of carbamates (*1,19*). There are several types of hydroxylation reactions which can be classified on the basis of the point of attack.

1. N-Alkyl

Several methylcarbamates are degraded by the hydroxylation of the *N*-methyl group (*19,20*). Carbaryl (**13**), for example, is hydroxylated in plants to the *N*-methylol analog, sometimes referred to as the *N*-hydroxymethyl derivative (**14**). This is not to be confused with *N* hydroxylation

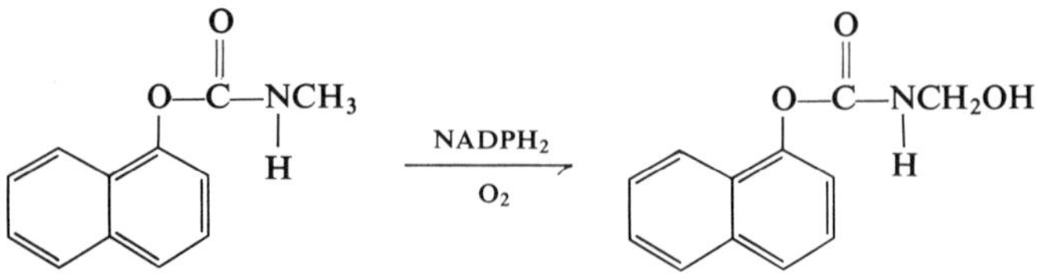

carbaryl

(**13**)

1-naphthyl hydroxymethylcarbamate

(**14**)

(see below). In vitro systems have proven particularly useful in the elucidation of nonhydrolytic pathways. Rat-liver microsomes supplied with reduced triphosphopyridine nucleotide ($NADPH_2$) and molecular oxygen, for example, will convert methylcarbamates such as Banol and carbaryl (22) and dimethylcarbamates such as p-nitrophenyl dimethylcarbamate (21–23) to their corresponding N-methylol derivatives. Generally, such an in vitro system will produce most of the metabolites found in plants prior to their conjugation with carbohydrates (21). To date, there is no in vitro system corresponding to the microsomal system of animals which has been developed for plants.

2. Aryl

Hydroxylation of aromatic rings is a common reaction in biological systems (24). Based on the ability to convert phenylalanine to tyrosine, there are major differences between various biological systems and their capability to hydroxylate aromatic rings (25). Although the phenylalanine hydroxylase isolated from spinach leaves was similar to the enzyme system present in animal (26), there are wide differences in hydroxylation activity within the plant kingdom. *Salvia, Coletricium*, and *Amaryllidaceae* do not hydroxylate phenylalanine (25), whereas *Hordeum diatechum, Salvia splendens, Triticum vulgare*, and *Fugopyrum tatoricum* show appreciable hydroxylation (28,29). It would seem reasonable, therefore, to expect differences in the rates of hydroxylation of pesticides between various plants.

The formation of 4-hydroxy-1-naphthyl methylcarbamate (15) and 5-hydroxy-1-naphthyl methylcarbamate (16) from carbaryl [reaction (16)] is a known (19) example of aromatic hydroxylation of a pesticide. A second example is the hydroxylation of Banol, presumably at either the 2 or 5 position (30). The position of the hydroxy group in the ring has not been established unequivocally. Data from the mass spectrometer indicated that attack occurred directly on the ring rather than on either of the methyl groups attached to the ring.

$$(17)$$

Aromatic hydroxylation does not necessarily involve a direct displacement of hydrogen by hydroxyl group (31–33). Substituted compounds such as p-chlorophenylalanine (31) or para-substituted acetanilide (34) undergo

$$(18)$$

hydroxylation in the para position with a concomitant migration of the para substituent. Udenfriend et al. (*34*) have termed this intramolecular migration the "NIH shift" (*33*). A portion of the mechanism which accounts for the migration of the chlorine atom is shown in reaction (18).

The complete mechanism (*33*) accounts for additional products. The point of initial hydroxyl attack and the kinetic factors involved in the rearrangement of the carbonium-ion intermediate determine the ratio of various products such as 3-chlorotyrosine (**17**) and tyrosine (**18**). The proposed mechanism (*33*) is useful in explaining how the action of one enzyme could result in a number of products. The NIH shift has been observed in a variety of organisms including a *Pseudomonas* but has not yet been found in plants (*33*). The importance of the NIH shift in the degradation of carbamates and related acyl anilides is yet to be established. The lack of specificity of aryl hydroxylases does suggest that hydroxylation reactions must be considered potential pathways important in the metabolism of aromatic compounds.

A second type of hydroxylation reaction involves an attack of benzylic carbon (alkyl carbon adjacent to an aromatic ring). Known examples of this type of reaction in nature include the formation of *d*-norpseudo ephedrine (**20**) from phenylalanine in the plant *Catha edulis* (*35*) labeled with ^{14}C in the benzylic carbon (**19**) and noradrenaline (**22**) from 2-(3,4-dihydroxyphenyl)ethyl amine (**21**) in beef tissue (*36*).

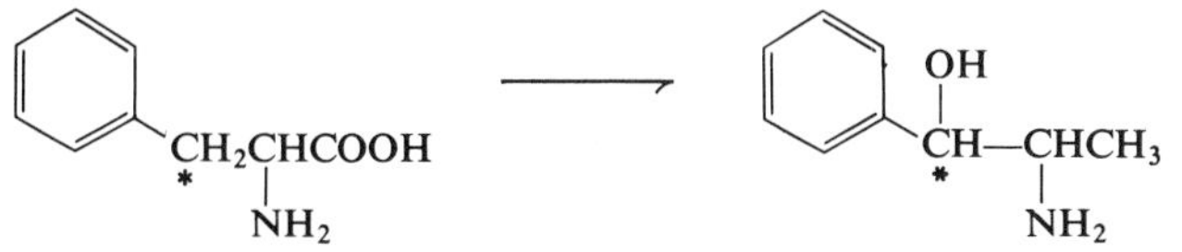

phenylalanine
(**19**)

d-norseudo ephedrine
(**20**)

(19)

2-(3,4-dihydroxyphenyl)ethyl amine
(**21**)

noradrenaline
(**22**)

(20)

This reaction does not proceed through an α,β-unsaturated intermediate; rather, it appears to be a direct hydroxylation of the benzylic carbon (*37*).

3. N Hydroxylation

The formation of N-hydroxy derivatives from carbamates has been suggested as a metabolic alteration in plants (38,39). This suggestion (38) was based on the intensity and character of the biological activity of synthetic N-hydroxy IPC (23). The N-hydroxy IPC was not actually isolated from IPC-treated plants. Boyland and Nery (41) reported that N-hydroxy-ethyl carbamate was essential for the production of chromosome damage in

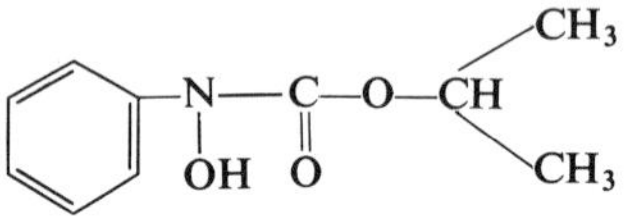

(23)

N-hydroxy IPC

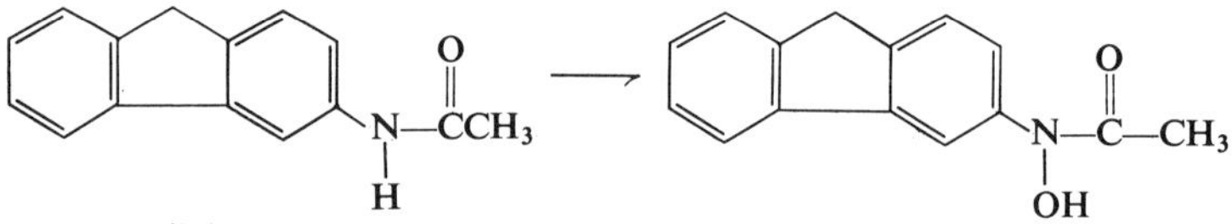

(24)

the root tips of *Vicia faba*. Ethyl carbamate was inactive, leading these workers to suggest that plants were unable to carry out this biotransformation. Kuhr and Casida (19) saw no evidence of N hydroxylation in their studies of eight different insecticidal methylcarbamates. N hydroxylations have been reported for 2-acetyiamino fluorene (24) (40) and urethane (6) (40) when incubated in the presence of animal microsomes. Thus N hydroxylations of carbamates and amides, a reaction which has been demonstrated in animals, appears to be of minor significance in plants.

C. N Dealkylation

Although phenylcarbamates obviously are not substrates for this biotransformation, the reaction is of considerable interest for methylcarbamates and related substituted amides. There is no evidence to suggest that monoalkylcarbamates such as carbaryl and Banol are dealkylated directly (21); rather, they are attacked by N-methyl hydroxylation as shown for carbaryl [reaction (15)] and then subsequently conjugated very rapidly (19). N,N-disubstituted carbamates are dealkylated by liver microsome–NADPH$_2$ systems presumably through an N-methylol intermediate (22,23). A similar stepwise degradation has been shown (42) for the disubstituted amide, Bidrin.

$$CH_3O-\!\!\!\!\overset{\displaystyle O}{\underset{\displaystyle}{P}}\!\!\!\!(CH_3O)-O-C=C(CH_3)-\overset{\displaystyle O}{C}-N(CH_3)_2 \quad\longrightarrow\quad CH_3O-\!\!\!\!\overset{\displaystyle O}{\underset{\displaystyle}{P}}\!\!\!\!(CH_3O)-O-C=C(CH_3)-\overset{\displaystyle O}{C}-N(CH_2OH)(CH_3)$$

Bidrin   (25)

$$CH_3O-\!\!\!\!\overset{\displaystyle O}{\underset{\displaystyle}{P}}\!\!\!\!(CH_3O)-O-C=C(CH_3)-\overset{\displaystyle O}{C}-N(H)(CH_3)$$

Azodrin   (22)

$$CH_3O-\!\!\!\!\overset{\displaystyle O}{\underset{\displaystyle}{P}}\!\!\!\!(CH_3O)-O-C=C(CH_3)-\overset{\displaystyle O}{C}-N(H)(CH_3) \quad\longrightarrow\quad CH_3O-\!\!\!\!\overset{\displaystyle O}{\underset{\displaystyle}{P}}\!\!\!\!(CH_3O)-O-C=C(CH_3)-\overset{\displaystyle O}{C}-N(H)(CH_2OH)$$

Azodrin   (26)

$$CH_3O-\!\!\!\!\overset{\displaystyle O}{\underset{\displaystyle}{P}}\!\!\!\!(CH_3O)-O-C=C(CH_3)-\overset{\displaystyle O}{C}-N(H)(H)$$

(27)

Injection of Bidrin into beans resulted in the appearance of trace amounts of the N-methyl-N-hydroxymethylamide analog (25) and 10 to 14% of the Bidrin level as Azodrin. The mono-N-hydroxymethylamide analog (26) and the unsubstituted amide (27) were not detected following injection of Bidrin but were observed in trace amounts (0.1 to 0.14% of the parent compound) following the injection of Azodrin. In another study with cotton plants (42a), none of the unsubstituted amide was detected following treatment with Azodrin and the importance of this oxidative pathway was questioned.

N Dealkylation has been demonstrated to be a significant reaction in the metabolism of dialkylphenylureas such as diuron (see Chapter 3). The inability of phenylureas to serve as substrates in the microsomal system (23) suggests they are not dealkylated through to the N-methylol intermediates by the system which attacks methylcarbamates.

A related disubstituted amide, diphenamid, undergoes stepwise dealkylation in fungi (43a). A similar pathway was initially reported in plants (43,44); however, subsequent study (43a) raised the question whether dealkylation was actually occurring in the plant or associated microorganisms. No dealkylation was observed in sterilized plants. There was no direct evidence to suggest the formation of intermediate *N*-methylol derivatives; however, trace amounts of at least two unidentified products (*44*) does not permit

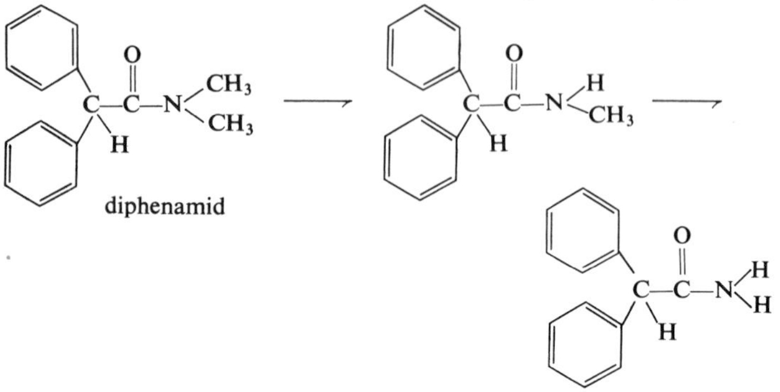

diphenamid

(23)

this possibility to be excluded. Based on the results obtained with Bidrin, the *N*-hydroxymethyl derivatives are present in extremely small amounts.

D. Sulfur Oxidation

A new insecticidal and miticidal carbamate, Temik, containing a thioether linkage has been described (*45*) which is metabolically transformed through an oxidative pathway (*46,47*). The initial oxidation to the sulfoxide (**28**)

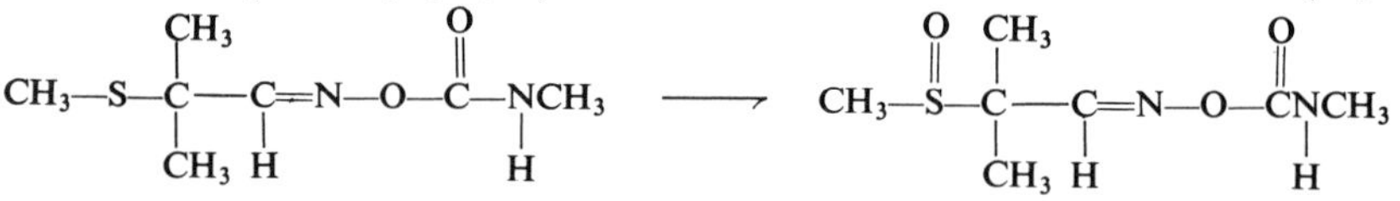

(**28**) (24)

is very rapid. The sulfoxide was then slowly metabolized through a further oxidation to the sulfone (**29**) and hydrolysis to the sulfoxide–oxime (**30**).

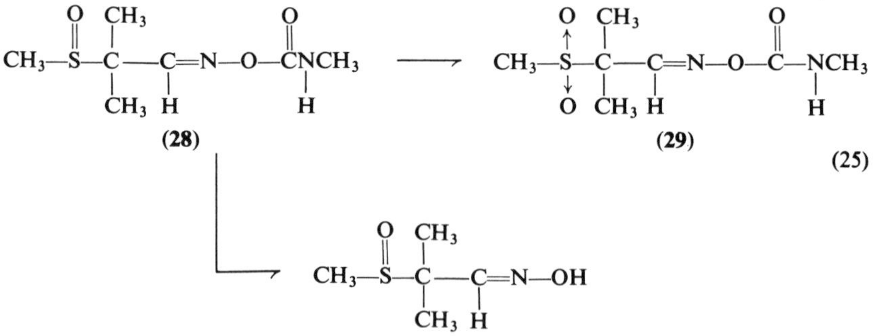

(**28**) (**29**) (25)

(**30**)

Additional work (*47*) suggested the sulfoxide–oxime (**30**) was degraded further to the corresponding nitrile (**31**). Coppedge et al. (*47*) also showed a similar pathway of degradation in three different soil types.

$$CH_3-\underset{\underset{(30)}{\overset{\displaystyle CH_3\;H}{|}}}{\overset{\overset{\displaystyle O\quad CH_3}{\|\quad|}}{C}}-C{=}N-OH \quad\longrightarrow\quad CH_3-\underset{\underset{(31)}{\overset{\displaystyle CH_3}{|}}}{\overset{\overset{\displaystyle O\quad CH_3}{\|\quad|}}{C}}-C{\equiv}N \qquad (26)$$

Another carbamate, Mesurol, containing a thioether linkage is also metabolized primarily through an oxidative mechanism to the corresponding sulfoxide (**32**) and sulfone (**33**) (*48*).

Mesurol   (32)   (33)

(27)

E. Conjugate Formation

The biotransformations described up to this point are those in which the parent compound has been attacked. Conjugates, on the other hand, are formed as a result of synthetic reactions involving condensation of endogenous or exogenous substances with naturally occurring compounds, generally carbohydrates or amino acids. These synthetic reactions are common reactions in plants (*49*) and result in the formation of highly polar, water-soluble products. Generally, these conjugates are glucosides formed from glucose (*49a*) or in certain specific instances (*49b*) from the disaccharide of glucose, gentitobiose. Glucosides are hydrolyzed enzymatically with β-glucosidase (*19*). Conjugates are also formed from certain amino acids such as alanine (*50,51*) and aspartic acid (*52*). Many xenobiotics (*53*) such as dithiocarbamates (*54*), maleic hydrazide (*55*), and phenols (*56*) are conjugated with naturally occurring substances. Compounds which do not

contain a phenolic group initially but are hydroxylated are ultimately
suitable for conjugation (57). Some aromatic amines such as 3-amino-2,5-
dichlorobenzoic acid (amiben) are conjugated with glucose to give N-(3-
carboxy-2,5-dichlorophenyl)glucosylamine (57a). It would be expected
that hydrolytic products such as aniline and 3-chloroaniline from the
phenylcarbamates would be likely candidates for conjugation; however,
there has been no description of such conjugates of these materials at the
present time. The 3,4-dichloroaniline formed from hydrolysis of propanil
3′,4′-dichloropropionanilide in treated rice formed a sugar conjugate
identified as N-(3,4-dichlorophenyl)glucosylamine (58,59). Recently an
enzyme, an arylamine N-glucosyltransferase, was obtained from soybeans
which forms glucosides with aromatic amines such as 3,4-dichloroaniline
(60).

4-3. DEGRADATION IN PLANTS

Pesticides applied to growing plants are subjected to a multiplicity of
external and internal degradative mechanisms (61). Material which remains
on the external surface of the treated plant is dissipated primarily by physical
factors. "Weathering" is a common term used to describe this loss and
represents the cumulative effects of volatility (62), photodecomposition
(63), physical abrasion, and washing.

Weathering on the surfaces of plants is of minimal importance for
herbicidal carbamates, which are generally applied as preemergence treatments to the soil prior to crop emergence. These factors are of considerable
importance for the insecticidal carbamates. Of major concern for both
types is the degradation within plants. Such degradation includes biochemical alterations, adsorption on inactive sites, and the formation of chemical
complexes (61).

Results of chemical analyses (64–69) of crop plants treated either directly
with insecticidal carbamates or indirectly with preemergent herbicidal
carbamates indicate that both methyl- and phenylcarbamates are rapidly
degraded. Only small amounts of the parent compound can be detected
1 week after treatment. The disappearance follows a first-order decay
curve (1).

Primarily due to work with animals (70), hydrolysis was considered as
the major degradative pathway in plants (67). This was also suggested by
the rapid disappearance of certain parent carbamates. Recent results

indicate that hydrolysis may be the major degradative pathway for CIPC (71) and the related acyl anilide, propanil, in resistant plants (58). However, when plant tissues were analyzed for the hydrolytic products such as α-naphthol from carbaryl (67), 3-chloroaniline from barban (66), and 3,4-dichloroaniline from both propanil (72) and swep (73), only limited amounts of these products were detected. In many instances (68,69,72,73) there were other products containing the intact carbamoyl linkage, suggesting that metabolitic transformations other than hydrolysis may play an important role in the degradation of carbamates.

Development of insecticidal methylcarbamates and subsequent studies of their metabolism in plants indicated quite clearly that hydrolysis was not necessarily a major degradative pathway (20,74). Carbaryl was hydroxylated in the plant to the three products shown in reactions (15) and (16). In addition, a fourth hydroxylated compound, tentatively identified as the 5,6-dihydro-5,6-dihydroxynaphthyl methylcarbamate on the basis of the chromatographic similarity to a product, formed in animals (75). Hydroxylation was rate limiting, as all the hydroxylated products were present in plants as conjugates—presumably glucosides. The hydoxylated compounds were generated by treatment with β-glucosidase.

Banol (30) was rapidly degraded in plants to a water-soluble product containing the intact carbamate linkage. The product of suggested ring hydroxylation [reaction (17)] was conjugated; however, small amounts of the free hydroxyl derivative (aglycone) were observed. There was no evidence to suggest alkyl hydroxylation of Banol to the N-methylol derivative.

Herbicidal methylcarbamates are relatively recent introductions (10,12). Initial metabolic studies with radioactive UC 22463 (76) indicate that it is rapidly modified in plants and only trace amounts of the parent carbamate can be detected within 7 days of treatment. The biotransformation in sensitive plants involves a conversion to a water-soluble product containing the intact carbamate. Tolerant plants, on the other hand, degrade either the parent carbamate or the water-soluble transformation product so rapidly that it is difficult to detect even 48 hours after treatment.

Riden and Hopkins (68) found that barban was rapidly degraded in both resistant wheat and sensitive wild oats to an unknown water-soluble substance (X) which released 3-chloroaniline on hydrolysis in 10% aqueous caustic. Hopkins suggested (77) that X was a metabolite which contained the intact carbamate linkage. Attempts to prove the latter hypothesis using two different ^{14}C-labeled materials were unsuccessful. Appearance of 3-chloroaniline ruled out the prospect of ring hydroxylation. The polar product was not N-hydroxybarban, as shown by the absence of a comparison of water solubility with an authentic sample. No data were shown to suggest a differential breakdown of X between sensitive and resistant plants.

Swep was not readily hydrolyzed in rice (73); instead it was metabolized without hydrolysis to a stable lignin complex. Only limited amounts of free 3,4-dichloroaniline were detected. Yih et al. (59a) observed incorporation of radioactivity from ring-labeled propanil into polymeric cell constituents, primarily lignin. In contrast to results obtained with Swep, there was no incorporation of the intact anilide. Incorporation occurred after hydrolysis to 3,4-dichloroaniline.

Recently Prendeville et al. (78) reported that CIPC was metabolized to water-soluble products which contained the intact carbamate linkage in sensitive plants. Polar metabolites were observed within 24 to 36 hours of application without any evidence of hydrolysis. There was no evidence that the resistant plant metabolized CIPC to similar water-soluble products; presumably hydrolysis was the favored reaction.

Propanil, which contains the carbamoyl group, was apparently metabolized to a water-soluble intermediate containing the intact amide bond (72,79,81) in a sensitive species such as barnyard grass. McRae et al. (72) apparently did not find any water-soluble product in tolerant rice under normal conditions. Either the unidentified water-soluble product was not formed or else it was subsequently metabolized rapidly. Absence of hydrolysis in rice of the much less selective 3,4-dichloromethylvaleranilide led the authors to conclude that the selective action of propanil was based on the ability of tolerant species to hydrolyze the herbicide to inactive products.

4-4. DEGRADATION IN SOILS

Herbicidal methyl- and phenylcarbamates are generally applied directly to the soil. Insecticidal carbamates, although generally applied to plants, eventually reach the soil either directly or indirectly. In both instances it is important to gain an understanding of the factors influencing persistency. Degradation of herbicidal carbamates in soil is the subject of a recent review (2).

Several factors are involved in the degradation of carbamates in soils (2,82). These include volatility, leaching soil moisture, adsorption, pH, temperature, photodecomposition, and microbial degradation.

Initially, it was believed that volatilization played a major role in the loss of phenylcarbamates from soil (83,84). This concept was developed from data based on losses from inert surfaces such as glass slides and filter paper. Studies (84) based on trapped vapors indicated that the adsorptive capacity of the soil was the major factor which influenced the volatility of IPC and CIPC. Initial studies indicated that CIPC was more persistent than IPC (84a). Recently it was demonstrated (85a) that IPC and CIPC showed similar dissipation patterns, but because CIPC was inherently more toxic than IPC, it appeared to persist longer in the field. Temperature is also a factor involved in the disappearance of carbamates from soils (84).

Both methyl- and phenylcarbamates resist leaching into the soil profile. CIPC was highly resistant to leaching in three different soil types (85). Over 90% of the recovered CIPC was found in the upper inch of the soil profile after 1.68 in. of rain (86). The methylcarbamate UC 22463 did not leach out of the upper $\frac{1}{4}$ in. of the soil profile after a 3-in. rainfall (87).

Moisture influences the rate of loss from both soil (84) and certain types of granulars (64). Residual herbicidal activity was longer in dry soils than in wet soils. Undoubtedly high moisture provides a more favorable environment for microbial action, particularly in upper regions of the soil profile. It is also probable that there is competition between the herbicide and free water for available adsorptive sites in soil colloids (84). Water could conceivably displace the carbamate from such sites and thus cause more rapid losses through volatility. Data obtained from granular formulations (88) tend to support this latter possibility. Danielson (88) observed that CIPC disappeared more rapidly from certain granulars which were exposed to moisture.

Early field observations (64) suggested that microbial degradation was a major factor in the degradation of carbamates. Environmental conditions that favored the growth and activity of microorganisms also favored degradation (2,85,89). Residual herbicidal activity persisted longer in sterile soil than in nonsterile soil for barban (89) and IPC (64).

The recent work (2,17,19,90–95) of the Beltsville group initiated a clear understanding of the importance of microbial degradation. Kaufman and Kearney (92) isolated and identified several soil microorganisms capable of hydrolyzing CIPC, as shown by the appearance of 3-chloroaniline. This suggested hydrolysis as a major degradative pathway. They were also able to demonstrate microbial degradation using soil-perfusion columns and ^{14}C-labeled CIPC. In contrast, methylcarbamate insecticide (Banol) disappeared only very slowly in both sterile and nonsterile soil. This suggested a major difference between degradation of methyl- and phenylcarbamates in the soil.

Barban applied to soil was not metabolized to the water-soluble substance X observed in plants. This suggested that the pathway leading to the water-soluble intermediate was unique to plants (*68*).

Bartha and Pramer (*96*) observed 3,4-dichloroanaline (*34*) in soil treated with propanil and suggested that degradation proceeded through a hydrolytic pathway. A second product was identified as 3,3′,4,4′-tetrachloroazobenzene (*36*) and they proposed the following scheme based on coupling of the product of biological oxidation (*35*) with the amine (*34*). Application of propanil to soil resulted in increased oxygen uptake (*96a*), suggesting

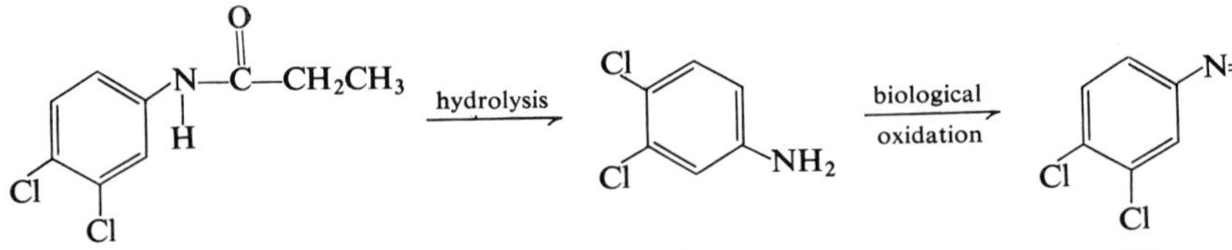

propanil　　　　　　　(*34*)　　　　　　　　(*35*)　　　　(28)

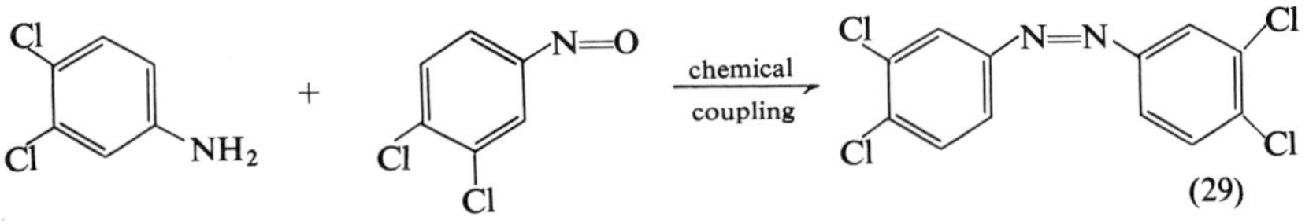

(*34*)　　　　　(*35*)　　　　　　　　　　(*36*)　　　　(29)

3,3′,4,4′-tetrachloro-
azobenzene

oxidation reaction possibly of the acyl side chain. Initially the authors suggested (*96*) that phenylcarbamates or phenylureas which yield aniline derivatives as a result of hydrolysis might be expected to yield the corresponding azo compound. Their subsequent studies (*97a*) showed that with *m*-chloroaniline, a hydrolysis product from CIPC but not aniline, the hydrolytic product of IPC was transformed to the expected dichloroazobenzene. There has been no evidence that the azobenzene (*36*) from 3,4-dichloroaniline is formed in plants (*59,59a*), although the reaction is catalyzed by peroxidase (*97a*).

4-5. ENZYMATIC STUDIES

There has been little work at the subcellular level concerning the actual enzymes involved in the degradation of phenyl- and methylcarbamates in plants. Indeed there has not been any work which parallels the animal microsomal studies on insecticides and drugs (97). Attempts to degrade CIPC by plant homogenates from tomato and spinach were unsuccessful (98) at pH of 4.2 or 5.8, respectively. Based on the pH optimum for the hydrolytic enzyme isolated from *Pseudomonas striata* (18), these conditions may have been too acidic. The latter enzyme was completely inactivated at pH 4.5.

The most exhaustive studies of cell-free systems responsible for carbamate degradation have been those of the Beltsville group. They have isolated and partially purified an enzyme from *Pseudomonas striata* which hydrolyzes the phenylcarbamates, as shown, for example, by the appearance of 3-chloroaniline from CIPC (17). It was suggested (95) that 3-chloroaniline was further metabolized by hydroxylation and that isopropanol was oxidized to acetic acid.

It was impossible, based on the end products, to determine if the enzyme isolated from *P. striata* was acting as an amidase or esterase or both. Relatively high activity of this enzyme on propanil suggested amidase activity. Methylcarbamates and ureas were not substrates for this enzyme.

Recent studies of the molecular parameters involved in enzymatic hydrolysis by Kearney (17) indicate that inductive, steric, and resonance effects as well as molecular size influence the rate of enzymatic hydrolysis. Kearney found decreasing rates of hydrolysis in the series:

$$C_2H_5 > n\text{-}C_3H_7 > \text{iso-}C_3H_7 > \qquad \underset{CH_2}{\bigcirc}$$

when these groups were in the alcoholic moiety. Correlation of acidity suggested that increased acidity resulted in increased rates of hydrolysis, possibly through an enhanced nucleophilic attack. Molecular size may be a factor in determining the rate.

Adachi et al. (79,80) prepared homogenates of rice which hydrolyzed propanil readily, while those of *Panicum crus-galli* and five other weed species showed low hydrolyzing activity. Maximum activity was observed at pH 8.4 and at 35°. This was in good agreement with the optimum of near pH 8.5, determined for the phenylcarbamate-hydrolyzing enzyme in bacteria (18). Recently, Still and Kuzirian (81) found a heat labile macromolecule which hydrolyzed propanil. There were six products. Only 13% of the transformed substrate was present as 3,4-dichloroaniline. Essentially all the remaining transformed substrate appeared as a polar, unidentified product. Frear and Still (99a) have isolated an aryl acylamine amidohydrolase, EC 3.5.1.a, from rice. They found 60 times more of the enzyme in resistant rice than in sensitive barnyard grass. They reported a pH optimum between 7.5 and 7.9, slightly lower than that observed by Adachi et al. (80).

A. Inhibitors and Synergists

The ability to alter biological activity of molecules by the addition of a second molecule is well documented in the insecticide literature. Synergists are chemicals which enhance the properties of other compounds. The relationship between synergist action and the metabolism of insecticides has been studied in some detail (99). Hodgson and Casida (23) observed that synergists were inhibitors of microsomal oxidation of dimethylcarbamates. Metcalf and Fukuto (99) have demonstrated that synergists block the nonhydrolytic degradation in insects. In the opposite sense, increased capability of insects to detoxify the parent molecule is considered as the basis for insect resistance (99,100).

Recently, interactions between various herbicides and insecticides have become important. Perhaps the best-known example is the increased herbicidal action of propanil when applied with certain carbamates and phosphates (100a,102). The combination of carbaryl and propanil results in increased phytotoxicity in rice (102); however, the increased herbicidal action has found utility for weed control in citrus in Japan. The biochemical basis for the increased herbicidal activity of propanil is evidently similar to the increased insecticidal action resulting from the use of a synergist. Carbaryl, acting as the synergist, is blocking the degradation of propanil. Only active cholinesterase inhibitors were effective in promoting the herbicidal activity of propanil; chlorinated hydrocarbons which are not cholinergic showed no influence (100a,102).

Studies on intact plants (72) indicated that carbaryl was altering the normal pathway in resistant rice. The water-soluble metabolite observed in the sensitive barnyard grass was absent in rice which had not been treated with carbaryl. Either the water-soluble metabolite was not formed or it was further metabolized so rapidly that it was not detected. Combinations of propanil and carbaryl resulted in the appearance of this water-soluble metabolite which indicated the potential existed to form this product in rice.

Inhibition of propanil hydrolysis (3,4-dichloroaniline production) was observed in cell homogenates (80, 100a). Frear and Still (99a) found that the inhibition of their isolated enzyme was competitive for carbaryl with a Ki of 1.51×10^{-8}. Kinetic studies (94a) of the enzyme from P. striata capable of hydrolyzing CIPC revealed that certain methylcarbamates such as carbaryl, Banol, and Zectran were competitive inhibitors. One methyl-carbamate, terbutol, was thought to be ineffective as an inhibitor because of the bulky *o-t*-butyl groups. Perhaps as a consequence of these steric factors, it also is a poor inhibitor of cholinesterase. A second methylcarbamate, UC 22463, which is inactive as a cholinesterase inhibitor presumably because of the lower reactivity of the aliphatic alcohols (*13a*), does not alter the herbicidal activity of propanil (*76*). Apparently inhibition of either esterase or amidase activity is associated with active cholinesterase inhibitors in plants and bacteria. In animals, arylamidase activity is inhibited by cholinergic agents (*101*).

4-6. METABOLISM AND SELECTIVE PHYTOTOXICITY

The relationship between metabolism and insecticidal activity has been recognized by the entomologists for some time (*100*). Several attempts have been made to relate the phytotoxicity of various compounds to their metabolism. Baskakow (*38*), for example, suggested that the basis for differential toxicity of IPC between sunflowers (tolerant) and oats (susceptible) was differential metabolism in various plant parts. IPC applied to the foliage was degraded rapidly. Degradation in the roots of sunflower was very rapid in comparison to the rate of degradation in oat roots (*103*).

Lemin (*43*) showed that *N* dealkylation of diphenamid to the much less phytotoxic monomethyl derivative proceeded rapidly in tomatoes and suggested that possibly a relatively slow dealkylation in sensitive species could account for differential toxicity. Kesner and Ries (*43a*) recently suggested that the monomethyl derivative was actually the phytotoxic moiety and dealkylation by fungi was an intoxication step necessary for the herbicidal activity of diphenamid. These contrasting results must await further clarification to establish any relationship between the metabolism and phytotoxicity of diphenamid. Swep was rapidly metabolized, as the intact carbamate appeared in the lignin fraction. The authors (*73*) suggest this effectively immobilized the compound and prevented it from reaching a toxic site of action.

Eshel and Warren (*104*) observed two different toxic responses in sensitive plants to foliar applications of CIPC. They postulated that a buildup of a toxic metabolite might be involved in these responses. Subsequent work (*78*) suggested that CIPC was metabolized differentially between sensitive and resistant plants. They found intact carbamates in sensitive plants which were not observed in the resistant plant.

Results with propanil (72,80) and UC 22463 (76) suggest that herbicidal activity may be associated with metabolism.

4-7. SUMMARY

Models of CIPC, propanil, and UC 22463 reveal striking similarities in their molecular architecture. The molecular dimensions of these molecules in both the extended and folded forms also show remarkable similarities (76).

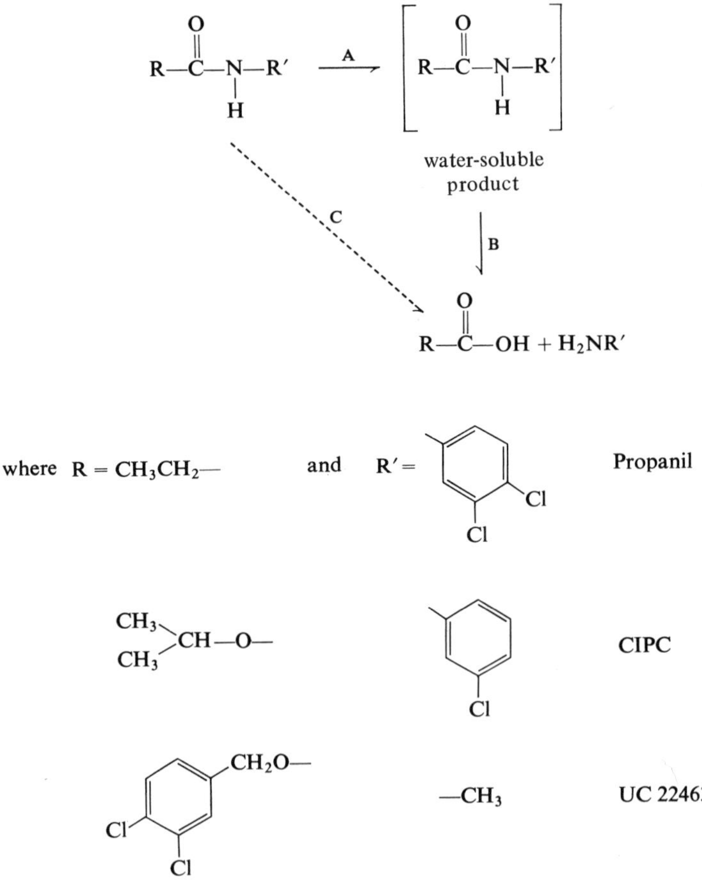

$$\begin{array}{ccc}
\text{R—C—N—R}' & \xrightarrow{\ \ A\ \ } & \left[\text{R—C—N—R}'\right]
\end{array} \tag{30}$$

where $R = CH_3CH_2$—   and $R' =$ Propanil

CIPC

—CH_3 UC 22463

The evidence reviewed in this chapter permits us to construct a working hypothesis relating the metabolism and herbicidal activity of the similar compounds. This hypothesis may be summarized in reaction (30). The compounds are readily transformed from highly lipophilic compounds to polar, hydrophilic products which contain the intact carbamoyl group (A) in sensitive species. The parent compounds are also readily degraded in tolerant plants either directly through hydrolysis (C) or subsequent to the formation of a water-soluble product containing the intact carbamoyl group (B). Results of inhibitor studies in the degradation of propanil in the resistant rice and the subsequent appearance of the water-soluble product suggest that such a biotransformation to a hydrophilic compound is also a potential reaction pathway in resistant plants. The extremely transient nature of the product makes it difficult to detect such a product under normal conditions in resistant plants.

This hypothesis may be developed on the basis of competing reactions. The hydrolytic (C) and the biotransformation reaction (A) to a hydrophilic compound compete for the parent compound. In sensitive plants the biotransformation reaction is favored, thus reducing the possibility of hydrolysis and degradation to herbicidally inactive products. In the tolerant plant under normal conditions, the hydrolytic pathway (C) is the preferred pathway and little or none of the hydrophilic product is evident. The addition of an inhibitor blocks the hydrolytic pathway and favors the formation of a water-soluble product.

Undoubtedly the drastic changes in solubility properties resulting from this biotransformation will alter the disposition of the compound within the cell. Availability to degradative enzymes would also be altered as a result of such a transformation. Certainly differences between species and their ability to metabolize compounds is not surprising. The differences between plants in hydroxylating phenylalanine to tyrosine is but one of many examples. The vast differences in content of the acylhydrolase enzyme between resistant rice and sensitive barnyard grass is another example. To study these potential differences in metabolism, the fate of a compound must be examined in both sensitive and resistant species. It is difficult to determine the function of metabolism on herbicidal activity from a single plant. Future studies directed toward the relative degradation rates of carbamates should provide clearer understanding of these relationships between differential phytotoxicity and metabolism.

It is evident that both methyl- and phenylcarbamates and chemically related phenylamides are subjected to a wide variety of biotransformations in plants and soils. While the hydrolysis of carbamates and acylanilides which has received the major attention is undoubtedly a significant pathway, the results of studies on the insecticidal carbamates strongly suggest the susceptibility of such molecules to other types of attack, especially oxidative attack. Hydroxylations of aromatic rings and N-alkyl groups, aliphatic side chains, must all be considered, not necessarily as alternative reactions but in relation to total degradation. Certainly, the multiplicity of reactions and the speed with which the carbamates are effectively degraded suggest a major reason for their increased ultilization in agriculture: methyl- and phenylcarbamates are generally not persistent in plants and soil.

REFERENCES

1. J. E. Casida, *Ann. Rev. Entomol.*, **8**, 39 (1963).
2. D. D. Kaufman, *J. Agr. Food Chem.*, **15**, 582 (1967).
3. G. Friesen, *Planta*, **8**, 666 (1929).
4. W. G. Templeman and W. A. Sexton, *Nature*, **156**, 630 (1945).
5. M. H. J. Weiden, A. J. Borash, E. L. Boyd, A. A. Sousa, and L. K. Payne, Jr., *J. Econ. Entomol.*, **60**, 873 (1967).
6. R. L. Metcalf, *Agr. Chem.*, **16**, 20 (1961).
7. M. J. Kolbezen, R. L. Metcalf, and T. R. Fukuto, *J. Agr. Food Chem.*, **2**, 864 (1954).
8. H. Gysin, *Chimia (Aarau)*, **8**, 205 (1954).
9. H. Gysin and E. Knuesli (to Geigy Chem. Corp.), U.S. Pat. 2,776,196 (1957).
10. A. H. Haubein (to Hercules Inc.), U.S. Pat. 3,140,167 (1964).
11. A. H. Haubein and J. R. Hansen, *J. Agr. Food Chem.*, **13**, 555 (1965).
12. R. A. Herrett and R. V. Berthold, *Science*, **149**, 191 (1965).
13. R. A. Herrett, *European Weed Res. Council Symp. New Herb.*, *2nd*, Paris, 1965, p. 221.
13a. R. L. Metcalf and T. R. Fukuto, *J. Agr. Food Chem.*, **15**, 1022 (1967).
14. L. W. Dittert and T. Higuchi, *J. Pharm. Sci.*, **52**, 852 (1963).
15. M. L. Bender and R. B. Homer, *J. Org. Chem.*, **30**, 3975 (1965).
16. T. R. Fukuto, M. A. H. Fahmy, and R. L. Metcalf, *J. Agr. Food Chem.*, **15**, 273 (1967).
17. P. C. Kearney, *J. Agr. Food Chem.*, **15**, 568 (1967).
18. P. C. Kearney, *J. Agr. Food Chem.*, **13**, 561 (1965).
19. R. J. Kuhr and J. E. Casida, *J. Agr. Food Chem.*, **15**, 814 (1967).
20. H. W. Dorough and J. E. Casida, *J. Agr. Food Chem.*, **12**, 294 (1964).
21. E. S. Oonnithan and J. E. Casida, *J. Agr. Food Chem.*, **16**, 28 (1968).
22. E. Hodgson and J. E. Casida, *Biochim. Biophys. Acta*, **42**, 184 (1960).
23. E. Hodgson and J. E. Casida, *Biochem. Pharm.*, **8**, 179 (1961).
24. S. Kaufman, in *Oxygenases* (O. Hayaishi, ed.), Academic Press, New York, **1962**, p. 129.
25. E. Leete, *Ann. Rev. Plant Physiol.*, **18**, 179 (1967).
26. P. M. Nair and L. C. Vining, *Phytochemistry*, **4**, 401 (1965).
27. J. Massicot and L. Marion, *Can. J. Chem.*, **35**, 1 (1957).
28. D. R. McCalla and A. C. Neish, *Can. J. Biochem. Physiol.*, **37**, 531 (1959).
29. O. L. Gamborg and A. C. Neish, *Can. J. Biochem. Physiol.*, **37**, 1277 (1959).

30. A. R. Friedman and A. J. Lemin, *J. Agr. Food Chem.*, **15**, 642 (1967).
31. G. Guroff, K. Kondo, and J. Daly, *Biochem. Biophys. Res. Commun.*, **25**, 622 (1966).
32. G. Guroff, M. Levitt, J. Daly, and S. Udenfriend, *Biochem. Biophys. Res. Commun.*, **25**, 253 (1966).
33. G. Guroff, J. W. Daly, D. M. Jerina, J. Renson, B. Witkop, and S. Udenfriend, *Science*, **157**, 1524 (1967).
34. S. Udenfriend, P. Zaltzman-Nirenberg, J. Daly, G. Guroff, C. Chidsey, and B. Witkop, *Arch. Biochem. Biophys.*, **120**, 413 (1967).
35. E. Leete, *Chem. Ind. (London)*, **1958**, 1088.
36. E. Y. Levin, B. Levenberg, and S. Kaufman, *J. Biol. Chem.*, **235**, 2080 (1960).
37. W. J. Smith and N. Kirshner, *J. Biol. Chem.*, **237**, 1890 (1962).
38. Yu. A. Baskakow, *Zashchita Rast. ot Vreiditelei. i Boleznei*, **6**, 34 (1961) (in Russian); through *CA*, **56**, 1796e (1962).
39. Yu. A. Baskakow and U. A. Zemskaya, *Fiz. Rast. Akad. Nauk SSR*, **6**, 67 (1959).
40. C. C. Irving, *J. Biol. Chem.*, **239**, 1589 (1964).
41. E. Boyland and R. Nery, *Biochem. J.*, **94**, 198 (1965).
42. R. E. Menzer and J. E. Casida, *J. Agr. Food Chem.*, **13**, 102 (1965).
42a. D. A. Lindquist and D. L. Bull, *J. Agr. Food Chem.*, **15**, 267 (1967).
43. A. J. Lemin, *J. Agr. Food Chem.*, **14**, 109 (1966).
43a. C. D. Kesner and S. K. Ries, *Science*, **155**, 210 (1967).
44. T. Golab, R. J. Herberg, S. J. Parka, and J. B. Tepe, *J. Agr. Food Chem.*, **14**, 592 (1966).
45. L. K. Payne, Jr., H. A. Stansbury, Jr., and M. H. J. Weiden, *J. Agr. Food Chem.*, **14**, 356 (1966).
46. R. L. Metcalf, T. R. Fukuto, C. Collins, K. Borck, J. Burk, H. T. Reynolds, and M. F. Osman, *J. Agr. Food Chem.*, **14**, 579 (1966).
47. J. R. Coppedge, D. A. Lindquist, D. L. Bull, and H. W. Dorough, *J. Agr. Food Chem.*, **15**, 902 (1967).
48. H. Niessen and H. Frehse, *Pflanzenschutz-Nachr. "Bayer,"* **16**, 205 (1963).
49. J. B. Harborne, *Biochemistry of Phenolic Compounds*, Academic Press, New York, 1964, Chap. 4.
49a. L. P. Miller, *Contrib. Boyce Thompson Inst.*, **11**, 271 (1940).
49b. L. P. Miller, *Contrib. Boyce Thompson Inst.*, **12**, 163 (1941).
50. P. Massini, *Biochim. Biophys. Acta*, **36**, 548 (1959).
51. J. Kaslander, A. K. Sijpesteijn, and G. J. M. Van der Kerk, *Biochim. Biophys. Acta*, **60**, 417 (1962).
52. W. A. Andreae and N. E. Good, *Plant Physiol.*, **32**, 566 (1957).
53. H. S. Mason, J. C. North, and M. Vanneste, *Federation Proc.*, **24**, 1172 (1965).
54. J. Kaslander, A. K. Sijpesteijn, and G. J. M. Van der Kerk, *Biochim. Biophys. Acta*, **52**, 396 (1961).
55. G. H. N. Towers and A. Hutchinson, *Nature*, **181**, 1535 (1958).
56. A. Hutchinson, C. Roy, and G. H. N. Towers, *Nature*, **181**, 841 (1958).
57. E. A. Williams, R. W. Meikle, and C. T. Redemann, *J. Agr. Food Chem.*, **12**, 453 (1964).
57a. D. S. Frear, C. R. Swanson, and R. E. Kadunce, *Weeds*, **15**, 101 (1967).
58. G. G. Still, *Weed Soc. Am. Abstr.*, 1967, 63.
59. G. G. Still, *Science*, **159**, 992 (1967).
59a. R. Y. Yih, D. H. McRae, and H. F. Wilson, *Science*, **161**, 376 (1968).

60. D. S. Frear, American Chemical Society, 154th Meeting, Chicago, 1967.
61. D. E. Moreland, *Ann. Rev. Plant Physiol.*, **18**, 365 (1967).
62. A. M. Abdel-Wahab, R. J. Kuhr, and J. E. Casida, *J. Agr. Food Chem.*, **14**, 290 (1966).
63. A. M. Abdel-Wahab and J. E. Casida, *J. Agr. Food Chem.*, **15**, 479 (1967).
64. V. H. Freed, *Weeds*, **1**, 48 (1951).
65. V. H. Freed and M. L. Montgomery, *Residue Rev.*, **3**, 1 (1963).
66. L. N. Gard, C. E. Ferguson, Jr., and T. L. Reynolds, *J. Agr. Food Chem.*, **7**, 335 (1959).
67. D. P. Johnson and H. A. Stansbury, *J. Agr. Food Chem.*, **13**, 235 (1965).
68. J. R. Riden and T. R. Hopkins, *J. Agr. Food Chem.*, **10**, 455 (1962).
69. C. R. Swanson, *U.S. Agr. Res. Serv.*, **ARS34-66** (1965).
70. R. T. Williams, *Detoxication Mechanisms*, Wiley, New York, 2nd ed., 1959, p. 161.
71. R. H. Hodgson, *Weed Soc. Am. Abstr.*, **1967**, p. 65.
72. D. H. McRae, R. Y. Yih, and H. F. Wilson, *Weed Soc. Am. Abstr.*, 1964, p. 87.
73. W. T. Chin, R. P. Stanovick, T. E. Cullen, and G. C. Holsing, *Weeds*, **12**, 201 (1964).
74. I. Y. Mostafa, A. Hassan, and S. M. A. D. Zayed, *Z. Naturforsch.*, **b21**, 1060 (1966).
75. N. C. Leeling and J. E. Casida, *J. Agr. Food Chem.*, **14**, 281 (1966).
76. R. A. Herrett, J. A. Kramer, Jr., and W. P. Bagley, American Chemical Society, 155th Meeting, San Francisco, 1968.
77. T. R. Hopkins, American Chemical Society, 139th Meeting, St. Louis, 1961.
78. G. N. Prendeville, Y. Eshel, G. F. Warren, and M. M. Schreiber, *Plant Physiol. Suppl.*, **42**, S-49 (1967).
79. M. Adachi, K. Tanegawa, and T. Uejima, *Noyaku Seisan Gijutsu*, **14**, 19 (1966) in Japanese); through *CA*, **66**, 75189q (1967).
80. M. Adachi, K. Tanegawa, and T. Uejima, *Noyaku Seisan Gijutsu*, **15**, 11 (1966) (in Japanese); through *CA*, **66**, 75190h (1967).
81. C. C. Still and O. Kuzirian, *Nature*, **216**, 799 (1967).
82. P. Burschel and V. H. Freed, *Weeds*, **7**, 157 (1959).
83. A. S. Newman and C. R. Downing, *J. Agr. Food Chem.*, **6**, 352 (1958).
84. J. V. Parochetti and G. F. Warren, *Weeds*, **14**, 281 (1966).
84a. H. R. De Rose, *Agron. J.*, **43**, 139 (1951).
85. R. E. Ogle and G. F. Warren, *Weeds*, **3**, 257 (1954).
85a. J. V. Parochetti and G. F. Warren, *Weed Sci.*, **16**, 13 (1968).
86. B. O. Pray and E. D. Witman, *Weeds*, **2**, 300 (1953).
87. R. A. Herrett and J. A. Kramer, *Weed Soc. Am. Abstr.*, 1966, p. 51.
88. L. L. Danielson, *Weeds*, **7**, 418 (1959).
89. K. P. Dubrovin, *Crops Soils*, **14**, 26 (1962).
90. P. C. Kearney and D. D. Kaufman, *Science*, **417**, 740 (1965).
91. P. C. Kearney, *Advan. Chem. Ser.*, **60**, 250 (1966).
92. D. D. Kaufman and P. C. Kearney, *Appl. Microbiol.*, **13**, 443 (1965).
93. D. D. Kaufman, American Chemical Society, 152nd Meeting, New York, 1966.
94. D. D. Kaufman, in *Pesticides and Their Effects on Soils and Water*, Soil Science Society of America, Inc., Madison, Wisc., 1967, p. 85.
94a. D. D. Kaufman and P. C. Kearney, *Weed Soc. Am. Abstr.*, **1967**, 74.
95. P. C. Kearney, D. D. Kaufman, and M. Alexander, in *Soil Biochemistry* (A. D McLaren and G. H. Peterson, eds.), Dekker, New York, 1967, pp. 318–342.
96. R. Bartha and D. Pramer, *Science*, **156**, 1617 (1967).

96a. R. Bartha, *J. Agr. Food Chem.*, **16**, 602 (1968).
97. B. B. Brodie, J. R. Gillette, and B. N. LaDu, *Ann. Rev. Biochem.*, **27**, 427 (1958).
97a. R. Bartha, H. A. B. Linke, and D. Pramer, *Science*, **161**, 582 (1968).
98. P. Koivistoinin and A. Karinpaa, *J. Agr. Food Chem.*, **13**, 459 (1965).
99. R. L. Metcalf and T. R. Fukuto, *J. Agr. Food Chem.*, **13**, 220 (1965).
99a. D. S. Frear and G. G. Still, *Phytochemistry*, **7**, 913 (1968).
100. T. R. Fukuto, *Ann. Rev. Entomol.*, **6**, 313 (1960).
100a. S. Matsunaka, *Science*, **160**, 1360 (1968).
101. C. H. Williams and K. H. Jacobson, *Toxicol. Appl. Pharmacol.*, **9**, 495 (1966).
102. C. C. Bowling and H. R. Hudgins, *Weeds*, **14**, 94 (1966).
103. U. A. Zemskaya and Yu. V. Rakitin, *Fiz. Rast. Akad. Nauk SRR*, **8**, 220 (1961) (in Russian); through *CA*, **55**: 24945f (1961).
104. Y. Eshel and G. F. Warren, *Weeds*, **15**, 237 (1967).

CHAPTER 5

Thiolcarbamates

S. C. FANG

DEPARTMENT OF AGRICULTURAL CHEMISTRY
OREGON STATE UNIVERSITY
CORVALLIS, OREGON

5-1. Introduction . . . . · 147
    A. Chemical and Physical Properties . . . . . · 147
5-2. Degradation . . . . · 148
    A. Degradation in Plants . . . . · 148
    B. Degradation in Soils . . . . · 158
5-3. Summary and Conclusion . . . . · 163
References . . . . · 164

5-1. INTRODUCTION

The first thiolcarbamate (EPTC) was introduced by Stauffer Chemical Company in 1954 to be used as an experimental herbicide for the control of annual grasses and many broad-leaved weeds. Low rates of EPTC were found to have marked inhibiting effects on nut grass with no injury to bean plants or potatoes. Since then, several thiocarbamate herbicides have been introduced.

A. Chemical and Physical Properties

All compounds in this group are clear liquids with an aromatic odor. They are miscible with most organic solvents including benzene, toluene, xylene, acetone, and alcohols, and their solubilities in water are generally low. Their structural formulas and physical properties are shown in Table 5-1.

Two methods, with good yield, have been used by Tilles (*1*) for the synthesis of numerous substituted thiolcarbamates. They are outlined in the following:

1. Sodium Dispersion Method

In this procedure, an anhydrous alkoxide-free sodium alkylmercaptide is refluxed with the appropriate dialkylcarbamoyl chloride in xylene. After removal of most of the solvent, the remaining product is then subjected to fractional distillation.

$$R_1SNa + ClC\!\!\overset{O}{\overset{\|}{-}}\!\!N\!\!\begin{smallmatrix}R_2\\R_2\end{smallmatrix} \xrightarrow[\text{xylene}]{} R_1\!\!-\!\!S\!\!-\!\!\overset{O}{\overset{\|}{C}}\!\!-\!\!N\!\!\begin{smallmatrix}R_2\\R_2\end{smallmatrix} + NaCl \qquad (1)$$

The yields of thiolcarbamate by this method were from 30 to 90%. Compounds prepared by this procedure include EPTC, vernolate, and sutan.

2. Chlorothiolformate Method

In this method an amine is reacted with an alkyl chlorothiolformate in ether to form a thiolcarbamate according to the following reaction:

$$R_1S\!\!\overset{O}{\overset{\|}{C}}\!\!-\!\!Cl + 2HN\!\!\begin{smallmatrix}R_2\\R_3\end{smallmatrix} \longrightarrow R_1S\!\!-\!\!\overset{O}{\overset{\|}{C}}\!\!-\!\!N\!\!\begin{smallmatrix}R_2\\R_3\end{smallmatrix} + \begin{smallmatrix}R_2\\R_3\end{smallmatrix}\!\!\!\!\searrow\!\!NH\cdot HCl \qquad (2)$$

The yields obtained by this method, which includes the preparation of pebulate and RO-Neet, were in the range 53–84%.

5-2. DEGRADATION

A. Degradation in Plants

1. Absorption

Most thiolcarbamate herbicides, when used for preemergence control, are applied as sprays to the soil surface and then mechanically incorporated into the soil immediately after application. It is possible that the chemical may be absorbed by the seed during the early stages of germination. In early experiments, Fang and Yu (*2*) covered the seeds of kidney bean, pea, corn, and oat with dry soils containing various levels of ^{35}S-labeled EPTC, ranging from 10 to 100 ppm, to determine whether or not EPTC was absorbed under these conditions. No significant amounts of radioactivity were found in the seeds after 6 days, indicating no absorption of EPTC by seeds in dry soil. However, when the germinating seeds were covered with wet soil containing ^{35}S-EPTC, a significant amount of radioactivity was taken up. EPTC was also taken up by seeds which were germinated between two sheets of filter paper moistened with EPTC solution.

In a study on the absorption from soil of a closely related herbicide, S-propyl butylethylthiolcarbamate (pebulate), Fang and George (3)

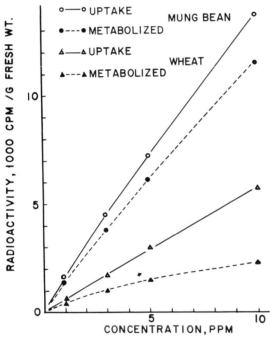

Fig. 5-1. Uptake and metabolism of ^{14}C–pebulate by mung bean and wheat seedlings.

reported that the amount of uptake and the rate of breakdown varied with the types of seed and herbicide concentration. The uptake of pebulate from soil was increased with time of germination and proportionally more with increasing concentration (Fig. 5-1). Bourke (4) studied the absorption of S-propyl-dipropylthiolcarbamate (vernolate) by soybean seedlings and reported that the absorption of vernolate–^{14}C reached its maximum in 48 hours. During this stage, no absorbed herbicide was degraded until the seedlings were 6 or 7 days old.

The absorption of EPTC by roots was reported by Appleby et al. (5) in

TABLE 5-1

Physical and Chemical Properties of the Thiolcarbamate Herbicides

Chemical name	Common designation in U.S.A.	Structural formula; molecular weight	Sp. gr. or density (°C)	Melting or boiling point, °C	mm Hg, °C	Solubility, g/100 ml (°C) Water	Solubility, g/100 ml (°C) Organic	N_D^{30}	H Solution, kcal/mole	Acute oral LD_{50} mg/kg
S-Ethyl N,N-dipropylthiol-carbamate	EPTC	$CH_3CH_2CH_2$ $\underset{CH_3CH_2CH_2}{\nearrow}NC\overset{O}{\overset{\|}{S}}CH_2CH_3$ (189.3)	0.955 (30)	127 (20 mm)	1.55×10^{-1} (25)	375 (20)	Soluble acetone, benzene, et al.; xylene, toluene, methanol isopropanol	1.4755	−3.93	1630 (rat) 3160 (mice)
Sodium N-methyldithio-carbamate	SMDC (metham)	$CH_3NHCSSNa \cdot 2H_2O$ (165.2)				72.2 (20)				820 (rat) 50 (mice)
S-Propyldipropylthiol-carbamate	Vernolate (R-1607)	$CH_3CH_2CH_2SCN\underset{CH_2CH_2CH_3}{\overset{CH_2CH_2CH_3}{\diagup}}$ (203.4)	0.954 (20)	140 (20 mm)		107 ppm (21)	Soluble xylene, kerosene	1.4736		1780 (rat)
S-Propyl butylethylthiol-carbamate	Pebulate (PEBC) (Tillam)	$CH_3(CH_2)_2SCN\overset{\overset{O}{\|}}{\underset{C_4H_7}{\diagup}}{}^{C_2H_5}$ (203.3)	0.945 (30)	142 (20 mm)	4.8×10^{-3} (25)	92 ppm (21)	Soluble acetone, benzene, xylene, toluene, methanol, isopropanol	1.4750	−2.74	1120 (rat)

Compound	Common name	Structure (mol. wt.)	Density	Boiling point	Water solubility	Solubility / n_D	LD_{50} (mg/kg)
2-Chloroallyldiethyldithio-carbamate	CDEC	CH₃CH₂\NCSCH₂CClCH₂ (S) / CH₃CH₂ (223.8)		128–130 (1 mm)	100 ppm (25)		850
S-2,3-Dichloroallyl-N,N-diisopropylthiolcarbamate	Diallate	(270.2)		150 (9 mm)	40 ppm		395
S-Ethyl hexahydro-1 H-azepine-1-carbothioate	Molinate	C₂H₅—S—C—N (O) (187.3)	1.06 (20)	137 (10 mm)	912 ppm	Soluble 1.516	720 (rat) 795 (mice)
S-Ethyl N,N-diisobutylthiol-carbamate	Sutan	C₂H₅—S—C—N(CH₂—CH(CH₃)₂)(CH₂—CH(CH₃)₂) (O) (217.4)	0.930 (30)	138 (21.5 mm)	45 ppm (22)	Soluble 1.470	3998 (rat)
S-Ethyl N,N-ethylcyclohexyl-thiolcarbamate	RO-Neet	C₂H₅—S—C—N(C₂H₅)(C₆H₁₁) (O) (215.4)		146 (10 mm)	85 ppm (22)		3190 (rat)
S-2,3,3-Trichloroallyl-N,N-di-isopropylthiolcarbamate	Triallate	Cl₂C=CCl—CH₂—S—C—N(CH(CH₃)₂)(CH(CH₃)₂) (O) (304.7)			4 ppm		1570 (rat)

oat and by Nalewaja et al. (6) in alfalfa. The absorbed EPTC was readily moved upward to the foliage. This chemical is also absorbed by coleoptiles and can be translocated downward to the roots.

2. Translocation

Studies on the translocation of thiolcarbamate herbicides have been conducted by Fang and co-workers (7–10) and Yamaguchi (11) using radio-autographic and direct counting techniques. ^{35}S–EPTC was absorbed from a preemergence soil application by a variety of horticultural crops and distributed throughout the entire plants (8,9,11). The radiosulphur from labeled EPTC has been found to accumulate in growing stem tips and root tips after application to the leaves. When the application was made to the roots, the distribution was more uniform (11). Nalewaja et al (6) reported that EPTC–^{14}C was readily taken up from nutrient solution by the roots of growing alfalfa plants. The amount of radioactivity accumulated in plants during the 5-day uptake period was approximately twice the amount accumulated in 2 days. The ^{14}C was accumulated throughout the entire plant, with greater accumulation in the youngest tissue. The uptake of ^{14}C–pebulate by tomato plants from soil receiving either pre- or post-emergence treatment has been reported (10). When pebulate was applied to soil, it was quickly absorbed by the root system and the radioactivity translocated upward to the foliage and fruits in the bloom stage. At 1 lb/acre treatment, the ^{14}C in the foliage reached a maximum concentration in 7 days and remained at a fairly constant level during the 70-day period. At 4 and 8 lb/acre, the maxima were not reached until the sixth or eighth week after treatment. The concentration of pebulate residue and total ^{14}C in the foliage correlated well with the rates of treatment. The distribution and accumulation of radioactivity in soybean and peanut plants after a preemergence application of 1-^{14}C–vernolate to soil have been reported (7). This herbicide was quickly absorbed from soil and translocated throughout the entire plant with higher concentrations occurring in the root and stem than in the foliage.

3. Metabolism

Fang and Yu (2) reported on the rate of ^{35}S–EPTC degradation in germinating seeds. Data in Table 5-2 show a greater degradation of EPTC in those seeds which are resistant to this herbicide than in those suscep-tible species. The radiosulfur from EPTC was incorporated into cysteic acid, cystine, methionine, methionine sulfone, and two unidentified compounds. The ratio of ^{35}S labeling in these compounds varied with plant species. In all cases only a small amount of radioactivity was found in inorganic sulfate.

Using ethyl-1-^{14}C–EPTC, Nalewaja et al. (6) reported the degradation EPTC to CO_2 by alfalfa plants. The ^{14}C was incorporated into fructose,

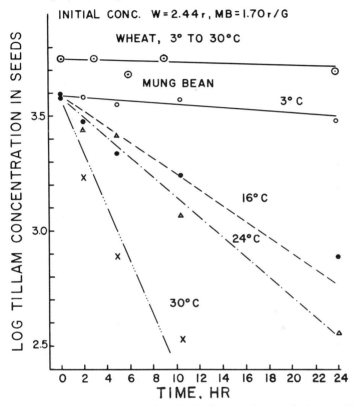

Fig. 5-2. Kinetic plot of ^{14}C–pebulate degradation by mung bean and wheat seedlings at different temperatures.

glucose, and several amino acids. A lack of radioactivity in cystine and cysteine (sulfur-containing amino acids) from ethyl-1-^{14}C–EPTC (6) and an incorporation of sulfur-35 from ^{35}S–EPTC in these compounds (2) suggests a further cleavage between the sulfur atom and the ethyl group.

Using ^{14}C-labeled pebulate, Fang and George (3) reported the rate of degradation of this herbicide in germinating mung bean and wheat seeds. In the mung bean seeds, which are quite resistant to pebulate, the degradation rate was higher and was dependent on the temperature (Fig. 5-2),

TABLE 5-2

Absorption of ^{35}S–EPTC and the Per Cent Incorporation of Radiosulfur in different Fractions of Various Plant Seedlings after Exposure to ^{35}S–EPTC for 48 Hours

Plant species	EPTC absorption, μg/seed	Per cent recovery in various fractions			
		EPTC residue	Inorganic sulfate	Hot water extract	H$_2$O Insoluble residue
Kidney bean	0.34	10.7	0.4	80.1	8.8
Mung bean	0.21	4.3	0.2	89.7	5.9
Pea	0.16	2.6	1.2	87.4	8.7
Corn	0.30	8.7	0.4	70.7	20.1
Wheat	0.11	8.0	0.6	74.2	17.2
Oat	0.25	23.0	0.3	62.8	13.9

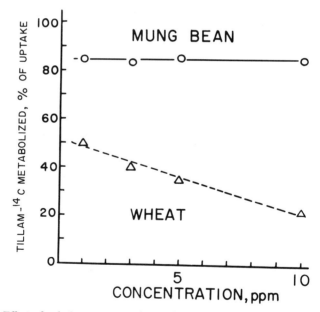

Fig. 5-3. Effect of pebulate concentration on its metabolism in mung bean and wheat seedlings.

whereas less pebulate degradation was evident in the susceptible wheat. Furthermore, the rate of pebulate degradation by mung beans remained quite constant and was not affected by concentrations below 10 ppm. On the other hand, the rate of degradation of pebulate in wheat decreased as its

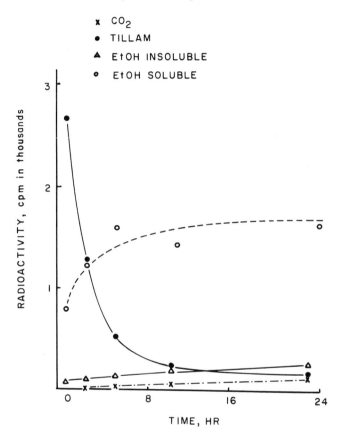

Fig. 5-4. Time course conversion of ^{14}C–pebulate in mung bean seedlings.

concentration increased (Fig. 5-3). This observation suggests the absence of a strong pebulate detoxication system in wheat seedlings.

The time course conversion of ^{14}C–pebulate (Fig. 5-4) illustrates a gradual disappearance of pebulate (Tillam) and an increase in other fractions, particularly the alcohol-soluble compounds. The incorporation of radioactivity into the alcohol-insoluble fraction and CO_2 were small, suggesting that the young seedlings did not have sufficient oxidative enzymes. However, the catabolic oxidation of this chemical to CO_2 is more rapid in both root and shoot tissues (Fig. 5-5). From 18.3 to 39.6% of the radioactivity was recovered as CO_2 from root and shoot tissues (Table 5-3).

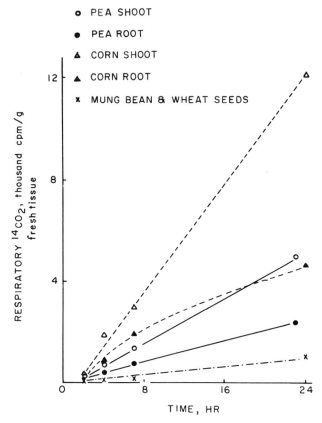

Fig. 5-5. In vitro $^{14}CO_2$ production from absorbed ^{14}C–pebulate by excised plant tissues and seedlings.

Bourke and Fang (12) reported the influence of soybean age on the metabolism of ^{14}C–vernolate. Figure 5-6 shows $^{14}CO_2$ production as a function of age of seedlings germinated either in water or in a 5-ppm solution of carrier vernolate. As can be seen from Fig. 5-6, the $^{14}CO_2$ production is low at the early stage of germination but increases gradually with age. Pre-exposure to vernolate resulted in reduced $^{14}CO_2$ production. This observation suggests that inhibition of enzyme synthesis may be the primary action

TABLE 5-3

In Vitro Metabolism of ^{14}C–Pebulate in Plant Tissues

Plant tissue	Fresh wt., mg	Total uptake, cpm	Per cent recovery of ^{14}C in various fractions			
			Pebulate residue	CO_2	EtOH soluble	EtOH insoluble
Pea shoot	1425	17840	14.6	39.6	43.8	2.1
Pea root	648	4270	25.1	37.8	26.2	10.8
Corn shoot	743	23744	34.3	24.9	39.7	1.1
Corn root	530	5793	13.1	36.9	43.0	6.9
Mung bean shoot	460	10667	21.9	18.3	50.1	9.7
Mung bean root	480	2612	30.9	22.2	39.0	8.0
Mung bean seed	723	30773	26.0	2.7	64.2	7.1
Wheat seed	528	21768	63.5	2.1	30.0	4.4

of the thiolcarbamates in germinating seeds. The overall absorptions are similar; 20.98 μg for water-germinated and 19.47 μg for carrier-germinated seedlings. Seedlings germinated in vernolate produced 3.25 μg equivalents of $^{14}CO_2$, whereas water-germinated seedlings produced a total of 7.40 μg equivalents. The difference in $^{14}CO_2$ production is reflected in the amount of radioactivity recovered in the ethanol-soluble fraction, of which 9.90 and

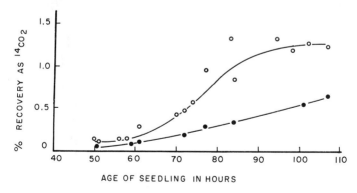

Fig. 5-6. Influence of age and pretreatment with vernolate on the rate of vernolate degradation by soybean seedlings.

14.74 μg were found in the water- and vernolate-germinated seedlings, respectively. Paper chromatographic separation of the ethanol-soluble fraction revealed the presence of four radioactive spots, with two of these containing most of the radioactivity. One of the highly labeled spots has been tentatively identified as citric acid by silica column chromatography.

Jaworski (13) reported that the 2-chloroallyl moiety of 2-chloroallyl-2-^{14}C–diethyldithiolcarbamate (CDEC) was extensively degraded in cabbage. Radioactivity associated with the major component corresponded to lactic acid by cochromatography.

B. Degradation in Soils

1. Persistence

Several factors are known to determine the persistence of herbicides in soil. These include uptake and degradation by soil microorganisms, a loss through physical processes (volatilization, leaching), and chemical changes (photodecomposition, chemical reaction). Volatilization is the most important factor for the loss of thiolcarbamate herbicides from soil. The loss of EPTC is greater in moist soils than in dry soils (14,15). Significant correlations have been shown to exist between the loss of EPTC by evaporation of soil moisture and the amount of organic matter, clay content, or both (14). During the first 15 min after spraying on the soil surface, 20% of the applied EPTC disappeared from dry soil, 27% from moist soil, and 44% from wet soil (16). The loss was 23, 49, and 69% after 1 day and 44, 68, and 90% after 6 days on dry, moist, and wet soils, respectively. Incorporation of EPTC to a depth of 2 to 3 in. prevented large losses of EPTC from soils.

Danielson et al. (17) demonstrated, with ryegrass bioassay tests, that equivalent rates of EPTC persisted longer in soils of relatively high organic matter and under subirrigation conditions than in soils of relatively low organic matter and under conditions of top-irrigation. In comparing the loss by vaporization of several thiolcarbamate herbicides, Gray (15) reported that vernolate and pebulate were much less volatile than EPTC and that S-ethyl hexahydro-1-H-azepine-1-carbothioate (molinate) was the least volatile. Horowitz (18) also indicated that the loss of pebulate by volatilization from dry soil did not seem to constitute an important factor of dissipation. However, the organic matter and clay content of soil seem to affect the herbicidal activity of pebulate. Under conditions where pebulate was applied to dry soil without incorporation, its activity persisted for 1 or 2 months. Fang (19) (Table 5-4) noted that the amount of pebulate loss from

TABLE 5-4

Effect of Soil Characteristics on the Vaporization Loss of Pebulate from Soils and on the Uptake of Pebulate by Mung Bean Seedlings

Soils[a]	Organic matter, %	Clay, % <20 μ	% Loss of pebulate from soil after evaporation of soil water			% Pebulate retention in dry soil, room temperature		Pebulate uptake[b] by mung bean seedlings, cpm/g fresh tissue
			33%	50%	60%	1.5 months	4 months	
Peat	83.3	—	0.0	4.7	8.5	51.9	55.5	245
Knappa	18.3	25.1	8.2	12.8	14.7	69.5	28.0	1330
Quillayutte	17.6	36.3	5.9	9.9	14.3	91.1	22.5	1120
Astoria	12.8	34.6	5.8	8.3	13.4	53.9	42.3	1140
Wingville	7.5	25.1	0.0	3.5	5.5	88.3	43.9	310
Aiken	6.8	57.3	18.6	18.8	26.6	62.8	63.4	2625
Barron	5.4	21.3	14.8	21.1	32.7	92.9	65.1	2780
Athena	5.0	29.0	12.1	14.3	23.6	57.8	70.6	3180
Williamette	4.0	29.1	15.3	26.8	28.5	80.8	38.1	3900
Medford	3.3	10.2	21.7	31.2	41.7	84.3	52.5	3720
Sams	2.9	30.6	19.7	28.3	35.8	89.7	67.3	3525
Baker	2.8	16.3	26.5	29.5	36.3	67.1	54.4	4290
Chehalis	2.2	18.6	13.9	12.8	19.5	100.0	56.7	1780
Walla Walla	2.2	18.5	17.5	31.2	30.8	87.1	51.9	4610
Powder	2.1	12.8	24.9	35.4	40.1	86.5	56.0	4740
Deschutte	1.6	8.1	27.3	37.5	48.8	84.8	37.0	3940

[a] General characteristics and some chemical and mineralogical properties of the soils were published in Soil Sci. Soc. Am. Proc., 26, 27 (1962).
[b] Pebulate concentration in soil was 3 ppm. The uptake was carried out at room temperature for 25 hours and calculated as counts per minute per gram of fresh tissue.

fifteen Oregon soils is linearly related to the time of storage, but the rate of loss from an individual soil is not correlated to the organic matter content in that soil. The loss of pebulate from wet soil is related to the amount of moisture loss and is correlated to the amount of soil organic matter. The adsorption process probably plays an important role in preventing the loss of thiolcarbamates from soil and also their availability for plant uptake (Table 5-4). Although there are no available data to prove directly that the volatilization of pebulate and vernolate is reduced by soil incorporation, an increase of herbicidal activity by this practice suggests a reduction in vaporization and, therefore, more persistence. The addition of nonvolatile solvents or solid materials will reduce the loss of EPTC (15,20). In contrast, Danielson et al. (17) reported a reduction of EPTC persistence when it was dissolved in kerosene and an increase of persistence by the addition of specific surfactants. At present, whether this additive will also modify the availability of herbicide to plants is not yet known and the advantage of this practice is difficult to evaluate. Other factors, such as leaching, photodecomposition, and chemical reaction will undoubtedly have some effects on the persistence of thiolcarbamates in soils. However, little research has been done to evaluate separately their influence on the persistence of these herbicides.

2. Metabolism

Soil microorganisms contribute significantly to the disappearance of thiolcarbamate herbicides when incorporated in soil (21–23). Sheets (23) reported that EPTC was inactivated about one-third as rapidly in autoclaved as in unautoclaved soil, suggesting that microbial breakdown is a major pathway of EPTC loss from soils. Therefore, EPTC persistence may be greatly prolonged in the field when conditions for microbial growth are less favorable. MacRae and Alexander (22) measured the microbial degradation of EPTC by determining the release of $^{14}CO_2$ from labeled EPTC applied to soil and by plant bioassay. They reported that EPTC was metabolized microbiologically, but the rate of $^{14}CO_2$ release from the ethyl moiety of the molecule was slow in comparison to the rate of inactivation of this herbicide as determined by bioassay test. A similar observation was reported by Kaufman in a Hagerstown silty clay loam soil (21). In this experiment approximately 25% ^{14}C–EPTC applied to soil was recovered as $^{14}CO_2$ in 35 days, whereas a complete inactivation of EPTC was revealed by bioassay. Since vaporization of EPTC takes place either in dry or in wet soil, the difference observed between the bioassay and the measurement of $^{14}CO_2$ could be due partially to vaporization loss of ^{14}C–EPTC during this period.

Also, it is conceivable that the ^{14}C from ethyl moiety of EPTC could be utilized anabolically by soil microorganism as it is observed in plants; thereby the label would not be immediately released as $^{14}CO_2$.

Isolation or identification of soil microorganisms capable of degrading thiolcarbamate and dithiocarbamate herbicides has not been reported, nor has the actual mechanism of microbial degradation been determined. Several sites of attack are possible, e.g., the alkyl groups, the amide linkage, or the ester linkage. Based on available data obtained from studies in plants and in animals, the thiolcarbamate molecule is probably hydrolyzed at the ester linkage with the formation of mercaptan, CO_2, and amine [reaction (3)]:

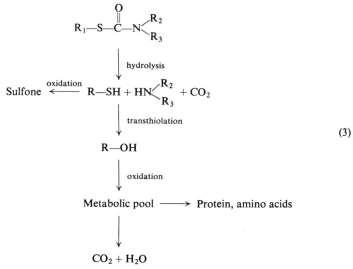

(3)

The mercaptan could then be converted to an alcohol and further oxidized. The fate of the aliphatic amines formed in the degradation of thiolcarbamates in soil is also unknown. Early workers reported that certain bacteria utilize amines as a source of nitrogen, based on their ability to support growth (24). Later, Gale (25) studied the oxidation of several amines by washed cells of *Pseudomonas aeruginosa* and reported that the amines were completely oxidized to ammonia, CO_2, and water. Williams (26) indicated that short-chain aliphatic amines are mainly degraded to the corresponding carboxylic acid and urea, whereas the intermediate amines are degraded to the corresponding aldehyde and ammonia.

The degradation of dithiocarbamate would yield carbon disulfide (CS_2). This compound is highly toxic and volatile; therefore utilization of CS_2 by soil microorganisms appears unlikely.

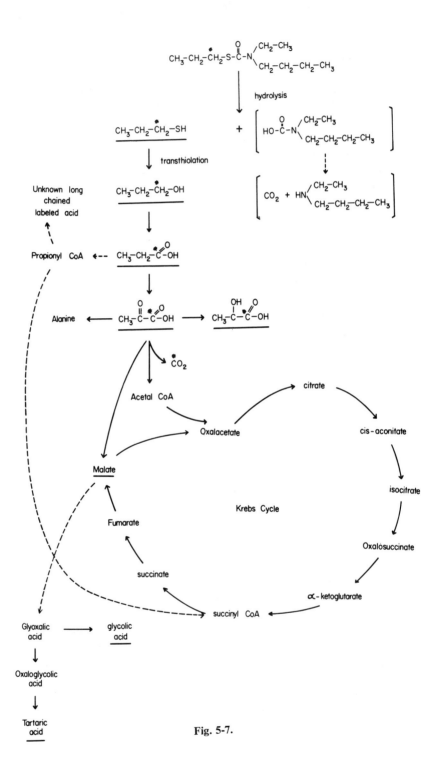

Fig. 5-7.

5-3. SUMMARY AND CONCLUSIONS

It is clear that the current knowledge on the metabolism of thiolcarbamate herbicides is rather limited. The result may be summarized as follows.

Thiolcarbamates are readily absorbed by plants but apparently do not remain as a residue for a very long period. Relatively little work has been done to investigate their possible metabolic products. It is generally believed that, upon hydrolysis, thiocarbamates yield a molecule of mercaptan, carbon dioxide, and dialkylamine (3). Evidence suggests a further cleavage of the sulfur atom from the mercaptan. Labeling experiments with ^{35}S–EPTC revealed that the sulfur-35 is incorporated into many sulfur-containing amino acids of plants. Use of ^{14}C-labeled thiolcarbamates (ethyl-1-^{14}C, n-propyl-1-^{14}C, and 2,3-dichloroallyl-2-^{14}C) has revealed that all label carbons gave rise to $^{14}CO_2$ and also are incorporated into many natural plant compounds—such as fructose, glucose, serine, threonine, alanine, aspartic acid, and glutamic acid from ^{14}C–EPTC; lactic acid from ^{14}C–CDEC; and citric acid from ^{14}C–vernolate. Cleavage may take place between the sulfur and carbon bond to yield an alcohol, carbonyl sulfide, and dialkylamine. However, there is no direct evidence to support this scheme.

Recent reports on degradation of phenylurea herbicides in soils show that dealkylation precedes hydrolysis (27,28). Demethylation of a number of closely related N,N-dimethylcarbamates has also been reported by an enzyme system from rat liver microsomes (28). However, Bourke (4), treating soybean seedlings with ^{14}C–vernolate, was not able to detect volatile labeled metabolites by steam distillation and gas–liquid chromatography. If dealkylation of vernolate takes place before hydrolysis in soybean seedlings, volatile metabolic products should result. At present, the precise nature of the metabolites of thiolcarbamate compounds is not known; pathways of degradation of these compounds by higher plants or by soils require further intensive study. The scheme given in Fig. 5-7 shows the proposed pathways for thiolcarbamate degradation. It is based on the work with animal (29) and some unpublished observations with tomato fruits (30). The underlined compounds have been identified in tomato fruits treated with ^{14}C–pebulate.

Fig. 5-7. Proposed pathways for pebulate degradation in plants. (The brackets enclose the hypothetical intermediate. The underlined compounds have been identified in tomato fruits treated with ^{14}C–pebulate.)

164   S. C. FANG

REFERENCES

1. H. Tilles, *J. Am. Chem. Soc.*, **81**, 714 (1959).
2. S. C. Fang and T. C. Yu, *Western Weed Control Conf. Res. Progr. Rept.*, 1959, p. 91.
3. S. C. Fang and M. George, *Plant Physiol. Suppl.*, **37**, xxvi (1962).
4. J. B. Bourke, Ph.D. thesis, Oregon State Univ., Corvallis, 1964.
5. A. P. Appleby, W. R. Furtick, and S. C. Fang, *Weed Res.*, **5**, 115 (1965).
6. J. D. Nalewaja, R. Behrens, and A. R. Schmid, *Weeds*, **12**, 269 (1964).
7. J. B. Bourke and S. C. Fang, *J. Agr. Food Chem.*, **13**, 340 (1965).
8. S. C. Fang and P. Theisen, *J. Agr. Food Chem.*, **7**, 770 (1959).
9. S. C. Fang and P. Theisen, *J. Agr. Feed Chem.*, **8**, 295 (1960).
10. S. C. Fang and E. Fallin, *Weeds*, **13**, 152 (1965).
11. S. Yamaguchi, *Weeds*, **9**, 374 (1961).
12. J. B. Bourke and S. C. Fang, *Weeds*, **16**, 290 (1968).
13. E. G. Jaworski, *J. Agr. Food Chem.*, **12**, 33 (1964).
14. S. C. Fang, P. Theisen, and V. H. Freed, *Weeds*, **9**, 569 (1961).
15. R. A. Gray, *Weeds*, **13**, 138 (1965).
16. R. A. Gray and A. J. Weierich, *Weeds*, **13**, 141 (1965).
17. L. L. Danielson, W. A. Gentner, and L. L. Jansen, *Weeds*, **9**, 463 (1961).
18. M. Horowitz, *Weed Res.*, **6**, 1 (1966).
19. S. C. Fang, unpublished data, 1967.
20. V. H. Freed, J. Vernetti, and M. Montgomery, *Proc. Western Weed Control Conf.*, **19**, 21 (1962).
21. D. D. Kaufman, *J. Agr. Food Chem.*, **15**, 582 (1967).
22. I. C. MacRae and M. Alexander, *J. Agr. Food Chem.*, **13**, 72 (1966).
23. T. J. Sheets, *Weeds*, **7**, 442 (1959).
24. J. R. Porter, *Bacterial Chemistry and Physiology*, Wiley, New York, 2nd ed., 1959, p. 1703.
25. E. F. Gale, *Biochem J.*, **36**, 64 (1942).
26. R. T. Williams, *Detoxication Mechanisms*, Wiley, New York, 2nd ed., 1959, p. 796.
27. R. L. Dalton, A. W. Evans, and R. C. Rhodes, *Proc. Southern Weed Conf.*, **18**, 72 (1965).
28. H. Geissbühler, C. Haselbach, H. Aebi, and L. Ebner, *Weed Res.*, **3**, 277 (1963).
29. S. C. Fang, M. George, and V. H. Freed, *J. Agr. Food Chem.*, **12**, 37 (1964).
30. S. C. Fang and E. Fallin, unpublished data, 1967.

CHAPTER 6

Chloroacetamides

ERNEST G. JAWORSKI

AGRICULTURAL DIVISION
MONSANTO COMPANY
ST. LOUIS, MISSOURI

6-1. Introduction 165
    A. Chemical and Physical Properties 166
6-2. Degradation of CDAA 167
    A. Chloroacetyl Moiety 167
    B. Allylic Moieties 171
    C. Degradation in Soil 173
6-3. Degradation of 2-Chloro-*N*-isopropylacetanilide 174
6-4. Uptake and Metabolism of Other 2-Chloroacetamides . . . 177
6-5. Mode of Action 182
6-6. Conclusions 184
References 185

6-1. INTRODUCTION

The metabolism of pesticides has received particularly wide and intensive study during the last 15 years. Although these investigations have been initiated in many instances because of a desire and need to know the persistence, metabolism, and fate of subsequent degradation products of a given pesticide in crop plants, in many cases such studies have resulted in collateral findings regarding detoxification mechanisms, possible modes of action, basis of selectivity, basis of resistance, and other facts of physiological and biochemical interest. Some of these collateral findings will be pointed out in the subsequent discussion of two preemergent chloroacetamide herbicides possessing unique qualities of specificity.

A. Chemical and Physical Properties

The first material is 2-chloro-N,N-diallylacetamide (CDAA) (**1**). This grass-specific, preemergent herbicide was commercially introduced in 1956 for use in corn and soybeans to control foxtail, bromegrass, cheatgrass, crabgrass, and certain broadleaf weeds (*1*).

$$\text{ClCH}_2\overset{\displaystyle\text{O}}{\overset{\|}{\text{C}}}\text{—N}\underset{\displaystyle\text{CH}_2\text{CH}=\text{CH}_2}{\overset{\displaystyle\text{CH}_2\text{CH}=\text{CH}_2}{<}}$$

(**1**)

The second material to be discussed is 2-chloro-N-isopropylacetanilide (**2**). This herbicide was introduced in 1965 and was designed to perform under abroad set of climatic and geographic conditions. It has been particularly effective in light, sandy soils where the water solubility of CDAA

$$\text{ClCH}_2\overset{\displaystyle\text{O}}{\overset{\|}{\text{C}}}\text{—N}\text{—}\bigcirc$$

$$\overset{|}{\text{CH}}$$

$$\overset{\diagup\quad\diagdown}{\text{CH}_3\quad\text{CH}_3}$$

(**2**)

precluded complete weed control due to rapid leaching. It was also designed as a preemergent herbicide for use in corn and soybeans to control a broader spectrum of broadleaf weeds as well as to control barnyardgrass, foxtail, bromegrass, cheatgrass, and crabgrass (*2,3*). As pointed out by Selleck et al. (*3*), this herbicide is effective against most annual grass weeds, *Chenopodiaceae*, and annual species of the *Compositae*.

CDAA (molecular weight, 173.6) is an amber liquid having a specific gravity of 0.990 at 25°. Its vapor pressure is 9.4×10^{-3} mm Hg at 20°. The water solubility is 1.97% at 22°, and it has a high degree of solubility in ethanol, acetone, xylene, and hexane.

2-Chloro-N-isopropylacetanilide (molecular weight, 211.7) is a white crystalline solid having a melting point of 78–79°. It is very soluble in ether (18%), acetone (31%), benzene (50%), ethanol (29%), and chloroform (38%). Its water solubility, however, is only 0.07%.

Both CDAA and 2-chloro-N-isopropylacetanilide are prepared by the reaction of chloroacetylchloride with the appropriate secondary amine, diallylamine and N-isopropylaniline, respectively, Each compound has an active halogen which can undergo nucleophilic displacement reactions and hydrolysis.

6-2. DEGRADATION OF CDAA

In 1954, when the first CDAA degradation studies were undertaken, no real precedent had been established for a study of metabolic degradation of pesticides, although a considerable literature existed with regard to the general reaction of haloacetamides such as iodoacetamide (4). Two types of studies were therefore undertaken as described by Jaworski (5); one in which the carbonyl carbon was labeled with ^{14}C and the other where the allyl moiety was labeled with ^{14}C in the number 2 carbon.

A. Chloroacetyl Moiety

Corn and soybeans were capable of rapid uptake of radioactivity from soil treated with carbonyl-labeled ^{14}C–CDAA. Uptake reached a maximum for both crops at 4 to 5 days following emergence, with a maximum specific activity of 85,000 cpm/g dry weight for soybeans at 5 days and 30,000 cpm/g dry weight for corn at 4 days. In subsequent harvests the specific radioactivity of both crops decreased at a rapid rate.

After the CDAA was shown to be readily taken up by plants, experiments were conducted to determine the nature of the radioactivity in the plants. Prior to doing this, the recovery procedure was established, and the results indicated that recoveries were greater than 90 % at a 0.1-ppm concentration of CDAA. A bioassay technique was developed to analyze the plant extracts for CDAA-like activity. Table 6-1 shows the standard results for CDAA responses, as well as those from corn plant extracts. This bioassay was described by Jaworski (5) and involved using germinating ryegrass seed. The data indicate that essentially complete metabolism of the molecule took place prior to the fourth day following emergence of the corn seedlings. Similar results were also obtained for soybean seedlings.

Chromatographic analyses were made of these extracts to determine the number and types of radioactive components present. Standard R_f values are shown in Table 6-2 for CDAA, as well as possible expected metabolites and degradation products. The analyses of corn and soybean extracts are shown in Tables 6-3 and 6-4, respectively. Four days following emergence of corn seedlings, the primary radioactive material was at R_f 0.00 in Solvent A and R_f 0.64 in Solvent B. These R_f values coincided with those for glycolic acid [(3); see Fig. 6-1]. A similar pattern was noted 7 days following emergence of the corn plants. The results further indicated the absence of unmetabolized CDAA, its 2-hydroxy analog, and 2-chloroacetic acid. Glycolic acid and possibly lactic or glyceric acids were therefore the most likely metabolite candidates. A number of other solvent systems were

TABLE 6-1

Ryegrass Bioassay of Corn Extracts[a] (carbonyl-^{14}C–CDAA treatment)

Concn. of CDAA ppm	Concn. of CDAA based on radioactivity ppm	Ryegrass growth mm	Concn. of CDAA based on bioassay, ppm
	Control		
—	—	21.3	—
	CDAA		
0.1	—	3.0	0.1
0.05	—	4.8	0.05
0.01	—	8.6	0.01
	Plant extract (4 days after emergence)		
—	0.12	16.6	0.01
—	0.06	20.8	0
	Plant extract (7 days after emergence)		
—	0.06	21.5	0
—	0.03	19.9	0

[a] The standards contained plant extracts from untreated plants equivalent to those of treated plant extracts.

TABLE 6-2

R_f Value of CDAA and Possible Degradation Products

	Solvent system[a]		
Compound	A	B	C
CDAA	0.89	0.91	0.93
α-Hydroxy analog of CDAA	0.89	0.76	0.89
Glycolic acid	0.00	0.61	0.59
Glyoxylic acid	0.00	0.47	0.15
Lactic acid	0.02	0.67	0.71
Glyceric acid	0.00	0.75	0.80
Oxalic acid	0.00	0.00	0.49
Chloroacetic acid	0.48	0.83	0.86

[a] Solvent system: A, benzene–methanol–H_2O (10:5:5); B, 80% aqueous phenol; C, butanol–acetic acid–H_2O (4:1:5).

TABLE 6-3

Chromatographic Analysis of Corn Extracts

Days after emergence	Solvent A[a]		Solvent B[a]		Solvent C[a]	
	R_f	Radioactivity %	R_f	Radioactivity, %	R_f	Radioactivity, %
4	0.00	92	0.64	98	0.63	97
	0.64	5	0.89	2	0.94	3
7	0.00	88	0.64	68	0.55	14
	0.21	4	0.88	20	0.69	68
	0.65	4			0.86	15
	0.90	5				

[a] For solvents, see Table 6-2.

TABLE 6-4

Chromatographic Analysis of Soybean Extracts

Days after emergence	Solvent A[a]		Solvent B[a]	
	R_f	Radioactivity, %	R_f	Radioactivity, %
2	0.00	70	0.42	64
	0.40	17	0.54	18
	0.77	13	0.66	5
			0.72	6
5	0.00	93	0.44	1
	0.71	6	0.66	98
			0.92	1
10	0.00	87	0.10	7
	0.44	7	0.25	7
	0.68	3	0.42	13
	0.92	3	0.59	73

[a] For solvents, see Table 6-2.

investigated and coupled with cochromatographic analyses to verify the presence of one of these components. Confirmation of glycolic acid as the major radioactive product formed was obtained by cochromatography of the labeled products with unlabeled glycolic acid in seven different solvent systems.

Examination of the results in Table 6-4 of soybean extracts 2 days after emergence indicated the presence of a compound behaving like glyoxylic [(4); see Fig. 6-1] rather than glycolic acid. In 5- and 10-day extracts this component was modified to one that behaved cochromatographically as glycolic acid. Zelitch and Ochoa (6) have shown that glyoxylic acid is a natural constituent of plants and is in equilibrium with glycolic acid. Zelitch has also pointed out (7) that glycolic and glyoxylic acids may function in tandem in plant respiration. On the basis of this information, it was not considered unusual to find the labeled glyoxylic acid. Furthermore, the relative proportions of these acids could vary widely, depending upon such factors as light, temperature, and time of harvest.

Additional information was obtained by growing carbonyl-labeled ^{14}C–CDAA treated plants in a closed system, in which CO_2 free air was introduced into the system and CO_2 evolution from the plant was assayed for radioactivity. Table 6-5 shows that more than 50% of the radioactivity absorbed through the root system of corn seedlings was evolved as $^{14}CO_2$, indicating that the plant readily degraded the CDAA molecule. This was also consistent with the finding of glycolic acid in the system.

TABLE 6-5

CO_2 Train Results with Carbonyl-^{14}C–CDAA-Treated Corn (24 days)

Fraction	Total activity, cpm $\times$ 10^{-7}	% Radioactivity based on:	
		Total	Plant
CO_2 collected	0.395	16.5[a]	54.4[a]
Plant	0.331	13.8	45.6
Soil	1.675	69.7	

[a] Data not corrected for $^{14}CO_2$ liberated by soil microflora.

On the basis of these studies, the generalized metabolic route for a portion of the CDAA molecule may be written as shown in Fig. 6-1. A mechanism involving the hydrolysis of both the α-chloro grouping and the amide linkage is postulated to account for the generation of glycolic acid. Glycolic acid may be in equilibrium with glyoxylic acid and the concentration of each will depend upon the circumstances of plant respiration and photosynthesis at the time of harvest. Once glycolic and glyoxylic acid are formed, $^{14}CO_2$ would be generated and photosynthetic fixation of the CO_2 as well as incorporation of labeled glycolic acid into a variety of biosynthetic sequences

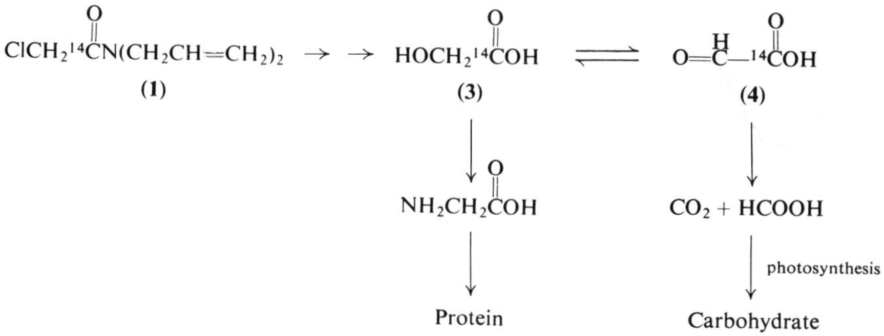

$$ClCH_2{}^{14}\overset{\overset{\displaystyle O}{\|}}{C}N(CH_2CH{=}CH_2)_2 \;\rightarrow\;\rightarrow\; HOCH_2{}^{14}\overset{\overset{\displaystyle O}{\|}}{C}OH \;\rightleftharpoons\; O{=}\overset{\overset{\displaystyle H}{|}}{C}{-}{}^{14}\overset{\overset{\displaystyle O}{\|}}{C}OH$$

$$\textbf{(1)} \qquad\qquad\qquad\qquad \textbf{(3)} \qquad\qquad\qquad\qquad \textbf{(4)}$$

$$\downarrow \qquad\qquad\qquad\qquad\qquad\qquad \downarrow$$

$$NH_2CH_2\overset{\overset{\displaystyle O}{\|}}{C}OH \qquad\qquad CO_2 + HCOOH$$

$$\downarrow \qquad\qquad\qquad\qquad\qquad \downarrow\ \text{photosynthesis}$$

$$\text{Protein} \qquad\qquad\qquad \text{Carbohydrate}$$

Fig. 6-1. Metabolism of CDAA.

would lead to the generation of numerous labeled products in the plant. Chromatographic analyses of plant extracts from harvests made more than 20 days postemergence always contained numerous radioactive components.

B. Allylic Moieties

The allylic radicals of CDAA were tagged in the 2-carbon position with ^{14}C and plants were treated in a manner similar to that described for the

TABLE 6-6

CO$_2$ Results with Allyl-^{14}C–CDAA-Treated Crops

Crop–treatment level (lb/acre)	Duration of study, days	% Radioactivity liberated[a] as $^{14}CO_2$ from plants
Corn (6)	13	14
Soybeans (6)	13	28
Peas (10)	12	23
Onions (6)	12	19
Sugar beets (6)	16	60
Cabbage sets (6)	10	46
Potato sets (6)	12	76
Tomato sets (6)	10	19
Strawberry sets (6)	15	24
Flax (10)	13	25
Barley (10)	14	60
Sorghum (6)	9	35

[a] Data are corrected for microbial breakdown of CDAA.

carbonyl studies. The enclosed CO_2-free system was utilized to measure $^{14}CO_2$ production and Table 6-6 summarizes the results obtained for a variety of crops including soybeans and corn. All plants studied were capable of metabolizing the allylic moiety to the extent where the 2-carbon atom was liberated as CO_2. In such a system, there is undoubtedly some photosynthetic reincorporation of respiratory CO_2 into the plants, because of the removal of CO_2 from air entering the system. The amount of $^{14}CO_2$ determined could therefore be expected to represent a minimal picture of the CO_2 evolved.

Chromatographic analyses of extracts of these plants did not elucidate the route of breakdown, possibly because of the lability and volatility of some of the intermediate products. None of the expected breakdown products arising from the cleavage of the amide linkage could be found in extracts of the plants. The type of degradation products sought included diallylamine, monoallylamine, allyl alcohol, acrylic acid, and acrolein.

TABLE 6-7

Radioactivity of Corn Seed Fractions

Fraction	Specific radioactivity, cpm/g	Concn. of radioactivity, ppm CDAA
Hulls		
Whole hulls	33.0	3.7
Petroleum ether extract	8.3	0.9
Aqueous extract	16.1	1.8
Residue	30.5	3.4
Germs		
Whole germs	26.9	3.0
Petroleum ether extract	6.4	0.7
Santomerse soluble	4.6	0.5
Protein	10.1	1.1
Residue	4.7	0.5
Endosperm		
Whole endosperm	22.6	2.5
Petroleum ether extract	5.0	0.6
Aqueous extract	5.7	0.8
Protein	4.4	0.5
Starch	16.9	1.9

From the data in Table 6-6, however, it is apparent that both dicotyledonous and monocotyledonous plants can readily metabolize the allylic moiety of CDAA.

To establish that the breakdown of the CDAA molecule was complete and that accumulation of some specific product derived from the allylic moiety was not taking place, plants were treated with allyl-^{14}C–CDAA and grown to maturity. Following maturation, the crops were harvested and fractionated as shown in Table 6-7. The table illustrates the various fractions isolated and shows their corresponding specific radioactivities. A low level of radioactivity was distributed among all fractions isolated. Since each fraction is morphologically, as well as in many instances chemically, different from the other, the random distribution of radioactivity throughout the fractions suggests that no unusual metabolite is formed as a result of the degradation of the allylic moiety of CDAA. Rather, the carbon atoms are presumed to be randomized and incorporated through normal metabolic pathways into many natural products. These results would be anticipated in the light of the CO_2 train studies with allyl-^{14}C-labeled CDAA. Similar fractionation studies were conducted with all the other crops shown in Table 6-6 and the results indicated the same type of general nonspecific distribution of radioactivity in all fractions.

Unfortunately, no mechanistic scheme can be proposed for the metabolism of the diallylamine portion of CDAA. It would not be unreasonable, however, to speculate that an amine oxidase could oxidize the amine to two acrolein molecules. These would be highly unstable and could be oxidized very rapidly.

C. Degradation in Soil

The degradation of CDAA in the soil has not been studied with labeled compounds, with the exception that studies using the CO_2 train showed $^{14}CO_2$ liberation from soil treated with either carbonyl-^{14}C- or allyl-^{14}C-labeled CDAA. The amounts generated represented approximately 20% of the total $^{14}CO_2$ trapped. Thus some decomposition of CDAA occurs in soil.

Dissipation studies in soil using chemical analyses for the determination of CDAA indicated a rapid loss of the parent compound. The half-life was estimated to be approximately 16 to 18 days and was fairly representative over a broad range of soil types and climatic conditions. Some of this loss would be attributable to volatility, as shown by Deming (8).

6-3. DEGRADATION OF
2-CHLORO-*N*-ISOPROPLYACETANILIDE

The uptake and metabolism of uniformly ring-labeled (^{3}H) 2-chloro-*N*-isopropylacetanilide in corn and soybeans has been reported by Jaworski and Porter (9). Both plants were capable of rapid uptake of radioactivity from soil treated with the acetanilide. As shown in Table 6-8, plant growth

TABLE 6-8

Specific Radioactivity of Corn and Soybean Plants Treated with 2-Chloro-*N*-isopropylacetanilide

Days after planting	80% Acetone soluble fraction	Insoluble fraction	Fresh wt./plant, g	ppm Expressed as the herbicide based on total radioactivity in plants
		Corn		
5	5.4×10^5	0.02×10^5	0.4	46
18	0.9×10^5	0.01×10^5	3.7	7.8
34	0.7×10^5	0.01×10^5	8.5	5.8
74	0.9×10^4		29	0.79
		Soybean		
5	1.5×10^5	0.06×10^5	0.8	12.8
18	0.6×10^5	0.01×10^5	2.3	5.5
34	0.2×10^5	0.01×10^5	4.8	1.4

was sufficiently rapid to cause a continued dilution of the amount of radioactivity in the plants on a per gram fresh weight basis. Residues of radioactivity in corn decreased from 46 ppm in plants harvested 5 days after planting to 0.79 ppm in plants harvested 74 days after planting. In soybeans a similar dilution of radioactivity was noted. Since the extraction of radioactivity from treated plants with 80% aqueous acetone was essentially quantitative and the insoluble fraction from plant tissues was extremely low in radioactivity, virtually all the radioactivity in the plants remained in a soluble form and was not fixed into polymeric, insoluble products.

Paper and thin-layer chromatographic analyses of the 80% aqueous acetone extracts of corn plants harvested at various intervals of time illustrated that the metabolism of the chloroacetanilide must be extremely rapid, since no tritiated 2-chloro-*N*-isopropylacetanilide was detected even at the earliest harvest. The chromatographic data suggested that the product or products formed were highly polar materials. A harvest made 18 days after planting indicated that the conversion of the chloroacetanilide to the hydrophilic material was virtually complete in 18 days. This was borne out by the appearance of a single radioactive peak upon cochromatography of extracts from 18-day plants with extracts from plants harvested 34 days after planting.

The partitioning characteristics of the corn metabolite indicated that more than 90% of the metabolite(s) was water soluble and would not partition into ether.

To study the nature of the metabolites, ion-exchange fractionation was performed on the crude 80% aqueous acetone extract and these results are shown in Table 6-9; 87% of the total radioactivity was found to be anionic in nature, suggesting the presence of an acidic functional group.

TABLE 6-9

Fractionation of Corn Metabolite(s) by Ion-Exchange Procedures

Fraction	Total radioactivity, %
80% Acetone extract	100
Cation (Dowex 50, H$^+$)	10
Anion (Dowex 1, HCOO$^-$)	87
Neutral	0

Since this water-soluble anionic radioactive metabolite could contain either N-isopropylaniline or aniline, it was isolated and subjected to rigorous base hydrolysis in a sealed tube. If an amide linkage existed, it would be cleaved by this procedure to liberate a moiety such as aniline or N-isopropylaniline. Vapor-phase chromatography of an ether extract from the base hydrolysis was conducted by adding cold carrier aniline and N-isopropylaniline to the extract. As shown in a vapor-phase chromatographic trapping experiment (Table 6-10), most of the radioactivity cochromatographed with carrier N-isopropylaniline. The recovery of radioactive N-isopropylaniline represented 84% of the total radioactivity injected into the column. It is therefore reasonable to assume that the corn metabolite contains N-isopropylaniline as an integral moiety. Further corroboration of the presence of N-isopropylaniline was obtained by thin-film chromatography of the ether extract from base hydrolysis.

TABLE 6-10

Vapor-Phase Chromatography (VPC) of Ether Extract from Base Hydrolysis of Corn Metabolite with N-Isopropylaniline and Aniline

VPC fraction no.	DPM in fraction
1	20
2 (aniline)	199
3	5
4 (N-isopropylaniline)	5377
5	118

Similar hydrolysis and vapor-phase chromatography trapping experiments were conducted using acidic rather than basic hydrolysis conditions. The conditions of the experiments were such that if the chloroacetanilide had been conjugated through its active chlorine to some natural product to form a glycosidic linkage, acidic hydrolysis would liberate the 2-hydroxy analog of 2-chloro-N-isopropylacetanilide. Vapor-phase chromatographic analysis of an ether extract from acid hydrolysis of the corn metabolite fortified with cold 2-hydroxy-N-isopropylacetanilide as a carrier indicated that the major radioactive peak coincided with the hydroxy analog (Table 6-11). These results again were verified by thin-film chromatography.

Similar studies with soybeans reported by Porter and Jaworski (*10*) are in complete agreement with the results found with corn. Thus these two highly resistant plant species metabolize 2-chloro-N-isopropylacetanilide in identical fashions.

While it is known that 2-chloro-N-isopropylacetanilide is rapidly metabolized by corn, soybeans, and a variety of other resistant crop plants

TABLE 6-11

VPC of Ether Extract from Acid Hydrolysis of Corn Metabolite with 2-Hydroxy-N-isopropylacetanilide

VPC fraction no.	DPM in fraction
1	30
2	164
3 (2-hydroxy-N-isopropylacetanilide)	2327
4	620
5	227

to a water-soluble acidic metabolite, the absolute structure of this metabolite has not been defined. It is known that the metabolite contains essentially the entire structure of the original herbicide, with the exception that the chloro group appears to have been displaced, probably by some nucleophilic endogenous substrate in the plant.

6-4. UPTAKE AND METABOLISM OF OTHER 2-CHLOROACETAMIDES

Studies by Smith et al. (*11*) defined the possible relationship between the degree of susceptibility of various plant species to selected 2-chloroacetamides and differential uptake or metabolism of the compounds by the

TABLE 6-12

Growth Inhibition by α-Chloroacetamides[a,b]

$$\text{ClCH}_2\text{C}\overset{\displaystyle O}{\underset{}{\|}}\text{N}\overset{\displaystyle R_1}{\underset{\displaystyle R_2}{<}}$$

Derivative					
R_1	R_2	Corn	Oats	Soybean	Cucumber
—CH$_2$CH=CH$_2$	—CH$_2$CH=CH$_2$	–	++	–	+
H	—CH$_2$CH=CH$_2$	–	++	–	+
—CH$_2$CH$_2$CH$_3$	—CH$_2$CH$_2$CH$_3$	–	+	–	+
H	—CH$_2$CH$_2$CH$_3$	–	++	–	+
H	—CH$<^{CH_3}_{CH_3}$	–	+	–	+
H	—(CH$_2$)$_5$CH$_3$	–	+	–	+
H	—⟨ S ⟩	–	+	–	+
H	—⟨ ⟩	–	+	–	+

[a] No inhibition, –; Slight inhibition, +; marked inhibition, ++.

[b] Inhibitor concentrations 10 ppm, except for diallyl derivative where concentration was 100 ppm.

plants. The seeds used in these studies were corn (*Zea-mays* L. CV US 13), oats (*Avena sativa* L.), soybean (*Glycine max* L. Merr CV Clark), and cucumber (*Cucumis sativus* L. CV Straight B). Oat and cucumber seeds were representative of susceptible monocotyledonous and dicotyledonous plant species, respectively, and corn and soybeans were representative of resistant plant species. The compounds studied are shown in Table 6-12, along with the relative sensitivities of the plant species to the chloroacetamides. The seeds used in these studies were surface sterilized with aqueous sodium hypochlorite, rinsed, dried, and placed in Scientific Product's seedpacks. The outer plastic pouch contained the chloroacetamide solutions and the inner paper wick held the seeds. All chloroacetamides were labeled at the carbonyl carbon with ^{14}C and the concentration of the compounds was 10 ppm, except for the diallyl derivative which was used at 100 ppm due to its low specific activity. At these concentrations, all four types of seeds germinated well. Following various times of germination, the seeds were removed from the pouches, rinsed with distilled water and diethyl ether, air-dried for 20 min, and weighed. The tissue was homogenized in 80% acetone, filtered, and reextracted with more acetone. Extracts were then assayed for radioactivity by liquid scintillation counting.

Two types of uptake curves were observed (as shown in Figs. 6-4 and 6-5). Corn, soybeans, and oats yielded a parabolic uptake curve, as shown in Fig. 6-2. While the uptake of only the diallyl derivative by oats is shown, the curve was typical for all derivatives. The uptake curve for cucumbers (Fig. 6-3) was sigmoidal in nature and was the same for all derivatives. A statistical analysis of the data from six sampling times indicated that all chloroacetamide derivatives were taken up to the same extent by a given seed. Corn, one of the more resistant species, invariably took up less chemical than the other seeds, but soybeans, the other resistant species, took up more than any other seed or about three times that of corn. Since oats and cucumbers are susceptible and corn and soybeans very resistant, it appears that the susceptibility is not determined by the amount of chemical absorbed.

The extent of metabolism of the chloroacetamides was studied by determining the amount taken up in 6 and 48 hours. The radioactivity of the plants was extracted and partitioned between chloroform and water since the chloroacetamides were found to have very high chloroform–water partition coefficients ranging from 5 to 25. Suspected breakdown products, such as chloroacetic acid and glycolic acid, had chloroform–water partition coefficients of less than 0.01. Thus it was assumed that all radioactivity found in the chloroform fraction was due to nonmetabolized chemicals, and the balance of the radioactivity remaining in the aqueous phase was

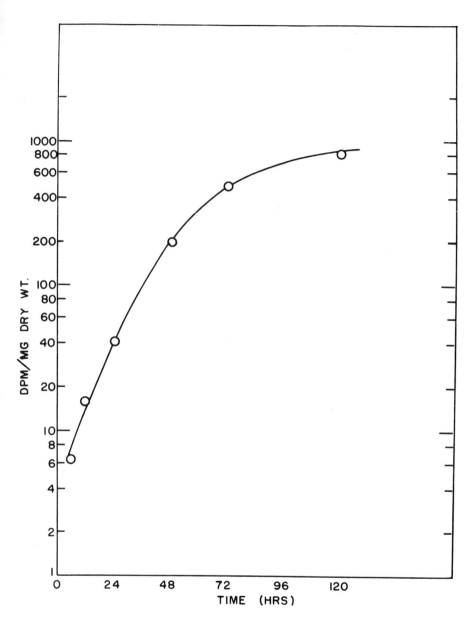

Fig. 6-2. Uptake of ^{14}C-labeled N,N-diallyl-2- chloroacetamide by germinating oat seeds.

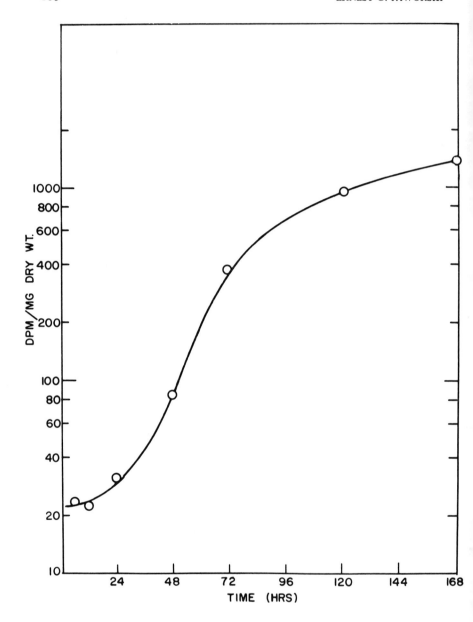

Fig. 6-3. Uptake of ^{14}C-labeled *N,N*-diallyl-2-chloroacetamide by germinating cucumber seeds.

attributed to metabolites. As seen in Fig. 6-4, both corn and oats metabolized a large fraction of the chemicals absorbed in 48 hours. Thus both the resistant and susceptible species clearly have the ability to metabolize 2-chloroacetamides. At 6 hours there was a definite difference between the amount of metabolism by corn and by oats. Corn metabolized significant amounts within a short time, but oats, the more susceptible species, metabolized essentially none.

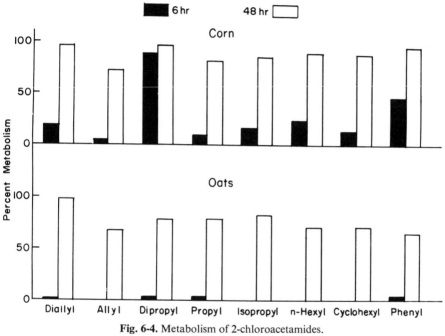

Fig. 6-4. Metabolism of 2-chloroacetamides.

The same relation was observed between soybeans and cucumbers, as shown in Fig. 6-5. Again, both metabolized large fractions in 48 hours, but only the resistant soybeans metabolized a significant amount in 6 hours.

The degree of susceptibility of various seeds to chloroacetamides could be directly related to the length of time required to initiate metabolism of these chemicals. Those species which are able to metabolize the chemical as soon as it enters or within a short time thereafter have only small amounts of the chemical present internally at any time. On the other hand, those species with delayed or slow metabolic capabilities accumulate relatively higher and therefore lethal concentrations. The basis for selectivity of the chloroacetamide herbicides could therefore be attributed to the ability of

resistant plants to metabolize them at a rate sufficient to keep cellular levels
below that required for growth inhibition.

Some selectivity based on the kinetics of absorption could also be expected
and might explain intermediate ranges of toxicity, such as shown between
cucumbers and oats. The latter are somewhat more susceptible to CDAA

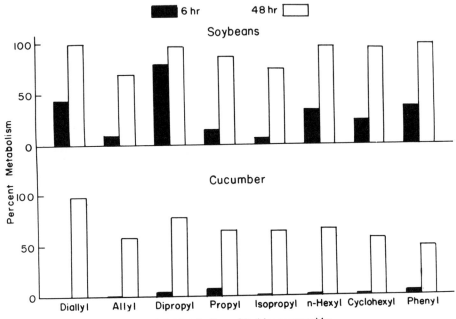

Fig. 6-5. Metabolism of 2-chloroacetamides.

than the former. In this case the metabolism rates appear to be comparable
in both species, but due to the parabolic uptake kinetics for oats, they would
be expected to absorb greater amounts of the herbicides per unit time
(compare Figs. 6-2 and 6-3) and build up higher intracellular concentrations.

6-5. MODE OF ACTION

Mechanistic studies on the mode of action of CDAA have been very
limited despite the fact that CDAA is a most interesting herbicide from the
aspect of its high degree of selectivity and high unit activity. Studies by
Jaworski (12) were conducted to evaluate the effects of CDAA upon respiration of germinating wheat and ryegrass seeds. Ryegrass respiration was
strongly inhibited by CDAA, whereas it was only moderately affected in

germinating wheat, a much less susceptible plant species. This was also demonstrated by a marked decrease in respiratory quotient in ryegrass seed. The RQ of wheat was only slightly affected. In both instances strong growth inhibition of the coleoptiles was achieved. Reversal studies demonstrated that glutathione, calcium pantothenate, and α-lipoic acid could reverse the respiratory inhibition of ryegrass by CDAA, but growth inhibition persisted. Although these data suggested that CDAA could inhibit certain sulfhydryl containing enzymes involved in respiration, the basic lethal effect must involve some mechanism more intimately connected with growth.

In a more recent study by Mann et al. (13), a survey of a variety of herbicides and their effects upon protein synthesis was reported. In these studies barley coleoptiles or Sesbania hypocotyls were preincubated with CDAA for 1 hour. L-Leucine–1-^{14}C was then added and incubation was continued for an additional 2 hours. The tissues were extracted with hot ethanol, and residual ^{14}C was assayed by liquid scintillation counting. The results of these studies with barley indicated a 51 and 70% inhibition of leucine ^{14}C incorporation in the protein at 2 and 5 ppm of CDAA, respectively. Results for Sesbania were approximately the same. Mann et al. (13) concluded that the inhibition of protein synthesis by CDAA is probably due to a more fundamental action, since even the uptake of amino acids (α-amino-n-butyric acid) was somewhat inhibited by CDAA. This latter effect could be attributed, however, to the inhibition of respiration and subsequent effects on active uptake of amino acids by the plant tissue.

The mechanisms that may be applicable in accounting for the detoxification of the chloroacetamides may also be involved in the mode of action of these compounds. That is to say that the haloacetamides can act as alkylating reagents, particularly with sulfhydryl groups which are highly effective nucleophiles. The studies of Lindley (14) on the reaction of thiol compounds with chloroacetamides are particularly illustrative of the potential of these compounds for interacting with sulfhydryl groups and hence various enzyme systems.

Very little work has been conducted on the investigation of the mode of action of 2-chloro-N-isopropylacetanilide with the exception of the work by Duke et al. (15). Duke reports that the inhibition of growth of cucumber roots by 2-chloro-N-isopropylacetanilide is closely correlated with the inhibition of protein synthesis in root tips and suggests that this is probably the primary site of action of the herbicide. He further suggests that the primary site of action is at the level of nascent protein formation and is probably due to the prevention of the transfer of aminoacyl-sRNA to the growing polypeptide chain. These results are consistent with studies conducted by Smith and Jaworski (*16*) where the inhibition of gibberellic-acid-induced (GA_3) amylase production in barley endosperm was demonstrated. Varner (*17*) demonstrated that GA_3 stimulated the *de novo* synthesis of α-amylase in the aleurone layers of barley. A 67% inhibition of amylase production resulted from the treatment of barley half-seeds with 3×10^{-4} M CDAA or 2-chloro-N-isopropylacetanilide (70 vs. 205 units of α-amylase per 10 half-seeds). This inhibitory response was concluded to be an effect on protein synthesis or some molecular level below that of protein synthesis, since the effect of CDAA was not reversed at higher levels of GA_3. Similar experiments using intact barley seeds indicated that 3×10^{-4} M CDAA resulted in a 27% inhibition of amylase production, and 10^{-2} M CDAA completely inhibited the formation of amylase in intact barley seeds. These levels of CDAA inhibited growth of barley by 78% when shoot lengths were measured over a 73-hour growing period. The growth of barley seed shoots was stimulated approximately 13% by GA_3 at 10^{-5} M; however, CDAA caused approximately the same degree of inhibition of growth in this instance as with non-GA_3-treated barley seeds.

This work and that reported by Duke et al. (*15*) suggests a role for CDAA and 2-chloro-N-isopropylacetanilide at the level of protein or nucleic acid synthesis. Interference at the site of action of plant-growth hormones, such as GA_3, could also be involved, but a direct interference with GA_3 activity cannot be involved, since the inhibition was irreversible even at very high levels of GA_3. It has also been demonstrated that CDAA and 2-chloro-N-isopropylacetanilide do not inhibit α-amylase activity per se even at 10^{-3} M.

6-6. CONCLUSION

Based on the present knowledge of the metabolism of chloroacetamide and chloroacetanilide herbicides, it is apparent that a generalization regarding their metabolic fates cannot be made. Whether the substitution of a phenyl group on the nitrogen results in a completely different detoxification mechanism than when the nitrogens are substituted with aliphatic moieties, such as in CDAA, must await further research. However, it would appear that crop species resistant to these herbicides are capable of rapid detoxification by one of two major mechanisms. One mechanism involves a reaction of the α halogen with endogenous substrates leading to the formation of water-soluble acidic metabolites, and the other involves the cleavage of the amide linkage and hydrolysis of the α halogen, as is the case with CDAA.

REFERENCES

1. P. C. Hamm and A. J. Speziale, *J. Agr. Food Chem.*, **4**, 518 (1956).
2. D. D. Baird, R. F. Husted, and C. L. Wilson, *Proc. Southern Weed Conf.*, **18**, 653 (1965).
3. G. W. Selleck, P. L. Berthet, D. M. Evans, and P. M. Vincent, *Symp. New Herb.*, *2nd*, Paris, 1965, pp. 277–285, 287–296.
4. J. Leyden Webb, *Enzyme and Metabolic Inhibitors*, Academic Press, New York, 1966, pp. 1–270.
5. E. Jaworski, *J. Agr. Food Chem.*, **12**, 33 (1964).
6. I. Zelitch and S. Ochoa, *J. Biol. Chem.*, **201**, 707 (1953).
7. I. Zelitch, *J. Biol. Chem.*, **201**, 719 (1953).
8. J. M. Deming, *Weeds*, **11**, 91 (1963).
9. E. G. Jaworski and C. A. Porter, American Chemical Society, 148th Meeting, Detroit, 1965.
10. C. A. Porter and E. G. Jaworski, American Society of Plant Physiologists, Urbana, Ill., 1965.
11. G. R. Smith, C. A. Porter, and E. G. Jaworski, American Chemical Society, 152nd Meeting, New York, 1966.
12. E. G. Jaworski, *Science*, **123**, 847 (1956).
13. J. D. Mann, L. S. Jordan, and B. E. Day, *Plant Physiol.*, **40**, 840 (1965).
14. H. Lindley, *Biochem. J.*, **82**, 418 (1962).
15. W. B. Duke, F. W. Slife, and J. B. Hanson, *Weed Soc. Am. Abstr.*, **1967**, 50.
16. G. R. Smith and E. G. Jaworski, unpublished work, 1966.
17. J. E. Varner, *Plant Physiol.*, **37**, 413 (1964).

CHAPTER 7

Amitrole

MASON C. CARTER

DEPARTMENT OF FORESTRY
AUBURN UNIVERSITY
AUBURN, ALABAMA

7-1. Introduction 187
    A. Physical and Chemical Properties 188
7-2. Degradation 188
    A. Degradation in Plants 188
    B. Degradation in Soil 189
    C. Metabolic Conjugation 191
7-3. Mode of Action 198
    A. Amino Acid and Protein Metabolism 198
    B. Purine Metabolism 199
    C. Flavin Synthesis 200
    D. Enzyme Inhibition 201
    E. Chlorophyll Synthesis and Plastid Development . . . 201
References 204

7-1. INTRODUCTION

Synthesis and chemistry of 3-amino-1,2,4-triazole (amitrole) have been known for many years (1); however, amitrole did not receive wide recognition as a herbicide and defoliant until 1952–1953 (2,3). Since its introduction, amitrole has been widely used for a variety of agricultural and industrial applications (4). Residues of this pesticide led to withdrawal of certain lots of cranberries from the market in 1959 when it was proposed that the phytocide could induce thyroid tumors in rats.*

* Report in *The New York Times*, International Edition, Weekly Review, Nov. 15, 1959.

A. Physical and Chemical Properties

Amitrole is a white, crystalline solid with a molecular weight of 84 and a melting point of 150–153° (5). It is soluble in water, methanol, ethanol, and chloroform; sparingly soluble in ethyl acetate; and insoluble in ether and acetone (5). Amitrole forms neutral aqueous solutions but acts as a weak base with a $k_b = 10^{-10}$ (6).

Potts (1) has reviewed the chemistry of s-triazoles in considerable detail. Although amitrole may be thought to exist in two tautomeric forms (Fig. 7-1), it is probably more correct to consider the imino hydrogen to exist as a charged atom bound to the triazole nucleus and stabilized by resonance (1). Amitrole behaves chemically as a typical aromatic amine (1); hence it will diazotize and couple with several dyes. Methods of detecting amitrole

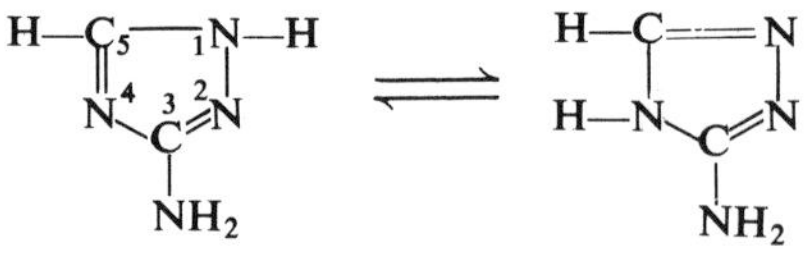

Fig. 7-1. Two possible tautomeric forms of 3-amino-1,2,4-triazole. A, 1H; B, 4H.

based on azo dye formation have been reported by several workers (7–9). Sund (10) reported an assay method utilizing a nitroprusside–ferrocyanide reagent.

7-2. DEGRADATION

A. Degradation in Plants

The s-triazole nucleus is highly stable (1); hence it is not surprising that few workers have reported evidence of ring cleavage under physiological conditions. Yost and Williams (11) reported a disappearance of amitrole–5-^{14}C from corn plants in approximately 6 weeks with a half-life of about 8 days. Disappearance was also observed in soybean but at a much slower rate (11). The possibility that amitrole was lost from roots, similar to other herbicides (12,13), was not investigated. These reports do not necessarily indicate ring cleavage.

Miller and Hall (14) could not detect amitrole in cotton 4 days after treatment. However, large quantities of metabolic products were present. These derivatives were probably conjugates which are discussed in Section 7-2.C.

Freed et al. (*15*) reported evolution of $^{14}CO_2$ from treated oats and barley, thus indicating ring cleavage. Resistant oats released CO_2 more readily than sensitive barley. Massini (*16*) found no loss of $^{14}CO_2$ from beans or tomatoes. Muzik (*17*) observed chlorosis in scions grafted on tomato plants 103 days after treatment with amitrole, indicating long persistence of the toxic moiety.

Hilton (*18*) and Castelfranco et al. (*19*) reported photodecomposition of amitrole in the presence of riboflavin. Ring cleavage occurred with the loss of ^{14}C as CO_2 or formic acid (*19*). This mechanism is discussed in Section 7-2.B.

Studies of amitrole degradation in plants have been complicated by the fact that the material is available commercially only with the 5-carbon labeled. Apparently, the 5-carbon is quickly lost (as CO_2 or formate) when ring rupture occurs and the remaining fragment(s) is thus unlabeled. However, if significant amounts of $^{14}CO_2$ or formate ^{14}C were produced from amitrole ^{14}C in higher plants, one would expect to find some incorporation of ^{14}C into normal metabolites. Such is not the case. The vast majority of the literature indicates that the extractable ^{14}C from plants treated with amitrole–5-^{14}C remains in the intact ring as free amitrole or conjugates (Section 7-2.C). Considerable amounts of amitrole are attached to protein (*20,21*) or somehow bound in an insoluble form (*8*). Conclusive evidence for rapid and extensive ring cleavage by higher plants has not been reported.

B. Degradation in Soil

Amitrole disappears rapidly from soils (*22–25*). Disappearance has been attributed to adsorption (*10,26*) and microbial degradation, although attempts to isolate organisms capable of degrading amitrole have not been successful (*22,25,28*).

Recently, Kaufman and co-workers (*27,28*) have proposed that most of the amitrole degradation occurring in soils proceeds by nonbiological reactions. Approximately 69% of the 5-carbon from amitrole was released as CO_2 in 20 days by nonsterilized soil (*28*). Autoclaved soil released only 2% in a comparable period, whereas soil treated with potassium azide or ethylene oxide released 46 and 35%, respectively (*28*). Reinoculation of autoclaved soil did not restore the capacity to metabolize amitrole (*28*). These authors propose that amitrole is degraded in soil by an oxidative mechanism involving an attack on the triazole nucleus by (OH·) or other free radicals.

Plimmer et al. (*29,30*) have studied the degradation of amitrole by free-radical generating systems. They further investigated the riboflavin-mediated photodecomposition of amitrole reported earlier (*18,19*). Carbon dioxide arising from the 5-carbon and cyanamid and urea arising from the 3-carbon and associated nitrogens were liberated from amitrole in the presence of riboflavin (*30*). Fenton's reagent produced the same products. However, the reagent of Castelfranco et al. (*19*), consisting of ascorbic acid, cupric sulfate, and molecular oxygen, liberated no CO_2, although amitrole was degraded (*30*). Plimmer et al. (*30*) concluded that riboflavin (and light) or Fenton's reagent promotes oxidation of amitrole, resulting in ring cleavage, the loss of CO_2, and the production of urea, cyanamid, and possibly molecular nitrogen (Fig. 7-2). The ascorbate–copper reagent evidently reduces amitrole to a free radical which then polymerizes.

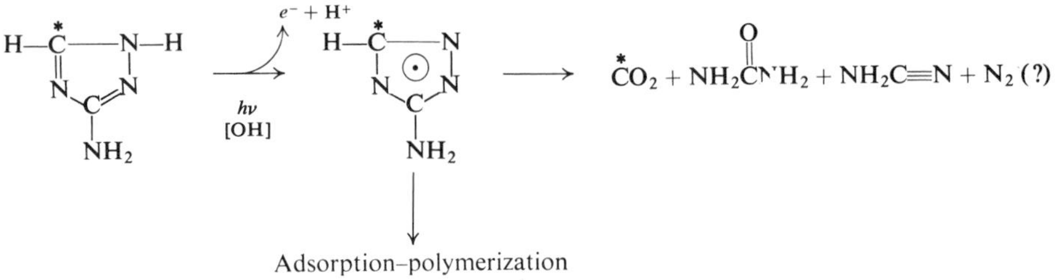

Fig. 7-2. Activation and degradation of amitrole. [After Plimmer et al. (*30*) and Castelfranco and Brown (*21*).]

This recent work provides strong evidence for nonbiological destruction of amitrole in soil; however, microbial attack cannot be totally discounted. Treatment with potassium azide failed to reduce amitrole degradation to the level of autoclaved soil but it produced a 40% or greater reduction of amitrole degradation over nonsterilized soil (*24,28*). Soil moisture, temperature, and pH markedly affected amitrole degradation (*24,26*), indicating possible microbial involvement. In Riempa's studies (*24*), amitrole degradation in soil exhibited a lag phase typical of microbial degradation, but the studies by Ercegovich and Frear (*26*) and Kaufman et al. (*28*) show that amitrole degradation obeys first-order kinetics, suggesting a chemical reaction. No one has reported an investigation of the possible involvement of extracellular enzymes.

Whatever the mechanism whereby the triazole ring is opened, there appears to be little doubt that ring opening does occur rapidly in soils and the resulting products (urea, cyanamid, and nitrogen) should be readily metabolized by soil microorganisms.

C. Metabolic Conjugation

Most literature on metabolic alteration of amitrole deals with the formation and properties of conjugates between amitrole and endogenous plant constituents. These "degradation" products contain the intact triazole nucleus which often may be regenerated by chemical treatment.

Rogers (*31,32*) reported a derivative of amitrole from several plants which was "chromatrographically identical" with an amine glucoside derivative of amitrole (*N-s*-triazol-3-yl-glucosylamine) (Fig. 7-3). The glucose derivative forms quite readily in vitro (*33*) and its occurrence in plant extracts is probably an artifact, since numerous attempts by other workers to detect the compound in plant extracts have failed (*8,14,16,34–36*). However,

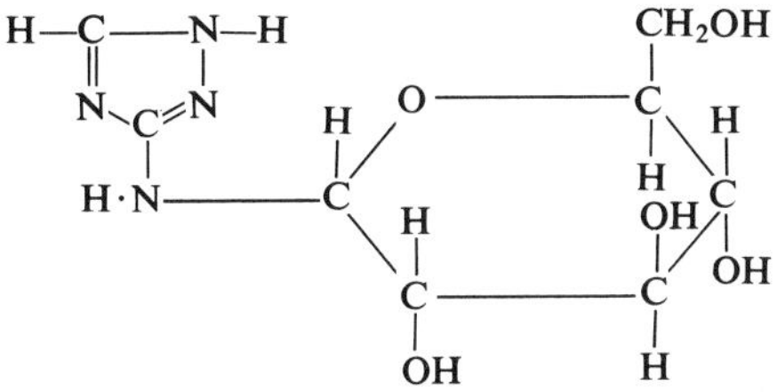

Fig. 7-3. Glucose adduct of amitrole (*37*).

Fredricks and Gentile (*33,37–39*) have published a series of studies on the properties and metabolism of the glucose derivative. In a recent paper (*39*) these authors suggest that the glucose adduct gives rise to a triose derivative through the action of aldolase, which would require isomerization of the glucose to fructose. Furthermore, these authors (*39*) suggest that the triose derivative represents the true structure of the amitrole derivatives reported by other workers (*8,14,16,35,36,40*), when, according to their own work (*33,39*), the glucose adduct will not diazotize and does not give a positive reaction with ninhydrin, two characteristics of amitrole derivatives reported by other workers (*8,16,40*). Fredricks and Gentile (*39*) suggest that the ninhydrin reaction found by others may have resulted from a contaminant—an unlikely possibility. The fact that the amitrole derivatives reported by most workers (*8,14,16,35,36,40*) are readily diazotizable and stable in strong acid makes it highly unlikely that the 3-amino group is substituted or that a glucose or a triose is part of the molecule. The existing evidence indicates that the glucose adduct of amitrole is simply an interesting artifact.

Racusen (*8*) reported the first comprehensive studies of amitrole metabolism. Two major metabolites were isolated from plants exposed to amitrole-5-^{14}C. The more abundant metabolite, termed "X" by Racusen, exhibited positive reactions with azo dyes and ninhydrin reagents and behaved as a zwitterion during electrophoresis at different pH's. The second metabolite, called "Y", exhibited only acidic properties above pH 4.5, gave no ninhydrin reaction, but did form azo dyes. Neither X or Y appeared to be as phytotoxic as amitrole. Both compounds were stable in 6 N HCl for 5 hours at 100°, indicating that neither compound is a simple amide or an amino-glucoside.

Shortly after Racusen's work, Massini (*6,16*) and Carter and Naylor (*40,41*) reported studies of amitrole metabolism. The principal metabolites reported by these workers exhibited azo dye reactions, ninhydrin sensitivity, and zwitterion behavior. In all probability "X" (*8*), ATX (*6*), "1" (*40*), and similar compounds reported by other workers (*14,35,36*) are the same compound which Massini (*16*) identified as 3-(3-amino-1,2,4-triazole-1-yl)-2-aminopropionic acid (3-ATAL) (Fig. 7-4). The suggestion by Carter and

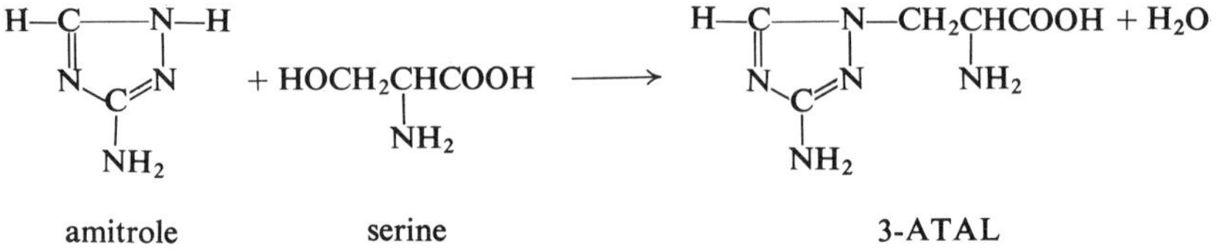

Fig. 7-4. Formation of 3-ATAL from amitrole and serine (*44*).

Naylor (*40*) that the alanine chain is attached to the triazole through the 3-amino group is not consistent with the azo-dye-forming properties of the compound. The existence of the C—N bond between the 3-carbon of alanine and the 1-nitrogen in the triazole ring has been confirmed by synthesis in our laboratory (*42*). Infrared spectra of natural and synthetic 3-ATAL are shown in Fig. 7-5. The spectra are not identical since the synthetic material is a mixture of D and L isomers. However, the functional groups correspond, and elemental analysis plus cochromatography in several solvents indicates that the compounds are identical.

Castelfranco and Brown (*21*) suggested that amitrole, in the presence of a free-radical generating system, accepts electrons and becomes a free radical, which is capable of alkylating proteins, and possibly amino acids, indiscriminately. However, Carter and Naylor (*43*) and Carter (*44*) have shown that ^{14}C from serine or glycine readily enters 3-ATAL, but labeling from glucose, succinate, alanine, glyoxylate, and formate is much less rapid. Most likely 3-ATAL is formed by the condensation of amitrole and serine (*16,44*) in a manner analogous to the formation of β-pyrazol-1-yl-α-alanine

(BPA) from pyrazole and serine (45) (see Fig. 7-4). The ability of BPA synthetase to catalyze 3-ATAL synthesis is currently under study in our laboratory.

The formation of 3-ATAL apparently represents detoxication, since the derivative does not appear to be nearly as toxic as amitrole (8,16,40) or as mobile (16). Furthermore, ammonium thiocyanate, which synergizes the action of amitrole, inhibits the formation of 3-ATAL (36,44). Donnalley (46) suggested that the synergism resulted from increased transport of amitrole, but increased mobility is probably a secondary result of reduced formation of the less mobile 3-ATAL (44). Other divalent sulfur compounds reduce 3-ATAL formation but none of those tested are as effective as thiocyanate (Table 7-1).

TABLE 7-1

Inhibition of 3-ATAL Formation by Organic Sulfur Compounds[a]

^{14}C Compound in extract	Sulfur compound, %				
	None	Thiocyanate	Thiourea	Thioacetamide	Cysteine
Amitrole	17.4	93.2	38.3	57.7	46.9
3-ATAL	63.1	6.7	57.2	36.8	45.8
"ATY"[b]	19.3	< 1	4.4	5.5	7.4

[a] Bean trifoliates given 5.0 μc of amitrole-5-^{14}C in equimolar solution of sulfur compound for 24 hours. Data expressed as percentage of total radioactive in 80% ethanol extract (Brown and Carter, unpublished data).

[b] Compound possessing characteristic of Y (8,14), unknown I (35), compound 2 (40).

In addition to 3-ATAL, another compound has been reported under various designations: "Y" (8,14), unknown I (35), and compound 2 (34). None of these workers reported sufficient chemical and physical properties to conclude that the compounds were identical. Chromatographic properties were similar and all compounds indicated positive azo dye reaction but negative ninhydrin reaction. Miller and Hall (14) reported that Y was the most abundant metabolite of amitrole in cotton leaves, whereas X (i.e., 3-ATAL) predominated in the seed. In beans, Canada thistle, and bindweed, silver maple, honeysuckle, and alfalfa, 3-ATAL was equal to or greater than other products (8,16,34–36).

Racusen (8) reported that Y was stable in 6 N HCl for 5 hours at 100°. Herrett and Linck (35) reported disappearance of their unknown I following

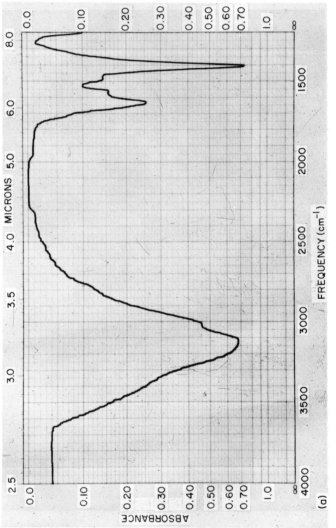

Fig. 7-5a.

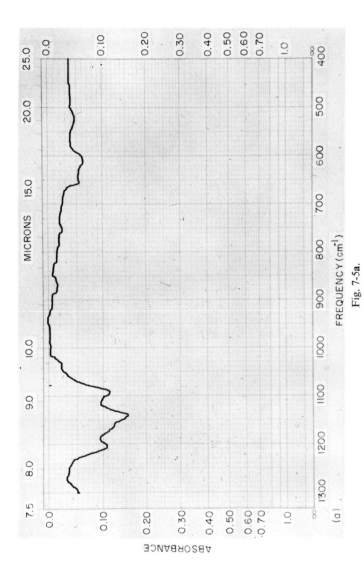

Fig. 7-5a.

Fig. 7-5. IR spectra of 3-ATAL (KBr pellet; Perkin–Elmer Model 337): (**a**) [pp. 194–195] spectra of 3-ATAL isolated from beans by the methods of Massini (*16*); (**b**) [pp. 196–197] spectra of 3-ATAL prepared from amitrole and α-acetamidoacrylic acid by Hutchinson (*42*). Synthesis yields a mixture of D and L isomers, whereas the natural product is all L form. Hence, the spectra are not identical.

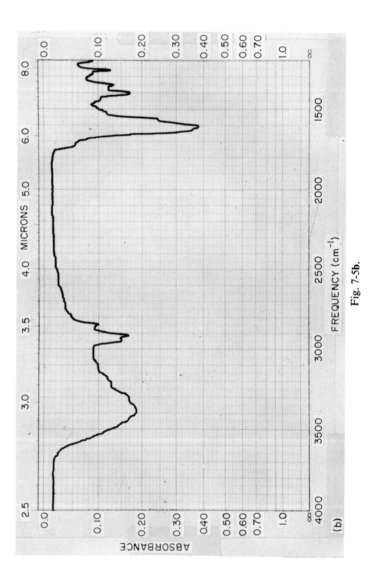

Fig. 7-5b.

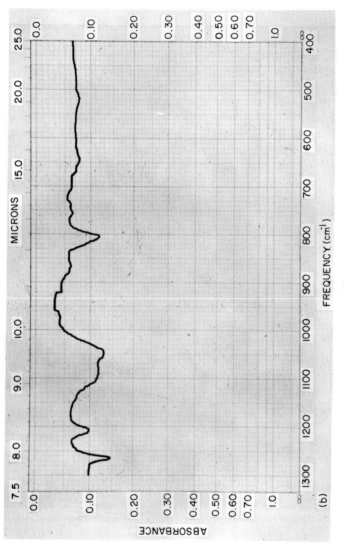

Fig. 7-5b.

similar treatment. 3-ATAL [X (*8*), unknown II (*35*)] was stable. Thus it would appear that compound Y of Racusen (*8*) and unknown I of Herrett and Linck (*35*) were not the same. Verification of the structure of products other than 3-ATAL must await further studies. Carter and Naylor (*34*) observed more than a dozen radioactive compounds derived from amitrole–5-^{14}C, none of which appeared to be normal metabolites arising from $^{14}CO_2$ fixation. Hence, most were probably conjugates.

Herrett and Bagley (*47*) reported a metabolic product of amitrole which they designated unknown III. This material was found to be five to eight times as effective as amitrole in suppressing the growth of tomato and lettuce roots (*47*). Unknown III was not reactive with ninhydrin and would not form azo dyes, suggesting substitution of the 3-amino group, but it was not the aminoglucoside. The compound was highly susceptible to hydrolysis, readily degrading during chromatography in acid solvents (*48*) and releasing free amitrole and, presumably, other fractions.

It is difficult to assess the significance of unknown III to plant metabolism. To obtain the compound, thistle plants must be extracted with water and concentrated in vacuo at room temperature (*48*). Many transformations could take place during such a procedure. Attempts to detect the compound in our laboratory using bean plants have been unsuccessful, and Smith et al. (*36*) were unable to detect the compound in three ecotypes of Canada thistle. The lack of confirmation casts serious doubts about the existence of unknown III in vivo. Like the amino-glucoside, unknown III may well be an artifact. However, an artifact which is several times as toxic as amitrole is well worth further study.

7-3. MODE OF ACTION

A. Amino Acid and Protein Metabolism

Amitrole blocks histidine biosynthesis in bacteria (*49*), yeast (*50,51*), and algae (*52*) by inhibiting imidazoleglycerol phosphate dehydrase (*49,53*) and imidazoleglycerol (IG) accumulates in the media. However, interference with histidine synthesis or utilization does not appear to be the primary site of action of amitrole in higher plants (*56,57*). McWhorter and Hilton (*57*) could find no reduction in histidine content of amitrole-treated corn, nor were they able to demonstrate IG accumulation. Brown and Carter (*20*) reported that amitrole did not affect the incorporation of histidine into bean protein.

Total free amino acid content increases in light-grown plants treated with amitrole, whereas protein content declines (57–59), indicating reduced protein synthesis. Bartels and Wolf (58) concluded that the effect of amitrole on protein synthesis is indirect, arising from interferences with purine metabolism. Brown and Carter (20) also found no evidence for a direct effect of amitrole on protein synthesis. McWhorter and Hilton (57) found that total free amino acids increased in amitrole-treated corn; however, free glycine and serine declined to very low levels. These authors suggested that formation of 3-ATAL may have depleted glycine–serine pools, as suggested earlier by Carter and Naylor (43). However, McWhorter and Hilton (57) could not detect 3-ATAL in treated corn tissue. Castelfranco and Brown (21) discounted amino acid conjugation and removal as a toxic mechanism on the basis of the large quantities of amitrole which would be required. Possibly amitrole interferes with C_1 metabolism and disrupts glycine–serine interconversion (57,60). Such a mechanism might also disrupt purine metabolism. Whatever the mechanism, depletion of glycine–serine pools could account for reduced protein synthesis in treated plants.

Williams et al. (61) suggested that amitrole was converted to 3-ATAL by *Escherichia coli*, and 3-ATAL, acting as a histidine analog, was incorporated into protein. Production of "lethal" protein could be responsible for part of amitrole's toxicity. Brown and Carter (20) were not able to demonstrate the incorporation of 3-ATAL into bean plant protein. Possibly the histidine-activating enzyme from beans cannot activate 3-ATAL, while the *E. coli* enzyme can. Peterson and Fowden (62) found that proline-activating enzyme from certain plants could activate azetidine-2-carboxylic acid, whereas the enzyme from other plants could not.

Brown and Carter (20) demonstrated conclusively that amitrole and 3-ATAL have no immediate effect upon the protein-synthesizing mechanism in bean plants. Hence, reduced protein content in treated bean plants must derive from a disruption in amino acid or nucleic acid metabolism.

B. Purine Metabolism

Blockage of histidine biosynthesis does not appear to be the only site of amitrole action in yeast and bacteria, since addition of histidine does not completely overcome amitrole inhibition of growth (49,54,55). A combination of histidine and adenine does totally nullify amitrole inhibition in yeast and bacteria (49,54,55). These findings have led Hilton (56) to suggest that amitrole interferes with purine synthesis. Klopotowski and Bagdasarian

(55) found that histidine plus cytosine was nearly as effective as histidine plus adenine in nullifying amitrole action on *Saccharomyces cerevisiae*, while only histidine plus adenine is effective with *Salmonella typhimirium* (49,55). Klopotowski and Bagdasarian (55) suggest that amitrole affects the availability of some common precursor of both purines and pyrimidines but give no suggestion as to the identity of this compound.

Sund et al. (63) found that 4-amino-5-imidazole carboxamide, several purines, and several ribosides reduced the growth inhibition of tomatoes produced by amitrole. Wart and Loughman (68) reported that amitrole reduced ^{32}P incorporation into the acid-insoluble fraction of barley roots and shoots, while Schweizer and Rogers (69) found that amitrole reduced soluble nucleotides in corn. But Wolf (64) reported that purines did not protect wheat against amitrole toxicity. Neither of these workers used well-purified extracts. In a more comprehensive study, Bartels and Wolf (58) grew wheat seedling in the presence and absence of amitrole in both light and darkness. Amitrole had no effect upon the DNA, RNA, or soluble nucleotide content per gram fresh weight of dark-grown plants. Likewise DNA and soluble nucleotide content was not reduced in light-grown plants, but cytoplasmic RNA (excluding nuclei, chloroplasts, and mitochondria) was reduced considerably. The base ratios of RNA were not affected, but amitrole reduced the incorporation of formate–^{14}C into adenine, guanine, and total acid-soluble nucleotide fraction. The incorporation of glycine–^{14}C into DNA and RNA was reduced by amitrole with the greatest reduction (60%) occurring in DNA. Although amitrole did not reduce the DNA per unit of fresh weight, it greatly reduced the synthesis of new DNA, suggesting an interference with cell division. Srivastava (70) reported that amitrole had an antimitotic effect upon certain plants. Feinstein (71) found that amitrole protected rats against X-radiation, also suggestive of reduced nuclear activity. Castelfranco and Bisalputra (72) found that amitrole inhibited cell division but not enlargement of *Scenedesmus quadricauda*. The general conclusion seems to be that amitrole disrupts purine synthesis or utilization in both higher plants and microorganisms, but the mechanism is yet to be elucidated (55,56,58,69,72).

C. Flavin Synthesis

Nullification of amitrole toxicity by several flavins plus a reduced riboflavin concentration in treated plants led Sund to suggest that amitrole inhibits riboflavin synthesis (63,66). As mentioned in Section 7-2, riboflavin mediates photodecomposition of amitrole in vitro (18,19) and Castelfranco

(*19*) discounted an inhibition of riboflavin synthesis on this basis. Hilton (*18*) found that both riboflavin and isoriboflavin nullified amitrole action in the light, but only riboflavin was effective in the dark. Hilton (*56*) suggests that riboflavin nullification is due to both photodecomposition and replacement of riboflavin deficiency produced by an interference with purine metabolism.

However, flavins may mediate decomposition of amitrole in vivo. Sund (*67*) observed that callus tissue cultured in the light was less sensitive to amitrole than tissue cultured in the dark. Also, biochemical reactions may be capable of driving riboflavin-mediated amitrole decomposition in the dark, as Castelfranco and Brown (*21*) demonstrated for several free-radical generating systems. No one has reported the fate of flavins in the reaction with amitrole, so it is not possible to say whether amitrole inhibits riboflavin synthesis or promotes destruction.

In solutions containing only riboflavin and amitrole, light drives the decomposition of amitrole with the loss of the 5-carbon as CO_2 (*21,30*), but if a protein (bovin serum albumin) is also present, amitrole is activated and attacks the protein (*20,21*). Intact amitrole is released upon hydrolysis (*20*). Thus flavins may react with amitrole in vivo, resulting in the destruction of flavin and the inactivation of amitrole through the attachment to protein.

D. Enzyme Inhibition

In addition to IGP dehydrase (*49,53*), amitrole has been found to inhibit several other enzymes (*73–75*). Catalase and fatty acid peroxidase are irreversibly inhibited (*21,74*). These observations have led Castelfranco to suggest that amitrole undergoes a one-electron oxidation to the free radical, which then attacks various enzymes, causing irreversible inhibition (*21*). Such a mechanism need not be specific for a given site or a given enzyme. Enzyme inhibition would depend upon the chance that alkylation with amitrole occurred at or near an active site. At high concentrations, amitrole produces rapid desiccation and defoliation and strongly inhibits growth (*76*); such action may be due to widespread nonspecific enzyme inhibition. However, at low concentrations growth may be affected only slightly (*76,77*), whereas other processes, such as chlorophyll synthesis, are strongly inhibited, suggesting a specific site of action.

E. Chlorophyll Synthesis and Plastid Development

Perhaps the most obvious effect of amitrole upon higher plants is the pronounced absence of chlorophyll in new growth arising subsequent to amitrole application (2,32,76). Amitrole does not promote chlorophyll degradation in extracts or plants grown in the dark (76,77), but bleaching follows treatment in the light. Chlorophyll content declines with increasing amitrole concentration in a linear relationship (79).

The structural similarity between amitrole and pyrrole led to speculation that the herbicide competed with normal assimilates in porphyrin synthesis. However, amitrole does not inhibit heme synthesis in avian erythrocytes (Table 7-2) and does not reduce the incorporation of δ-amino levulinic

TABLE 7-2

Effect of Amitrole upon the Incorporation of Succinate–2,3-^{14}C into Heme[a]

	Reaction ingredients[b]			Spec. act. of heme,
Amitrole	Succinate–2,3-^{14}C	Glycine	Glucose	cpm/mM
0	2 μc	400 μM	20 mg	97,300
400 μM	2 μc	400 μM	20 mg	124,750

[a] M. C. Carter and B. Jacobson, unpublished data.
[b] Washed red cells from 20 ml of duck blood suspended in 10 ml of isotonic buffer. Procedures taken from Shemin and Kumin (78).

acid (ALA) or porphobilinogen (PGB) into porphyrins in plant systems (80,81). Thus the effect of amitrole has been attributed to an interference with plastid development (32,80,82,83).

Proplastids in amitrole-treated etiolated plants appear to be structually identical to proplastids from normal etiolated plants, but changes associated with greening do not occur in treated plant plastids (83). Chloroplasts from light-grown amitrole-treated plants are completely lacking in fraction I protein and 70S ribosomes, but proplastids from treated etiolated plants contain both fraction I protein and 70S ribosomes (84). Cytoplasmic 80S ribosomes are not affected by amitrole in either light or darkness (84). Amitrole appears to be fostering the disappearance of 70S ribosomes upon illumination.

If plastid development is inhibited by amitrole through an interference with purine metabolism (56,58,80), there must be a highly specific type of interference, since cell enlargement, which requires considerable nucleic acid metabolism, is not greatly affected by amitrole concentrations which strongly inhibit chlorophyll formation. The effect seems restricted to the chloroplast and occurs only in the light (83,84). It is difficult to attribute the highly specific effect of low amitrole concentrations upon plastid development to a general interference with purine metabolism.

Bogorad (85) states that the control of chlorophyll synthesis probably resides at the level of ALA synthetase. Plants which are chlorotic due to iron deficiency produce little or no porphyrins but are capable of synthesizing chlorophyll if given ALA (86). Etiolated beans and wheat, two plants quite sensitive to amitrole, exhibit a lag period of 6–8 hours after being placed in the light before beginning rapid accumulation of chlorophyll (87,88). If these etiolated seedlings are given a few minutes of illumination and returned to the dark for a few hours, they exhibit no lag period upon reillumination (87,88). Chloramphenicol added prior to preillumination will greatly inhibit chlorophyll synthesis, but the longer the period between preillumination and chloramphenicol treatment, the less the inhibition of chlorophyll synthesis (89). Amitrole's effect is quite similar. When added just prior to preillumination, amitrole causes a 50% inhibition of chlorophyll synthesis; but if added just prior to final illumination, the inhibition is much less (90).

Amitrole apparently blocks light-induced changes in the proplastid, resulting in a reduced capacity for chlorophyll synthesis. Amitrole may repress certain enzymes necessary for chlorophyll synthesis, possibly ALA synthetase. Unfortunately, attempts to demonstrate ALA synthetase activity in leaf extracts have not been successful (85). The inhibition of structural changes in the proplastid caused by amitrole may be an indirect effect of the lack of chlorophyll synthesis. Chloroplasts from amitrole-treated plants (83) appear similar to those from chlorophyll-lacking mutants of *Cyanidinium caldarium* (91).

A further interesting observation concerning the action of amitrole upon chlorophyll synthesis is the fact that new growth, where chlorosis is most severe, contains considerable 3-ATAL but little or no amitrole (8,14,16,34). But Racusen (8), Carter and Naylor (40), and Massini (16) found that 3-ATAL was apparently nontoxic to a number of plants. If so, what is producing the chlorosis? Hilton et al. (92) reject 3-ATAL itself and the reaction which forms it as having any contribution to the toxicity of amitrole, because 3-hydroxy-1,2,4-triazole (3-OT) also produces 3-ATAL in plants, but 3-OT is nonphytotoxic. The metabolism of 3-OT was studied by Massini (93), who states that 3-OT "is transformed into a compound with similar chromatographic properties (to those formed from amitrole)." However, 3-ATAL and most of the other amitrole derivatives studied possess the diazotizable amino group of amitrole. 3-OT does not form azo dyes and would have to be transaminated in the plant to form 3-ATAL. The possibility still exists that 3-ATAL may produce a chronic localized toxicity in cells where it occurs, and its abundance in chlorotic tissue may well be associated with the impairment of chlorophyll synthesis and plastid development.

REFERENCES

1. K. T. Potts, *Chem. Rev.*, **61**, 87 (1961).
2. W. C. Hall, S. P. Johnson, and C. L. Leinweber, *Texas Agr. Expt. Sta. Bull.*, **759** (1953).
3. R. Behrens, *Proc. N. Central Weed Conf.*, **10**, 61 (1953).
4. R. A. Alverson, *Annotated Bibliography of Amino Triazole*, Am. Cyan. Co., 1957.
5. American Cyanamid Co., *Tech. Data Sheet: Amino Triazole*, 1956.
6. P. Massini, *Acta Botan. Neerl.*, **7**, 524 (1958).
7. F. D. Aldrich and S. R. McLane, *Plant Physiol.*, **32**(2), 153 (1957).
8. D. Racusen, *Arch. Biochem. Biophys.*, **74**(1), 106 (1958).
9. R. W. Storherr and J. Burke, *J. Am. Offic. Agr. Chemicals*, **44**(2), 196 (1961).
10. K. A. Sund, *J. Agr. Food Chem.*, **4**, 57 (1956).
11. J. F. Yost and E. F. Williams, *Proc. Northeast. Weed Conf.*, 1958, pp. 9–15.
12. J. B. Hanson and F. W. Slife, *Illinois Res.*, **3–4** (1961).
13. C. L. Foy and W. Hurtt, *Weed Soc. Am. Abstr.*, 1967, p. 40.
14. C. S. Miller and W. C. Hall, *J. Agr. Food Chem.*, **9**, 210 (1961).
15. V. H. Freed, M. Montgomery, and M. Kief, *Proc. Northeast. Weed. Conf.*, 1961, pp. 6–16.
16. P. Massini, *Acta Botan. Neerl.*, **12**, 64 (1963).
17. T. J. Muzik, *Weeds Res.*, **5**(3), 207 (1965).
18. J. L. Hilton, *Plant Physiol.*, **37**, 238 (1962).
19. P. Castelfranco, A. Oppenheim, and S. Yamaguchi, *Weeds*, **11**(1), 111 (1963).
20. J. C. Brown and M. C. Carter, *Weed Sci.*, **16**(2), 222 (1968).
21. P. Castelfranco and M. S. Brown, *Weeds*, **11**(2), 116 (1963).
22. C. D. Ercegovich, Ph.D. thesis, Pennsylvania State Univ., University Park, 1958.
23. D. D. Bardarenko, *Proc. N. Central Weed Conf.*, 1958.
24. P. Riempa, *Weed Res.*, **2**, 41 (1962).
25. F. M. Ashton, *Weeds*, **11**(2), 167 (1963).
26. C. D. Ercegovich and D. E. H. Frear, *J. Agr. Food Chem.*, **12**, 26 (1964).
27. D. D. Kaufman, *Weed Soc. Am. Abstr.*, 1967, pp. 78–79.
28. D. D. Kaufman, J. R. Plimmer, P. C. Kearney, J. Blake, and F. S. Guardia, *Weed Sci.*, **16**(2), 226 (1968).
29. P. C. Kearney and J. R. Plimmer, *Weed Soc. Am. Abstr.*, pp. 76–77, 1967.
30. J. R. Plimmer, P. C. Kearney, D. D. Kaufman, and F. S. Guardia, *J. Agr. Food Chem.*, **15**, 996 (1967).
31. B. J. Rogers, *Weeds*, **5**(1), 5 (1957).
32. B. J. Rogers, *Hormolog.*, **1**, 10 (1957).
33. J. F. Fredricks and A. C. Gentile, *Physiol. Plantarum*, **13**, 761 (1960).
34. M. C. Carter and A. W. Naylor, *Botan. Gaz.*, **122**(2), 138 (1960).
35. R. A. Herrett and A. J. Linck, *Physiol. Plantarum*, **14**, 767 (1961).

36. L. W. Smith, D. E. Bayer, and C. L. Foy, *Abstr. Weed Soc. Am.*, 1967, pp. 61–62.
37. J. F. Fredricks and A. C. Gentile, *Biochim. Biophys. Acta*, **92**(2), 356 (1961).
38. J. F. Fredricks and A. C. Gentile, *Physiol. Plantarum*, **15**, 186 (1962).
39. J. F. Fredricks and A. C. Gentile, *Phytochemistry*, **4**, 851 (1966).
40. M. C. Carter and A. W. Naylor, *Physiol. Plantarum*, **14**, 20 (1961).
41. M. C. Carter and A. W. Naylor, *Plant Physiol. Suppl.*, **34**, 6 (1959).
42. J. R. Hutchinson, Ph.D. Dissertation, Auburn University, Auburn, Ala., 1968.
43. M. C. Carter and A. W. Naylor, *Physiol. Plantarum*, **14**, 62 (1961).
44. M. C. Carter, *Physiol. Plantarum*, **18**, 1054 (1965).
45. P. M. Dunnill and L. Fowden, *J. Exptl. Botan.*, **14**, 237 (1963).
46. W. F. Donnalley, Ph.D. thesis, Michigan State Univ., East Lansing, 1964.
47. R. A. Herrett and W. P. Bagley, *J. Agr. Food Chem.*, **12**(1), 17 (1964).
48. R. A. Herrett, personal communication, 1968.
49. J. L. Hilton, P. C. Kearney, and B. N. Ames, *Arch. Biochem. Biophys.*, **112**(2), 544 (1965).
50. T. Klopotowski and D. Hulanicka, *Acta. Biochim. Polon.*, **10**(2), 209 (1963).
51. J. L. Hilton, *Weeds*, **8**(3), 392 (1960).
52. J. N. Siegel and A. C. Gentile, *Plant. Physiol.*, **41**(4), 670 (1966).
53. T. Klopotowski and A. Wiater, *Arch. Biochem. Biophys.*, **112**(2), 562 (1965).
54. F. W. Weyter and H. P. Broquist, *Biochim. Biophys. Acta*, **40**, 567 (1960).
55. T. Klopotowski and G. Bagdasarian, *Acta Biochim. Polon.*, **13**(2), 153 (1966).
56. J. L. Hilton, *Symp. Use Isotopes Weed Res.*, IAEC.FAO Vienna, 1965.
57. C. G. McWhorter and J. L. Hilton, *Physiol. Plantarum*, **20**(1), 30 (1967).
58. P. G. Bartels and F. T. Wolf, *Physiol. Plantarum*, **18**(3), 805 (1965).
59. C. G. McWhorter, *Physiol. Plantarum*, **16**(1), 31 (1963).
60. M. C. Carter, D.F. thesis, Duke Univ., Durham, N.C., 1959.
61. A. K. Williams, S. T. Cos, and R. G. Eagon, *Biochem. Biophys. Res. Commun.*, **18**(2), 250 (1965).
62. P. J. Peterson and L. Fowden, *Nature*, **200**, 148 (1963).
63. K. A. Sund, E. C. Putala, and H. N. Little, *J. Agr. Food Chem.*, **8**, 210 (1960).
64. F. T. Wolf, *Plant Physiol.*, *Suppl.*, **36**, xxxix (1961).
65. J. L. Hilton, *Plant Physiol.*, **37**(2), 238 (1962).
66. K. A. Sund and H. N. Little, *Science*, **132**, 622 (1960).
67. K. A. Sund, *Physiol. Plantarum*, **14**, 260 (1961).
68. D. J. Wart and B. C. Loughman, *Can. J. Botan.*, **39**, 339 (1961).
69. E. E. Schweizer and B. J. Rogers, *Weeds*, **12**(4), 310 (1964).
70. M. G. Srivastava, *Trans Bose Res. Inst. Calcutta*, **21**, 119 (1956–1959).
71. R. N. Feinstein, *Science*, **125**, 936 (1957).
72. P. Castelfranco and T. Bisalputra, *Am. J. Botan.*, **52**(3), 222 (1965).
73. W. G. Heim, D. Appleman, and H. T. Pyfrom, *Am. J. Physiol.*, **186**, 19 (1956).
74. E. Margoliash and A. Novogrodsky, *Biochem. J.*, **68**, 468 (1958).
75. P. Castelfranco, *Biochim. Biophys. Acta*, **41**, 485 (1960).
76. W. C. Hall, S. P. Johnson, and C. L. Leinweber, *Texas Agr. Expt. Sta. Bull.*, **789** (1954).
77. F. T. Wolf, *Nature*, **188**, 164 (1960).
78. D. Shemin and S. Kumin, *Federation Proc.*, **11**, 285 (1952).
79. E. B. Minton, W. H. Preston, Jr., and W. H. Orgell, *Plant Physiol. Suppl.*, **33**, xlviii (1958).

80. P. G. Bartels, *Proc. Assoc. Southern Agr. Workers*, **60**, 305 (1963).

81. L. Bogorad, *J. Biol. Chem.*, **233**, 501 (1958).

82. H. Linser and O. Kiermayer, *Planta*, **49**, 498 (1957).

83. P. G. Bartels, *Plant Cell Physiol.*, **6**, 361 (1965).

84. P. G. Bartels, K. Matsuda, A. Siegel, and T. E. Weier, *Plant Physiol.*, **42**(5), 736 (1967).

85. L. Bogorad, in *Plant Biochemistry* (W. Bonner and J. E. Varner, eds.), Academic Press, New York, 1965.

86. H. V. Marsh, H. J. Evans, and G. Matrone, *Plant Physiol.*, **38**(6), 638 (1963).

87. R. B. Withrow, J. B. Wolff, and L. Price, *Plant Physiol. Suppl.*, **31**, xiii (1956).

88. L. Price and W. H. Klein, *Plant Physiol.*, **36**(6), 733 (1961).

89. M. M. Margulies, *Plant Physiol.*, **42**(2), 218 (1967).

90. M. C. Carter, unpublished data, 1968.

91. L. Bogorad, F. V. Mercer, and R. Mulens, *Photosynthetic Mechanisms of Green Plants*, A Symposium, B. Kok, Chairman, Natl. Acad. Sci., Washington, D.C., 1963, pp. 560–570.

92. J. L. Hilton, L. L. Jansen, and H. M. Hull, *Ann. Rev. Plant Physiol.*, **14**, 353 (1963).

93. P. Massini, *Proc. Intern. Conf. Peaceful Uses At. Energy*, 2nd meeting, 1959, pp. 58–62.

CHAPTER 8

The Chlorinated Aliphatic Acids

C. L. FOY

DEPARTMENT OF PLANT PATHOLOGY AND PHYSIOLOGY
VIRGINIA POLYTECHNIC INSTITUTE
BLACKSBURG, VIRGINIA

8-1. Introduction 207
    A. Physical and Chemical Properties 208
8-2. Degradation 212
    A. Degradation in Plants 212
    B. Degradation in Animals 217
    C. Degradation in Soils 218
    D. Pathways of Degradation in Soil 232
8-3. Mode of Action 238
References 249

8-1. INTRODUCTION

The halogenated aliphatic acids have been known for many years, but their use as herbicides is very recent. Patent citations on their use as herbicides were made by Bousquet (1) for trichloroacetic acid (TCA) in 1944 and by Barrons (2,3) for 2,2-dichloropropionic acid (dalapon) and for 2,2,3-trichloropropionic acid in 1951 and 1957, respectively. A patent citation by Toornman (4) for 2,2-dichlorobutyric acid was made as recently as 1959.

In 1950, in a comprehensive review on herbicides by Norman et al. (5), only four references were quoted in relation to halogenated aliphatic acids. All referred to TCA, and the earliest was in 1948. However, other chlorinated aliphatic acids have become well known as herbicides or growth regulators within the past twenty years. A recent literature search (6) revealed over 700 papers on dalapon alone between 1958 and 1962. In addition, monosubstituted and trichloro-substituted acetates, propionates, butyrates, and other analogs have been investigated. Numerous additional references on the chlorinated aliphatic acids have appeared since 1962.

Most citations are concerned with relatively few of these derivatives. The major ones, in order of their appearance, are TCA, dalapon, 2,2,3-trichloropropionic acid, 2,2-dichlorobutyric acid, and 2,3-dichloroisobutyric acid. α Chlorination appears to be a major requirement for activity, with TCA, dalapon, and 2,2-dichlorobutyric acid being herbicidally most active. The unsubstituted aliphatic acids, including formic, acetic, acrylic, butyric, and oleic (among others), are essentially inactive as herbicides.

The herbicidal action of a 1 % chloroacetic acid was described in 1951 by Zimmerman et al. (7). They claimed that several weed species were killed in 1 to 24 hours. A selective action was also found since no damage was sustained by corn plants, roses, and carnations. Subsequently TCA and dalapon found a place in agricultural practices. The now well-known grass-killing properties of TCA were observed early by McCall and Zahnley (8). The announcement of dalapon in 1953 as a systemic grass-selective herbicide (9) represented a promising new approach to chemical weed control. Sodium 2,2 dichloropropionate (dalapon, sodium salt) was first made available by the Dow Chemical Company for industrial weed control; it later showed considerable promise for certain selective agricultural uses (9). Both TCA and dalapon are somewhat selectively toxic to annual and perennial grasses in much the same way that 2,4-D is to broad-leaved species. Several such uses for each compound, in various food or feed crops, are listed in the current USDA Summary of Registered Agricultural Pesticide Chemical Uses (10).

Sodium 2,3-dichloroisobutyrate has received considerable research attention since the late 1950s as a male gametocide in cotton, tomatoes, and several other crops (11,12).

A. Physical and Chemical Properties

Replacement of hydrogen with a halogen in the aliphatic acids yields derivatives which ionize to a greater extent if unsubstituted. The halogens, being strongly electronegative, tend to attract electrons. Thus the inductive effect of the chlorines makes the chlorinated aliphatic compounds stronger acids than the corresponding acetic or propionic acids. The effect of chloro substitution on the pK_a values of several acids is shown in Table 8-1.

The strongly electronegative chlorine atoms in 2,2-dichloropropionate greatly influence other properties of the molecule such as the rotation of the methyl group around the α carbon.

Chloroformic acid, chloroacetic acid, and dichloroacetic acid are all inactive as selective grass-control herbicides. Within the propionic acid and

TABLE 8-1

Effect of Chloro Substitution on Acidity of Acetic and Propionic Acids at
25° (*13,14*)

Acetic acid	pK_a	Propionic acid	pK_a
Acetic	4.76	Propionic	4.88
Monochloroacetic	2.81	2-Chloropropionic	2.80
Dichloroacetic	1.29	3-Chloropropionic	4.10
Trichloroacetic[a]	0.08	2,3-Dichloropropionic[b]	1.71

[a] Refers to a 0.03 *M* solution which is 89.5% ionized (*33*).

[b] pK_a value reprinted by permission from Kearney et al. (*14*); all others reprinted by permission of Reinhold Book Corporation from Fieser and Fieser (*13*).

the butyric acid series, α chlorination results in herbicidal activity, with the 2-chloro compounds being highly active. Chlorination in other positions alone does not result in activity and in combination with α chlorination may weaken the effects of α chlorination (*6*).

Increasing chain length reduces activity, even with α chlorination. The 2,2-dichlorovaleric acid is only weakly active, and the 2,2-dichlorohexanoic acid is inactive. The substitution of other halogens for chlorine generally reduces activity throughout the series (*6*).

Freed (*15*) conducted certain physical and chemical examinations on pure 2,2-dichloropropionic acid and 2,2,3-trichloropropionic acid, as shown in Table 8-2.

TABLE 8-2

Selected Physical Properties of Dalapon and 2,2,3-Trichloropropionic Acid (*15*)

Physical property	2,2-Dichloropropionic acid	2,2,3-Trichloropropionic acid
Melting point	20°	65–66°
Density	1.399	1.491
pH (aqueous)	1.32 (0.099 *N*, 23°)	1.21 (0.10 *N*, 24°)
Ka	2.94×10^{-2}	9.94×10^{-2}
pK_a	1.53	1.00
Ref. index	1.453	1.485
Molar volume	102.20 cc	119.00 cc
Molecular weight	142.98	177.43

Table 8-3 presents another interesting property of chlorinated aliphatic acids investigated by Freed and Montgomery (*16*), the relative molar volume (V_m).

TABLE 8-3

Molar Volumes and Partial Molar Volumes of Several Chlorinated Aliphatic Acids (*16*)

Acid	Molar volume, cc	Partial molar volume, cc
Monochloroacetic	59.8	65.0
Trichloroacetic	101.1	97.5
2,2-Dichloropropionic	102.2	102.2
2,2,3-Trichloropropionic	118.9	131.0

The relationship of structure, including three-dimensional configuration, to biological activity is very complex. Since dalapon is probably in an aqueous phase in most biological systems, the authors suggest that the partial molar volume (or the volume contribution of the constituent at infinite dilution) might be pertinent to activity. They regarded it significant that dalapon, a systemic herbicide, is the only acid showing no appreciable volume change in solution. Actually, the position of dalapon relative to molar volume is not inconsistent with known physical chemical principles. Rather, this property may be considered a logical consequence of its other properties based on strength of acids and hydrogen bonding among different species in solution.

The chlorinated aliphatic acids are water-soluble, anionic compounds that do not possess functional groups generally associated with hydrogen bonding. These facts suggest little or no adsorption of these compounds on soil colloids (*14*). Likewise, one should expect little adsorption or binding in plant tissues, except through metabolic accumulation and/or mechanical trapping.

Some of the most important physical properties of dalapon and TCA are compared in Table 8-4.

Since dichloropropionic acid or trichloroacetic acid can exist in the acid form only at very low pH values, Kearney et al. (*14*) have suggested that the ionic species encountered under most biological conditions will be the anions dichloropropionate or trichloroacetate. They concluded that the appearance of the acid or undissociated form would be extremely rare under most physiological conditions.

TABLE 8-4

Physical Properties of Dalapon and TCA $(14)^a$

	Dalapon	TCA
Empirical formula	$C_3H_3Cl_2NaO_2$	$C_2Cl_3NaO_2$
	$(C_2H_4Cl_2O_2)$	$(C_2HCl_3O_2)$
Specific gravity or density, °C	1.0049^b at 25°C	—
	1.2978^c at 25°C	$(1.6225^d/4)$
Melting point	193–197	Decomposes
		(56.9)
Vapor pressure, mm Hg at °C	—	(760 at 196–197; 1 at 51.0)
pH	5.7^b	5.5–6.0
	6.0^c	(0.5)
Solubility, water	90% at 25°C	Soluble
		(54% at 25°)
Solubility, organic	Methanol, < 0.18 g/100 g; ethanol, 82.7 g/100 g; low solubility in other solvents	Slightly soluble in organic solvents (alcohol)

^{a} Values listed are for the sodium salts; values in parentheses refer to the acids. [Reprinted by permission from (14).]
^{b} 1% solution. ^{c} 50% solution. ^{d} 5% solution.

Investigation of several derivatives of dalapon has failed to reveal any with greater biological activity than the sodium salt (9,17). However, activity has been considerably enhanced by changing the pH or by adding any of several suitable surfactants. The latter alter the physiologically important ionic and polar properties of dalapon solutions (17–23) (see Section 8-3).

Sodium 2,2-dichloropropionate is a white to tan-white, free-flowing powder prepared by neutralizing 2,2-dichloropropionic acid with sodium hydroxide. An anionic wetting agent (a polyglycol of Dow manufacture) is also formulated in the commercial product.

The chemistry of such compounds as TCA and dalapon is deceptively simple. The compounds are easily prepared and the products undergo standard reactions (6). In the laboratory, α-chlorinated acids can undergo dehydrochlorination, yielding (according to reaction conditions) hydroxy acids, amino acids, or cyano acids. These reactions apparently do not take place in plant tissue, however. Freed et al. (26) indicated that dalapon undergoes the typical reactions of salt formation, esterification, and acyl chloride formation.

In aqueous solutions these acids decompose at room temperature (6). TCA breaks down in solution to form chloroform and carbon dioxide. Dry dalapon sodium salt is stable, but aqueous solutions are subject to decomposition, undergoing the probable reaction shown in Eq. (1).

$$
\underset{\text{dalapon}}{\overset{\displaystyle \overset{\text{Cl}}{\underset{\text{Cl}}{\vert\vert}}}{CH_3-\overset{\vert}{\underset{\vert}{C}}-COONa}} + H_2O \longrightarrow \underset{\text{pyruvic acid}}{CH_3-\overset{\displaystyle O}{\overset{\Vert}{C}}-COOH} + NaCl + HCl \qquad (1)
$$

The reaction does not take place readily under acid conditions and proceeds very slowly at temperatures below 20°. The sodium salt of dalapon is almost as hygroscopic as TCA. The two chlorine atoms on the second carbon are of considerable interest. As shown, these can be removed by alkaline hydrolysis to yield pyruvic acid and inorganic chloride.

Another reaction involving the chlorine in dalapon has been demonstrated in vitro (26). This reaction, with sulfhydryl groups of organic compounds, presumably forming thioether linkages, may prove to be of biological importance. Preliminary experiments showed this reaction to proceed at a physiological pH. Reaction of halogen-substituted alkyl acids with sulfhydryl-containing metabolites is not new. For example, monochloroacetic acid and TCA react with glutathione. By comparison, dalapon reacted much more slowly (27). It has been suggested, without further explanation, that this difference in reaction rate with the SH groups may, in part, account for differences in their effects on plants. This particular reaction with the ubiquitous, physiologically active compound glutathione may or may not be important. However, the fact that the SH group is an active functional group in certain enzymes seems relevant. For example, it is by such an alkylation reaction that iodoacetic acid exerts its toxic action (28).

2,2,3-Trichloropropionate is stable in water solutions and also in weakly acidic or weakly basic solutions (29). In very strongly acidic solutions, propionic acid is formed. Loss of chlorine also occurs by prolonged exposure to strong alkaline media (pH 9 or higher).

8-2. DEGRADATION

A. Degradation in Plants

Higher plants do not readily attack or metabolize dalapon (30–34) or TCA (35,36). Barrons and Hummer (37) and Tibbetts and Holm (38) demonstrated the presence of TCA in plants grown in TCA-treated soils. The colorimetric method used by Tibbetts and Holm (38), however, did not distinguish between TCA and its possible degradation products. Blanchard (35) treated pea and corn plants with ^{14}C-labeled TCA, extracted the sap, and found only a single radioactive spot which cochromatographed with labeled TCA. No physiological variables were introduced. The presence of trichloromethyl compounds, in addition to TCA, in treated tomato and tobacco plants has been reported (36). Only intact TCA could be detected in flax, black radish, maize, barley, and dandelion plants from soil applications of the herbicide. Thus the virtual lack of metabolic alteration of TCA in plants is based on just three reports. Conclusive as these reports may appear, it would seem that more complete study is needed on the metabolic fate of TCA in plants.

Dalapon is absorbed, translocated, and accumulated in plants largely as the original chemical (18,31–34,39–42). The most intensive series of studies on dalapon metabolism in plants employed autoradiography, extraction and fractionation, counting, and paper chromatographic techniques to analyze for the herbicide and its possible metabolic products.

Absorption of dalapon by roots or leaves of cotton resulted in extensive distribution throughout the plant (32,33,40), and accumulation was greatest in regions of high metabolic activity (32–34, 41). Similar accumulations have been noted for sugar beets (30,39), barley (40), corn (18), sorghum, and wheat (33,41).

Foy (32,33,41) in studies on cotton (a tolerant species), sorghum (a susceptible species), and wheat found that dalapon was absorbed, translocated, redistributed, and accumulated in higher plants, principally as the intact molecule or its dissociable salt. It remained essentially nonmetabolized for long periods, especially in dormant or quiescent tissues. The metabolic stability and persistence of dalapon is emphasized by the fact that it accumulated in the seeds of cotton and wheat and was transmitted from one generation to the next (33,41,43). Indeed, dalapon stimulus was traced to the third generation in wheat; it was carried over in the seeds after exposure of first-generation seedlings to preplant applications of dalapon at the rate of 4 lb/acre in the field (Fig. 8-1).

In an intensive study of dalapon metabolism in cotton, Foy (33) incubated tissue homogenates with dalapon–2-^{14}C and dalapon–[36]Cl for short periods; no metabolic changes were detected by extraction, fractionation, and chromatography. Moreover, 7 days after foliar application to intact cotton and sorghum, dalapon, and no other prominent radioactive species, was recoverable with water or ethanol from all plant parts (Fig. 8-2).

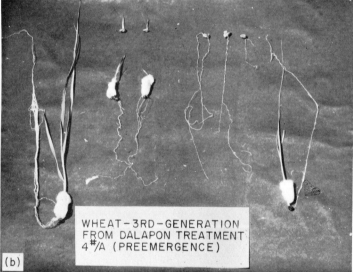

Fig. 8-1. Carry-over effect of characteristic dalapon symptoms in (left) second-generation (a) and (right) third-generation (b) wheat following inhibition of first-generation plants by preplanting application of dalapon at 4 lb/acre. Groups of heads in (a) are arranged left to right in order of occurrence on the same plant. In (b) the seedling at left is normal and others show inhibition or other anomalies. [Reprinted by permission from (*33*).]

Loss of radioactivity has been found to occur from the roots of cotton (*32,34*) and sorghum (*32*). However, the excreted radioactive material was chromatographically indistinguishable from authentic dalapon (*32*). Excretion of dalapon from the roots was increased by creating an unfavorable ionic balance in the nutrient medium.

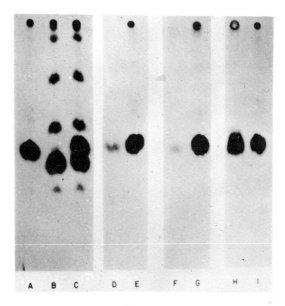

Fig. 8-2. Radioautograms of representative cochromatograms. A, 5 μl of 96% dalapon–2-^{14}C stock solution; B, 5 μl of impure 2,2,3-trichloropropionate-2-^{14}C (TCP); C, dalapon plus TCP, 5μl of each; D, aqueous extract from roots of dalapon-treated cotton plants; E, extract in D plus dalapon; F, aqueous drop (from ether extract) of nutrient solution in which dalapon-treated cotton was grown; G, extract in F plus dalapon; H, aqueous extract from dalapon-treated leaves of sorghum; I, extract in H plus dalapon. [Reprinted by permission from (*33*).]

In long-term studies, however, a small amount of nonextractable radioactivity appeared in both cotton and sorghum. In one phase of the cotton study (*33*), for example, dried ground fruits of various ages were extracted and fractionated according to the scheme shown in Fig. 8-3. Nine to 10 weeks after treatment with dalapon–2-^{14}C (through severed petioles), approximately 85 to 90% of the radioactivity was recoverable as dalapon. The remainder was associated with the ether-soluble portion, the neutral and cationic fractions of the ethanol extract, and the insoluble plant residue.

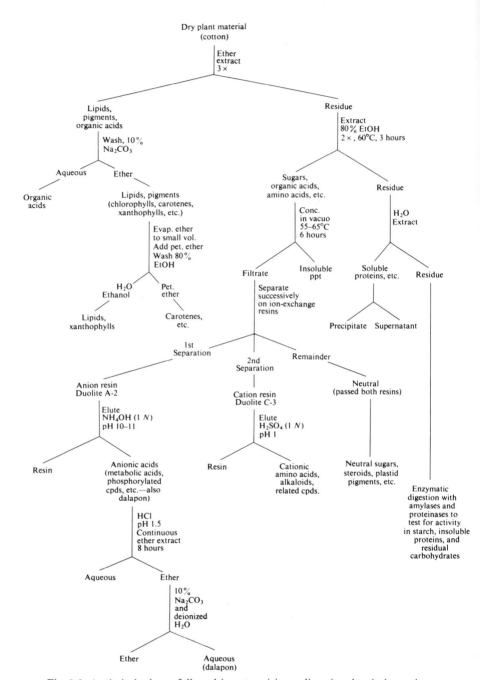

Fig. 8-3. Analytical scheme followed in categorizing radioactive chemical constituents from fruits and leaves of cotton 10 weeks after treatment with 96% Na-2,2-dichloro-propionate–2-^{14}C. [Reprinted from (33) by permission of the American Society of Plant Physiologists.]

Some dalapon may be slowly degraded and the ^{14}C incorporated metabolically into the plant constituents. The presence of nonextractable radioactive residues in cotton has been interpreted differently by Smith and Dyer (34). They suggested that this was occluded or trapped, but chemically unaltered, dalapon. Quantitatively it accounted for only a very small percentage of the applied chemical.

Very small amounts of radioactivity (possibly ^{36}Cl) were detected in the water of guttation from hydathodes of sorghum 6 to 8 days after treatment (33,41). None was detected in the case of plants treated comparably with dalapon-2-^{14}C. As in the preceding situation, however, the low levels of radioactivity precluded further characterization of the chemical substance(s). The degradation of dalapon in higher plants is very slight. Eventual breakdown, if indeed it does occur, may possibly involve an initial dehalogenation followed by normal or modified propionate oxidation. Giovanelli and Stumpf (44) stated that the oxidation of propionate in animal tissues occurs by a carboxylation pathway through methyl malonate to succinate. The same reaction might perhaps be acceptable for dalapon and 2,2,3-trichloropropionate in plant tissue after dehalogenation.

Most studies with dalapon have been of relatively short duration. Blanchard et al. (31) agreed that dalapon resisted degradation based on their studies with soybean and corn in which no metabolic products were found 4 days after herbicide application to roots or foliage. Care must be exercised in long-term studies, however, to correctly interpret the decline of herbicide content. As Schreiber (45) indicated, what seems to be loss of a chemical may actually be dilution due to growth. Also, in long-term studies, microbial contamination of injured plant tissue and subsequent degradation by microorganisms may sometimes become a factor. McIntyre (46) has suggested that differences in the rate of translocation of dalapon in the light and in the dark could be attributed to the formation of a chemical or physical combination of the herbicide with a photosynthate. However, no direct experimental evidence exists to support this hypothesis.

No detailed degradation studies of other chlorinated aliphatic acids in higher plants were found in the literature.

B. Degradation in Animals

Leasure (6), in a recent review, found certain similarities between the behaviour of dalapon in plant, soil, and animal systems. Dalapon fed to animals was quickly excreted (nonmetabolized) in herbicidal concentrations in the urine. According to Leasure, limited evidence indicated that the relatively small amount of dalapon remaining in the animal system was decomposed along the same general lines as in soil systems.

Dalapon residues reported in milk were much less than 1 % of the amount ingested in the feed in one study (47). In another report, cited by Leasure (6), Redemann and Hamaker found only two labeled compounds in milk from a cow whose feed contained ^{36}Cl-labeled dalapon. These were dalapon and chloride ion, and the latter was present in much larger quantities than was the dalapon. It was postulated that dalapon hydrolyzes to pyruvate, which then breaks down to acetate and carbon dioxide.

C. Degradation in Soils

Some portions of practically all herbicides used, whether soil- or foliar-applied compounds, eventually contact the soil. Herbicides reaching the soil, accidentally or by design, normally become dissipated or removed with time, in one or more of several ways, as follows: (a) volatilization; (b) photodecomposition; (c) soil absorption–inactivation; (d) leaching; (e) chemical breakdown; (f) microbiological degradation; (g) plant uptake, followed by metabolic degradation and/or physical removal at harvest. The ways in which herbicides may encounter the soil and the possible ensuing courses of events are depicted schematically in Fig. 8-4, from Holly (156).

In most critical studies conducted thus far on herbicide disappearance from within soils, degradation by soil microorganisms has proved to be very significant—perhaps indeed the most important factor in many instances. In contrast to their strong persistence in higher plant tissues, the chlorinated aliphatic acid herbicides, in general, are readily subject to soil microbiological decomposition. Virtually no problems from soil residues of these herbicides have been detected after their wide-scale commercial use over a period of more than 10 years.

1. Physical Properties of the Herbicides that Influence Degradation

Little work has been done to determine the effect of molecular structure of aliphatic acids on the ease of decomposition by soil microorganisms. As a rule—but with distinct exceptions—short-chain aliphatic hydrocarbons are not as readily metabolized as those of higher molecular weight, as shown by a number of research workers (49,50,51). Also, unsaturated aliphatics tend to be more readily attacked than the corresponding saturated acids (52).

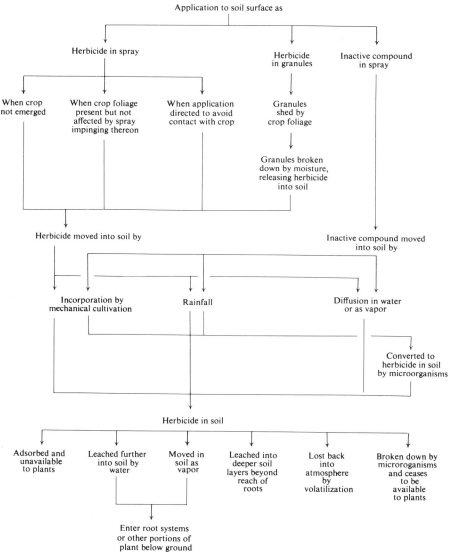

Fig. 8-4. Scheme showing the sequence of events following application of herbicides by acting through the soil. [Reprinted by permission from (*156*), p. 453, courtesy Academic Press, London and New York.]

A few scattered reports describe the relative persistence of the various chlorinated aliphatic acid herbicides in soils, As reviewed by Kearney et al. (*14*), Jensen (*53*) found that the number of chlorine substituents appeared to determine the rate of decomposition. In pure culture studies, he observed that a group of *pseudomonad*-like bacteria readily decomposed both monochloro- and monobromoacetate. The same organisms only moderately decomposed 2-chloropropionate, but had little effect on dalapon or dichloroacetate and no effect on TCA. Another group of bacteria (probably *Agrobacterium*) readily decomposed dalapon and dichloroacetate, but was only partially effective on 2-chloropropionate, and was ineffective on mono- or trichloroacetate. Other genera of soil microorganisms manifested still different specificities.

Hirsch and Alexander (*54*) also investigated the decomposition of propionic and acetic acids having varying numbers of chlorine, bromine, fluorine, and iodine substitutions by a *Pseudomonas* sp. and a *Nocardia* sp. Significant differences existed between isolates in the types of halogen-containing aliphatic acids utilized, as well as the effect of halogen number and position. Both microorganisms grew well on yeast extract in the presence of fluorinated compounds but were unable to degrade these compounds. Although both microorganisms were effective on dalapon and 2-chloro-, 2-bromo-, and 2-iodopropionate, they were more effective on the 2,2-dichloroaliphatic acids than the corresponding 2-chloro-substituted compound. Also, in each case, the organisms were more effective on the α-halogenated propionate than the corresponding acetate. The inability of either strain to dehalogenate 2,3-dibromo- or 2,2,3-trichloropropionate suggests that the β-substituted forms are less susceptible to degradation.

In contrast, Kaufman [(*55*), cited in Ref. (*14*)] observed that eight of nine isolates which effectively degraded dalapon were more effective on 3-chloropropionic than on 2-chloropropionic acid. Two of these organisms were also more effective on 2,3-dichloroisobutyric than on 2,2-dichlorobutyric acid. The ninth isolate was about equally effective on 2-chloropropionic acid and dalapon, but it was less effective on 3-chloropropionic acid than on 2-chloropropionic acid. This same isolate was apparently effective in varying degrees on 10 chlorinated acetates, propionates, and butyrates examined. The effectiveness of all microorganisms decreased with each increase in the number of chlorine substituents. Kaufman observed (*56*) that the chlorinated propionates were decomposed more rapidly than the chlorinated acetates. One isolate, however, was more effective on the chlorinated butyrates than on either the propionates or acetates.

Kaufman (*56*), in using a soil-enrichment technique, found that the rate of microbial decompositon of halogenated acetic and propionic acids decreased as the number of halogens on the molecule increased. Microbial decomposition of the β-substituted aliphatic acids occurred more slowly than the corresponding α-substituted compounds. Halogenated propionic acids were decomposed more rapidly than the corresponding acetic and butyric acids.

2. Degradation of the Herbicides in the Soil by Microorganisms

General soil studies indicate that both dalapon and TCA are subject to microbial decomposition, but that TCA is degraded more slowly than dalapon. Loustalot and Ferrer (57) reported that the disappearance of TCA from soil was favored by warm, moist conditions. Ogle and Warren (58) also found that breakdown of TCA in soils was most rapid under conditions conducive to high microbiological activity. TCA breakdown was low in sandy soils. Similar results have been obtained with dalapon (59,60). Thiegs (59) also found that dalapon degradation in soils was most rapid under warm, moist conditions. He further reported that subsequent additions of dalapon to soil were decomposed more rapidly than the initial application. Holstun and Loomis (60) found that the decomposition of dalapon is primarily a function of an undetermined fraction of the soil microorganisms. Sterilization of the soil essentially stopped all degradation, which began again after recontamination of the soil.

In other studies, using both dalapon-1-^{14}C and dalapon-2-^{14}C, Thiegs (61) reported the recovery of $^{14}CO_2$ in both instances and concluded that the decomposition of dalapon in soil was complete to CO_2. The degradation of 2,2-dichlorobutyric acid in soil apparently follows the same pattern as dalapon and TCA, but proceeds much more slowly (6).

The final proof of the dominating role of bacteria or other microorganisms in detoxification processes in the soil is the isolation of the responsible organism, its growth in pure culture using the herbicide as a source of carbon or nitrogen, and the demonstration that it can inactivate the herbicide. Most bacterial genera seem to confine their attack to one specific group of herbicides, but some seem to be capable of decomposing chemical compounds of widely divergent structures. The genera *Nocardia* and *Arthrobacter*, for example, attack both the phenoxy and the chlorinated aliphatic herbicides.

Hirsh and Alexander (54) isolated and characterized strains of *Pseudomonas* and five strains of *Nocardia* which decomposed dalapon, liberating 90 to 100% of the halogen within 3 weeks. Other workers have reported additional species of bacteria, fungi, and actinomycetes which have decomposed chlorinated aliphatic acids. For example, Magee and Colmer (62) reported *Agrobacterium*, Thiegs (61) reported *Flavobacterium*, and Jensen (53,63) added *Penicillium, Trichoderma, Clonostachys*, and *Arthrobacter*.

Numerous authors (*53,54,61,63,64–69*) have reported that soil micro-organisms can utilize chlorinated aliphatic acids as a source of energy. The current literature records a wide variety of microorganisms that have been isolated and proved effective in degrading various chlorinated alphatic acid compounds (Table 8-5). Nearly all these organisms have been isolated by means of an "enrichment technique." This technique, in its several forms, consists mainly of exposing several grams of soil to an aqueous solution of the herbicide in question. The solution is then periodically analyzed for breakdown products of the herbicide. A soil-perfusion technique similar to the one described by Lees and Quastel (*70*) has proved to be useful as an enrichment technique for studying pesticide degradation processes (*14*). Newman and Downing (*71*) stated that it appears that the disappearance of TCA and dalapon results from removal by leaching and microbial decomposition. The relative importance of these two means depends on soil and environment.

Kaufman (*78*) found that the microbial degradation of dalapon was inhibited in the presence of amitrole. Phytotoxic residues of the herbicides persisted longer in the soils when the herbicides were applied in combination than when each was used individually.

Dehalogenation of TCA by soil microorganisms has been reported by several investigators (*53,54,65,69,79*). Most of the isolated microorganisms grow feebly on TCA as a sole source of carbon. Jensen (*69*) reported that TCA and its theoretical dehalogenation product, oxalate, could serve as a carbon source for two species of *Arthrobacter*.

3. Degradation of the Herbicides in Culture Solution by Microorganisms

A range of halogenated fatty acids can be metabolized by a number of soil microorganisms in culture (*33,54,65*). The attack of microorganisms on the herbicide has been followed by measuring the release of ionic chlorine into the culture medium.

Foy (*33,41*) found that pure dalapon-^{36}Cl in aqueous stock solution was metabolized over a period of several months in the refrigerator by some species of microorganism(s), possibly *Alternaria* sp., which produced five new ^{36}Cl-labeled substances (Fig. 8-5). Two of the substances were tentatively identified as inorganic ^{36}Cl and monochloropropionate-^{36}Cl. No attempt was made to identify the other three labeled compounds. Although serendipitous, this early (1957) observation offered positive proof that a microorganism was capable of using dalapon as sole substrate to synthesize new labeled compounds. He postulated that similar conversions probably occur in soils, accounting for the disappearance of dalapon toxicity under favorable conditions.

In Jensen's work (65) three species showed quite different behavior in relation to the chloroacetic and propionic acids fed to them. Thus a *Pseudomonas* species most vigorously attacked mono- and dichloroacetic acids. An *Arthrobacter* sp. was most active on dichloroacetic acid and dalapon. The experiments of Hirsch and Alexander (54) were rather more ambitious

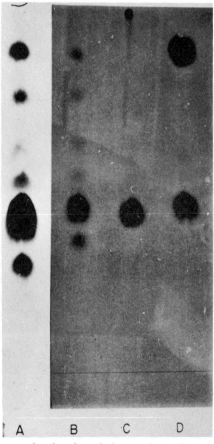

A   B   C   D

Fig. 8-5. Radioautograms showing degradation products after decomposition of pure dalapon–^{36}Cl by some species of microorganism, possible *Alternaria* sp. Point of drop application on the chromatogram is at extreme top edge. (A) 10-μl drop, after contamination; (B) 5-μl drop, after contamination; (C) pure dalapon; (D) impure dalapon, the remainder of the activity being represented as inorganic chloride (Li^{36}Cl). [Reprinted by permission from (153).]

TABLE 8-5

References to Soil Microorganisms which Decompose Chlorinated Aliphatic Acids (14)[a]

Organism	Monochloroacetic acid	Dichloroacetic acid	Trichloroacetic acid (TCA)	2-Chloropropionic acid	3-Chloropropionic acid	2,2-Dichloropropionic acid (dalapon)	2,2,3-Trichloropropionic acid	2,2-Dichlorobutyric acid	2,2-Dichloroisobutyric acid	2,3,3-Trichloroisobutyric acid
Bacteria										
Agrobacterium sp.	—	55,63,67	—	55	55	55,63,67 62,72	—	55	55	55
Pseudomonas sp.	—	54,55	55	54,55	54,55	54,72,73 62,74	55	55	55	55
Arthrobacter sp.	55	55	55,67,75	55	55	53,55,66	55	55	55	55
Micrococcus sp.	—	—	—	—	—	74	—	—	—	—
Alcaligenes sp.	55	—	—	55	55	55,66	—	55	55	55
Bacillus sp.	—	55	—	55	55	55,66	—	55	55	55
Pseudomonas dehalogens	—	—	68,76	—	—	68,76	—	—	—	—
Flavobacterium sp.	—	—	—	—	—	61	—	—	—	—

Fungi									
Trichoderma viride	63,67,77	63,67,75	63,67	77	—	66	—		
Clonostachys sp.	63,77	77	77	77	—	54,66	—		
Penicillium sp.	—	—		—	—	54,66	—		
Aspergillus sp.	77	77		77	—	54	—		
Acrostalagmus sp.	—	—			—		—		
Penicillium lilacinum	—	—			—	66	—		
Penicillium rouqueforti	63	—				—	—		
Actinomycetes									
Nocardia sp.	54,55	54	54,55	54,55	—	54,55,66		55	
Streptomyces sp.						54,66		55	55	55

[a] Reproduced by permission of John Wiley & Sons, Inc.

TABLE 8-6

Dehalogenase Induction in *Pseudomonas dehalogenans* (65)

P. dehalogenans group	Inducing molecule	Simultaneous adaptation to:			
		Monochloroacetic	Dichloroacetic	Trichloroacetic (TCA)	2,2-Dichloropropionic (dalapon)
I–II	Monochloroacetic	+	+	−	−
III	Monochloroacetic	+	+	−	+
III	Dichloroacetic	+	+	−	+
III	Trichloroacetic	+	+	+	+
III	2-Monochloropropionic	+	+		+
III	2,2-Dichloropropionic	+	+	+	+

in that they employed a greater range of substrates, some labeled with ^{14}C to follow independently the release of chlorine and the utilization of carbon. Species of *Pseudomonas* and *Nocardia* were shown to utilize 2-monosubstituted propionic acids with great ease, irrespective of the halogen. The metabolism of the corresponding β-substituted acids was found to be much more difficult. The authors also found a difference in behavior of the two organisms in relation to Cl, Br, and I. On the strength of this, they suggested that the responsible enzyme could not be a nonspecific dehalogenase which removes a halogen from a utilizable substrate. Both organisms decomposed dalapon with the utmost vigor but had no effect at all on 2,2,3-trichloropropionate. Behavior with the acetic acids was equally complex. Two features of particular importance were that TCA was attacked by *Pseudomonas* but not by *Nocardia*, whereas the opposite behavior was shown with iodoacetic acid.

Jensen (*65*) found dehalogenase induction in a *Pseudomonas* sp. (Table 8-6), which he explained by assuming that the bacteria can form two different chloride-liberating enzymes, one of which is induced by monochloroacetic acid and is active toward that compound only, while the other is induced by dichloroacetic acid and can dechlorinate several compounds.

4. Mechanism through which Microbes Develop the Ability to Degrade the Herbicides

The mechanism through which a soil microbial population develops the capacity to degrade a pesticide is not completely understood. Audus (*48*) has suggested two major possibilities that would involve either (1) chance mutation or (2) adaptive enzymes. According to Audus (*48*), the first theory is supported by the random manner in which a wide variety of microbial genera decompose certain herbicides. However, the tendency of several samples of a single soil to develop similar effective populations of microorganisms repeatedly, when independently enriched, conflicts with this theory.

The second theory which proposes the induction of adaptive enzymes in certain responsive microbial genera is in agreement with the views of induced microbial changes presented by Cohn and Monod (*80*). This theory has been criticized, however, by Walker and Newman (*81*) on the basis that effective populations would not persist in soils after complete detoxication and that subsequent herbicide additions would also require a lag phase. Conversely, as discussed by Kearney et al. (*14*), mutants would retain their effective characteristics in the absence of the herbicide substrate.

The finding that pure cultures quickly lose their ability to utilize certain herbicides when supplied with a less complex substrate like glucose (54) lends support to the induction or adaptive enzyme theory. The results of investigations conducted more recently (65,82) with pure cultures of microorganisms lend support to the adaptation theory.

Although the mechanism by which an organism becomes effective is unknown, proliferation is an important feature of this phenomenon, as pointed out by Kearney et al. (14). Dramatic demonstration of the importance of proliferation was shown by Leasure (6), who treated potted soil with dalapon at 50 lb/acre at weekly intervals for a period of 6 weeks. After 6 weeks, the pots were seeded to Japanese millet, wild oats, radishes, and cranberry beans, and immediately treated again with a preemergence application of dalapon at 50 lb/acre. All seedlings grew normally in pots which had received a total of 350 lb of dalapon per acre within a period of less than 7 weeks. Drastic effects of the herbicide were noted on all four species planted in pots treated with dalapon for the first time.

5. Effects of Herbicides on Soil Microorganisms

The literature contains many conflicting viewpoints of the effects of herbicides on soil microorganisms. Both stimulatory and inhibitory effects on soil microorganisms in response to applications of TCA or dalapon to soils have been observed. In a few instances initial reductions in growth have been followed by increases in activity. Increases may be due either to adaptation and proliferation of "effective" microorganisms or to proliferation of organisms resistant to the effects of the herbicide. Herbicide concentrations found to be inhibitory in the laboratory do not necessarily occur in the soil under ordinary field conditions. Herbicides are effective to the extent to which they are dissolved in soil water (83). As pointed out by Kearney et al. (14), application rates must be distinguished from concentrations which may result in small areas in the soil. They cite the following example: An application rate of 10 lb/acre is equivalent to 5 ppm, assuming even distribution in 2 million lb of soil (6-in, plow depth). If complete solubilization and no adsorption occurs, the concentration in the soil solution is 25 ppm in a soil with 20% water at field capacity. Since field soils are seldom maintained at field capacity, these concentrations are often even greater. Although some microorganisms may be inhibited in areas of relatively high concentrations, adjacent areas in the soil may be essentially free of herbicides and therefore represent a source of repopulation.

Nitrifying organisms are among the most sensitive microorganisms to herbicides (*14*). Otten et al. (*84*) observed that nitrification in soil was inhibited by both TCA and dalapon. Douros (*85*) also observed an inhibition of nitrification by dalapon, but according to Worsham and Giddens (*86*) depression was only temporary. Mayeux and Colmer (*87*) observed that dalapon had little effect on nitrite oxidation. Since these compounds tend to persist in most soils from a couple of days to months, it seems likely that the nitrifying organisms may slowly acquire a tolerance to them.

Azotobacter bacteria appeared to be resistant to both dalapon and TCA (*71,83,88–90*). *Azotobacter* is very resistant to the chlorinated aliphatic herbicides, concentrations of 1000–20,000 ppm being required to produce substantial inhibitions of growth and respiration in the three species tested by Colmer (*90*) and Magee and Colmer (*91*). The species showed markedly different sensitivities to TCA, which decreased in the order of *A. chroococcum*, *A. agile*, and *A. vinelandii*. Resistance to dalapon is of the same order as that to TCA, but all three species seem equally sensitive (*91*). There is little or no threat to nitrogen fixation by *Azotobacter* by this group of weed killers when used at normal rates (*71*).

Little is known about the effect of TCA or dalapon on symbiotic nitrogen-fixing bacteria, although Worsham and Giddens (*86*) have reported that dalapon had no effect on soybean nodulation at application rates up to 68 lb/acre.

Several investigations have been conducted to determine the effects of halogenated aliphatic acids on soil microbial populations in general. Kratochvil (*92*) observed that TCA significantly reduced the soil microbial activity of treated soils. In contrast, Hoover and Colmer (*93*) found that rates of TCA higher than normally used in field application had no deleterious effect upon bacteria, actinomycetes, and fungi in sugarcane fields. The methods used to investigate this action by the different investigators may account for the different results.

Magee (*94*) observed that dalapon stimulated the multiplication of soil bacteria, actinomycetes, and fungi. Worsham and Giddens (*86*) also observed an increase in numbers of actinomycetes and bacteria present in treated soil. Elkan et al. (*95,96*) observed that sodium propionate greatly increased both respiration and total numbers of fungi. Hale et al. (*97*) found that low concentrations (50 to 150 ppm) of dalapon increased oxygen uptake by soil microorganisms, whereas higher concentrations (600 ppm) slightly inhibited oxygen uptake.

Dalapon and TCA also have an effect on certain plant diseases, as observed by Richardson (*98,99*); however, neither compound had an appreciable effect on the causative organism under pure culture conditions. Most other references in the literature concerning the effects of chlorinated aliphatic acids on soil microorganisms are negative.

6. Influence of Certain Physical Soil Constants on Degradation

It is well known that clays, and specifically montmorillonite clays, adsorb organic complexes on their surfaces. The clay hindrance of degradation may result from adsorption not only of the substrate but also of the enzyme. The latter type of adsorption is likely of prime or sole importance to the activity of extracellular enzymes. The degree of substrate binding varies with the nature of the compound, its molecular weight, the pH of the system, and the individual clay mineral. The vast potential for binding is suggested by the enormous surface exposed by clays.

TABLE 8-7

Soil Properties and Adsorption Percentages for Dalapon (14)[a]

Soil type	pH	% Clay	% Organic matter	C.E.C., me/100 g	% Adsorption dalapon
Barnes clay loam	7.4	34.4	6.90	33.8	0
Hagerstown silty clay loam	5.5	30.0	4.31	12.5	2
Sharkey clay	6.2	67.1	3.90	40.2	0
Celeryville muck	5.0	—	—	142.0	20

[a] Reproduced by permission of John Wiley & Sons, Inc.

The chemical structure of chlorinated aliphatic acids suggest little or no adsorption of these compounds on the soil colloid. This has been demonstrated experimentally (100,101) and is illustrated in Table 8-7.

Dalapon exhibited a high degree of mobility in several soil types studied by Holstun and Loomis (60). Warren (102) reported that a group of 17 herbicides, dalapon and TCA were the most mobile. Kearney et al. (14) presented further evidence that the physical interactions between soil particles and dalapon are relatively unimportant. They concluded that the high initial concentration of TCA and dalapon in the soil and the short period of action reduce the significance of leachability as an important factor which might produce inconsistent performance as a herbicide.

At low rates of application, phytotoxic residues of dalapon disappeared from several soils within 2 to 4 weeks (102–104); at high rates of application, dalapon persisted for several months (103). Residual activity of TCA usually persisted longer in soils than that of dalapon (*102,105*), but conflicting data have been reported in at least one case (*103*).

In their studies Day et al. (*106*) concluded that "the capacity of the soil to decompose dalapon was essentially random with respect to soil series, texture, C.E.C., total organic matter, and geographical source." Other researchers (*53,59,66,103,104*) have also reported differences among soils.

In 1955 Thiegs (*59*) demonstrated that temperature and moisture were factors affecting the rate of breakdown of sodium dichloropropionate in soil. Dalapon was decomposed most rapidly in warm, moist soil but was relatively stable in moist soil at 40°F and dry soil at 100°F. Thiegs found that fresh additions of dalapon to soil were decomposed more rapidly than the initial application. He also reported that the addition of organic matter increased the rate of disappearance of dalapon and that dalapon did not disappear from sterilized soil.

Holstun and Loomis (*60*) stated that dalapon decomposition was adversely affected by low soil moisture, low pH, temperatures below 20–25°, and large additions of organic matter, and they therefore concluded that it was a function of microbiological activity. Jensen (*64*) observed that dalapon was decomposed only feebly at pH levels below 5. Kaufman (*66*) found with five soils in greenhouse and laboratory studies that dalapon degradation by effective microorganisms was affected by organic matter level, pH, cation-exchange capacity, and aeration.

Phytotoxic residues of TCA usually disappear from soil within 30 to 90 days. However, TCA may persist longer, especially at high rates of application (*57,107*). As we have seen, this herbicide is readily moved downward with water (*58,102*); the absence of leaching, especially in greenhouse and laboratory experiments, may account at least in part for the extended phytotoxicity.

Under the conditions imposed by Ogle and Warren (*58*), the residual activity of TCA was greatest in a fine sandy soil and least in a muck. Similarly, Crafts and Drever (*103*), in a greenhouse experiment, and Barrons and Hummer (*108*) reported more inactivation of TCA in soils high in organic matter than in low organic matter soils. Rai and Hammer (*107*), on the other hand, found that toxic residues had a greater persistence in the organic soil than in the sandy soil. They suggested greater retention by the clay in soil levels where seeds germinate. They, however, had worked with metal cans where leaching was restricted. This may account, in part, for the results. The rate of disappearance of TCA varied with temperature (*57,58,105*) and was usually higher with higher temperatures, the optimum being at about 45°.

General soil persistence of chlorinated aliphatic acids other than TCA and dalapon has not been thoroughly investigated. In tests conducted at two locations in Tennessee, initial and residual activities of sodium 2,2,3-trichloropropionate in soil were approximately equal to those of dalapon (*104*).

One additional herbicide, erbon (the 2,4,5-trichlorophenoxyethyl ester of dalapon) deserves mention. This potent nonselective soil sterilant may persist in soils for several months to 1 year or more, depending upon dosage and environmental conditions. The residual activity of erbon is probably due to a slow hydrolysis which yields dalapon and 2,4,5-trichlorophenoxyethanol. The chlorophenoxy alcohols are known to be oxidized to their corresponding acids (*72,75*), thus, 2,4,5-trichlorophenoxyethanol would be converted to the potent and relatively persistent herbicide 2,4,5-trichlorophenoxyacetate (2,4,5-T).

7. Volatilization of the Herbicides

The volatility of the chlorinated aliphatic acids from soil would depend on the chemical form and the presence and magnitude of physical interactions between the molecules and soil particles (*14*). Since there is little interaction with soil particles, as previously noted, volatility at any given temperature is then, primarily, a function of the chemical form of the molecule and air movement.

Kutschinski (*109*) reported high dalapon losses at high temperatures when dalapon was applied to the soil as an acid. Day (*110*) and Day et al. (*106*) suggest a rapid enough loss by volatilization to eliminate significant soil residues in their studies with some esters of dalapon. Foy (*111*) found that the dalapon acid volatilized rapidly from an aluminum surface at room temperature, whereas neglible amounts of the sodium salt form disappeared in 64 hours under the same conditions (Fig. 8-6). Significant loss of the sodium salt of dalapon under normal field use conditions appears unlikely.

In general the same relationship between the acid and sodium salt forms would be expected to exist for the other chlorinated aliphatic acids as well.

D. Pathways of Degradation in Soil

Abundant evidence exists that soil microorganisms can dehalogenate chlorinated aliphatic acid herbicides, particularly dalapon and TCA, and use the carbon as a sole source of energy (*53,54,65,67–69*). At least eight species of soil bacteria, seven or eight species of fungi, and two species of

actinomycetes have been shown to be effective in degrading certain chlorinated aliphatic acids [(*14*); see also Table 8-5].

The initial reactions associated with fragmentation of the halogenated
aliphatic acids have been ascribed to enzymatic catalysis. Foy's early
observation (*33,41*) of the microbial decomposition of dalapon-^{36}Cl in
vitro could be explained on this basis. The results of Jensen's work (*53*)
suggested that degradation of the chlorinated organic acids occurred by a

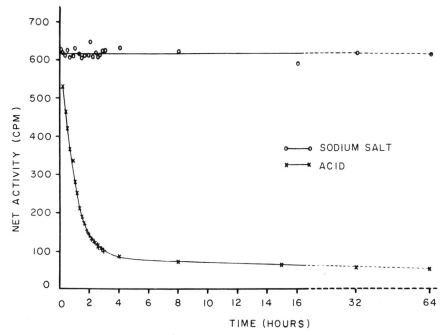

Fig. 8-6. Comparison of volatilization losses of the acid and the sodium salt of dalapon–
^{36}Cl from an inert surface. Counts were taken continuously or at intervals in a laboratory
hood, under a gentle fan, without change in geometry. [Reprinted by permission from
(*111*).]

dechlorination process involving substrate-induced enzyme. These observations were supported by the findings of Magee and Colmer (*62*). Hirsch and
Alexander (*54*) concluded that it was unlikely that the responsible enzyme
was a nonspecific dehalogenase which removed any halogen from meta-
bolizable halogenated fatty acids.

Jensen has made a very extensive study of adaptation phenomena in
various organisms which can degrade the chlorinated aliphatic acids. He
used the accumulation of ionic chlorine as a measure of the progress of

degradation. Although Jensen has not done any experimental studies to determine the fate of the intermediates produced, he suggested (53) that the first step probably is a hydroclastic removal of the chlorine atom and the substitution of a hydroxyl group, as shown in Eq. (2):

$$R\underset{\underset{Cl}{|}}{-COO^-} + H_2O \longrightarrow R\underset{\underset{OH}{|}}{-COO^-} + H^+ + Cl^- \qquad (2)$$

The products resulting from this general scheme of metabolism would then be the corresponding hydroxy or keto acids [Eq. (3) through (7)].

$$CH_2ClCOOH + H_2O \rightarrow CH_2OHCOOH + H^+ + Cl^- \qquad (3)$$

$$CHCl_2COOH + H_2O \rightarrow CHOCOOH + 2H^+ + 2Cl^- \qquad (4)$$

$$CCl_3COOH + 2H_2O \rightarrow (COOH)_2 + 3H^+ + 3Cl^- \qquad (5)$$

$$CH_3CHClCOOH + H_2O \rightarrow CH_3CHOHCOOH + H^+ + Cl^- \qquad (6)$$

$$CH_3CCl_2COOH + H_2O \rightarrow CH_3COCOOH + 2H^+ + 2Cl^- \qquad (7)$$

The products resulting from hydrolysis are all common metabolites found in many microbiological systems. The authenticity of many of these reactions in biological systems has yet to be established.

Hirsch and Alexander (54) reported a unique case of utilization of dalapon without halide liberation. A *Streptomycete* sp., isolated from soil, decomposed 11.6% of the dalapon without significant accumulation of ionic chloride. The most plausible explanation offered for this phenomenon was that the organically bound chlorine was never cleaved from the molecule, but remained in solution while a portion of the carbon chain served as a carbon source. An alternative suggestion was that the chlorine was released in a volatile organic form from solutions.

The metabolism of dalapon–^{14}C has been studied in an organic soil, in mixed bacterial populations (*Arthrobacter* sp.) from the organic soil, and in pure cultures (112). A comparison of dalapon–1-^{14}C and dalapon–2-^{14}C metabolism in the above system showed a rapid evolution of $^{14}CO_2$ from the carboxyl-labeled dalapon, whereas the labeled carbon from the 2 position of dalapon was found primarily in the lipid, nucleic acid, protein, and cold TCA-soluble fractions of the organisms. A study of the soluble labeled products extracted from microorganisms incubated with ^{14}C–dalapon showed activity in the amino acids alanine and glutamic acid (14). These observations would be consistent with a pathway involving pyruvate as one of the early products in the metabolic degradation of dalapon. Early labeled metabolic degradation products of dalapon–2-^{14}C in the presence of pure cultures of *Arthrobacter* sp. grown under aerobic conditions were pyruvate and alanine (112).

Recently Kearney et al. (*82*) reported the isolation and partial purification of an enzyme from an *Arthrobacter* sp. that removed the organically bound chlorine from dalapon. The enzyme had an optimum pH of 8.0, was rapidly inactivated at high temperatures, and was fairly specific for dalapon. The partially purified enzyme showed no metal-ion requirement and was not enhanced by reducing conditions. It is difficult, however, to determine a requirement for reducing conditions since many of these reagents have copious quantities of halide ion. The product resulting from enzymatic dehalogenation of dalapon was pyruvate. Several mechanisms can be proposed for such a transformation. The immediate precursor of pyruvate in this system is probably 2-chloro-2-hydroxypropionate (*113*). Kearney (*113*) suggested that one reaction system by which the enzyme could form 2-chloro-2-hydroxypropionate from dalapon would involve a direct substitution reaction:

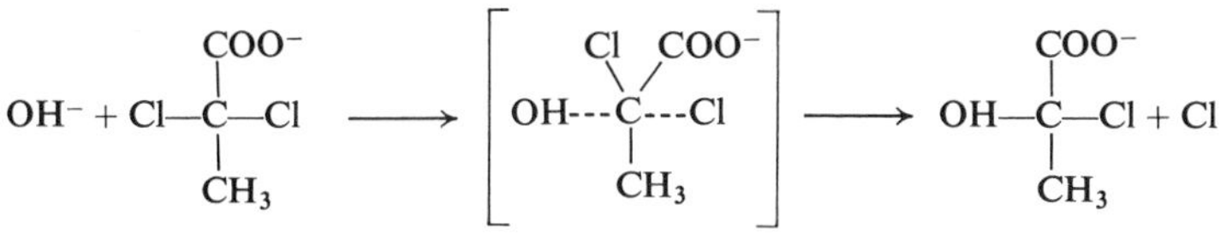

$$OH^- + Cl\text{—}\underset{\underset{CH_3}{|}}{\overset{\overset{COO^-}{|}}{C}}\text{—}Cl \longrightarrow \left[OH\text{---}\underset{\underset{CH_3}{|}}{\overset{\overset{Cl\quad COO^-}{\diagdown\diagup}}{C}}\text{---}Cl \right] \longrightarrow OH\text{—}\underset{\underset{CH_3}{|}}{\overset{\overset{COO^-}{|}}{C}}\text{—}Cl + Cl \quad (8)$$

In this case there would be a direct nucleophilic attack on carbon-2, led by a hydroxyl group to form the desired product. A second reaction would involve β elimination (*113*), i.e., some basic group on the enzyme surface could abstract a proton from the β carbon of dalapon to form 2-chloro-acrylate or the 1-chloropropene:

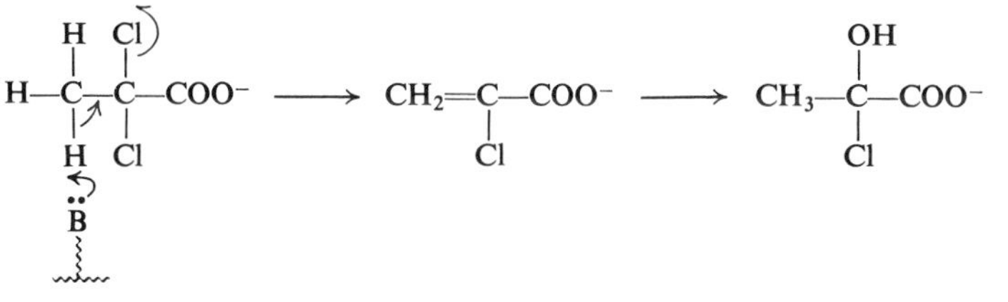

$$H\text{—}\underset{\underset{\underset{\underset{B}{\vdots}}{H}}{\overset{\overset{H}{|}}{C}}}{}\text{—}\underset{\underset{Cl}{|}}{\overset{\overset{Cl}{|}}{C}}\text{—}COO^- \longrightarrow CH_2{=}\underset{\underset{Cl}{|}}{C}\text{—}COO^- \longrightarrow CH_3\text{—}\underset{\underset{Cl}{|}}{\overset{\overset{OH}{|}}{C}}\text{—}COO^- \quad (9)$$

Energetically, reaction (9) would be far simpler for the enzyme to carry out.

Smith [cited in Ref. (*14*)] prepared this 2-chloro-2-hydroxypropionate compound and found that it rapidly went to pyruvate. This reaction is probably chemical. As seen above, two mechanisms—one involving direct substitution and the other β elimination—have been proposed for the enzymatic formation of the 2-chloro-2-hydroxypropionate. Evidence thus far collected for the metabolism of dalapon by the *Arthrobacter* sp., used in the studies of Beall et al. (*112*) and Kearney and co-workers (*82,114*), suggested the sequence of reactions shown in Fig. 8-7.

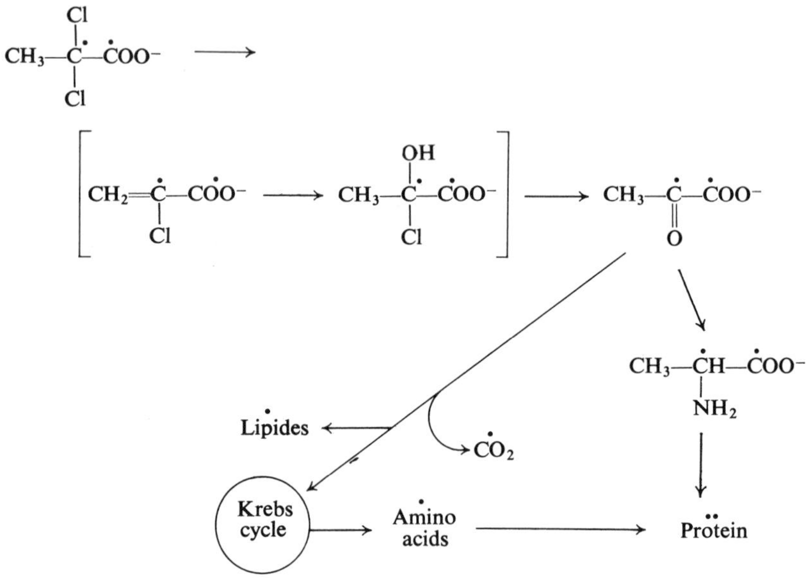

Fig. 8-7. Proposed pathway of metabolism of dalapon by an *Arthrobacter* sp. isolated from soils. (The dots designate the location of ^{14}C in dalapon. The brackets enclose hypothetical intermediates involved in the enzymatic conversion of dalapon to pyruvate.) [Reprinted by permission from (*14*), p. 26, courtesy of John Wiley & Sons, Inc.]

In preliminary studies using cell-free extracts, Kearney et al. (*14*) found that chloride liberation from TCA was slower than the enzymatic dehalogenation of dalapon. The substrate specificity of their crude system was very broad, attacking both mono- and dichlorinated acetates and propionates. Another enzyme isolated by research workers at Cornell University, however, is apparently more specific in that it will hydrolyze 3-chloropropionate but not 2,2-dichloropropionate (*115*).

Thiegs (*61*), using both 1–^{14}C dalapon and 2–^{14}C dalapon, reported the recovery of labeled CO_2 in both experiments and concluded that the decomposition of dalapon in soil was complete to CO_2.

Metabolic studies with an unidentified soil microorganism incubated with TCA–1-^{14}C and TCA–2-^{14}C indicate rapid evolution of $^{14}CO_2$ from both forms of labeled TCA (*116*). Coinciding with $^{14}CO_2$ evolution is the release of Cl⁻ into the solution. Although growth is limited on TCA alone, radio-activity from TCA–1-^{14}C and TCA–2-^{14}C was incorporated into all cellular components, namely, transient intermediates, lipids, nucleic acid, and proteins. One of the early products detected in TCA metabolism was the amino acid serine.

The degradation of 2,2-dichlorobutyric acid in soil reportedly follows the same pattern as dalapon and TCA, but proceeds much more slowly.

From the foregoing discussion, it is obvious that microbial degradation is an important factor affecting the persistence of the chlorinated aliphatic acids. Experimental evidence at present is not sufficient to explain, precisely, all the physical chemical and biological mechanisms involved. However, the several major factors which probably affect the biodegradability or decomposition rate of organic chemicals (including the chlorinated aliphatic herbicides) have been well summarized by Alexander (117) as follows:

1. Inaccessibility of the substrate. The compound may be deposited in a microenvironment which precludes microbial approach; it may be adsorbed to clay or other colloidal matter; or it may become entrapped or embedded within a nonmetabolizable or slowly degraded substance that prevents the organism or its enzymes from reaching the substrate.

2. Absence of some factor essential for growth. For example, no activity would occur should water, nitrogen, or a biologically utilizable terminal electron acceptor be unavailable.

3. Toxicity of the environment. This could result from biologically generated organic inhibitors, microbially formed inorganic toxins, high salt concentrations, extremes of temperature, acidity, or some other environmental condition outside of the range suitable for microbial proliferation.

4. Inactivation of the requisite enzymes. Enzymes may lose activity by adsorption to clay minerals or other colloids, as they may be inhibited by their substrates or products.

5. A structural characteristic of the molecule which prevents the enzyme from acting. An example cited by Alexander (117) was terminal quaternary groups, nonalkyl substituents, or extensive branching on an aliphatic moiety which might markedly affect the microbial decomposition of alkyl benzene derivatives, particularly where the degradation must be initiated by α or β oxidation of the alkyl portion of the molecule. Similarly, Alexander points out, substituents that do not permit enzyme approach to the site upon which it acts could delay or prevent decomposition. Some evidence summarized above suggests that the introduction of halogens, methyl, or other substituents imparts resistance to certain herbicidal compounds.

6. Inability of the community of microorganisms to metabolize the compound because of some physiological inadequacy. An enzyme capable of degrading the compound may simply not exist. Alternatively, the substrate may not be able to penetrate into cells which have the appropriate enzymatic composition.

8-3. MODE OF ACTION

Although the effects of higher plants on the chlorinated aliphatic acids are very slight, these compounds exhibit a wide range of effects on plant systems. The precise mechanisms of action of these compounds at the cell level in higher plants are unknown. However, the following discussion should prove useful in promoting further research in this area of plant physiology and biochemistry.

The phytotoxic effects of the chlorinated aliphatic acid herbicides as a group are very similar in some respects: All cause leaf chlorosis and abnormal growth responses typical of growth regulators (118,119). TCA, absorbed by grass roots, causes formative effects which indicate profound physiological disturbances. Dalapon causes similar formative effects through either foliar or root absorption. In addition to these systemic effects, the mono-, di-, and trichloroacetic acids cause a pronounced contact toxicity which is associated with an inability to be translocated from leaves. An acute toxicity of dalapon similar to that of TCA is evident at higher rates and may also be manifested under special circumstances favoring rapid penetration (16,31).

Trichloroacetic acid is widely used as a general protein precipitant. The acid is comparable in strength to many of the mineral acids. Redemann and Hamaker (120) have shown that dalapon is almost as effective as TCA in precipitating egg yolk and egg albumen. Whether this is important in the phytotoxic action of these two compounds is debatable, since the acid or undissociated form is reasoned to be encountered rarely under physiological conditions. It should be noted, however, that halogenated acetates and propionates are theoretically able to alkylate the sulfhydryl or amino groups in enzymes.

Dalapon characteristically exhibits two physiologically distinct types of action—acute toxicity (on occasion) and slower growth inhibition. Presumably the acute toxicity—defined as immediate and localized—is due to its action as an acid and protein precipitant (120,121), which causes drastic permeability changes in the plasma membranes and nonselective, localized destruction of cellular constituents. Wilkinson (122) has suggested that the toxic effects of dalapon at high rates are typical of those of strong acids, disrupting lipoidal membranes. This destruction of the plasma membrane might result equally well, however, from an attack on protein, since the ectoplast is visualized as consisting of two monolayers of lipids surrounded on either side by a monolayer of proteins (123).

Acute toxicity produced by dalapon solutions may be brought about by a high concentration of the herbicide, of a toxic spray additive, or of hydrogen ion, or by other factors such as temperature, relative humidity, stomatal behavior, etc., which may react indirectly with these and thus favor rapid penetration. Toxicity at the point of spray application can reduce or even prevent translocation and subsequent expression of systemic plant-growth-regulating action (17,32). This factor may be much more important in herbicidal efficacy than has been commonly supposed.

Whereas acute toxicity may be considered disadvantageous when trans-location and systemic action are desired, it is conceivable that a slight amount of local injury to plant cells may be advantageous under certain circumstances, by weakening membranes and so increasing permeability.

The more subtle, delayed response to solutions with lower initial concentrations is manifested in the meristematic regions of a plant, following the transport of dalapon with food materials, as discussed by Foy (32). In this case dalapon may accumulate to toxic levels in meristematic cells and act against one or more enzymes or, perhaps, against the membranes of organelles. Dalapon is known to inhibit mitotic activity in meristems (124). To accomplish systemic toxicity, the herbicide must move across cell membranes without destruction of the cellular contents and accumulate to toxic concentrations in remote tissues.

There are as yet no absolute criteria for determining relationships between the chemical and the biological behavior of a compound such as dalapon. However, both ionic and polar properties are significant.

Ions and molecules behave differently in at least three properties— chemical reactivity, adsorption at surfaces, and penetration of membranes— and some of the selectively toxic agents are active only in the nonionized state. The ease with which some acids are absorbed by plants is inversely proportional to their degree of ionization, except at the point where $pH \leq pK$. Dalapon showed this trend in studies with red-beet-root slices, Johnsongrass foliage, corn coleoptiles, and corn foliage (17).

Nondissociated dalapon molecules, in aqueous solution at low pH, penetrated corn leaves more readily than did the anions in alkaline solutions. Systemic herbicidal response was most pronounced at pH 5 to 7, however, because acute toxicity at lower pH's prevented translocation of the herbicide along with the products of photosynthesis.

Acetic and propionic acids, weaker members than their chlorinated analogs in the two series, are usually considered rather nontoxic, but in the nondissociated state either may be highly toxic to plant cells (*125*). Thus their highest activity occurs in oil, an apolar solvent; in aqueous solutions they are active only at low pH.

The distinction between polar and nonpolar (apolar) compounds is often stressed in literature on the action of herbicides. Nonpolar compounds are generally regarded as oil-like, hence more lipophilic; polar compounds as more water-like, or hydrophilic. Daniels (*126*) refers to a relationship between the ionic character of a compound and its relative polarity: Polar compounds exhibit chiefly electrostatic attraction, which results in the formation of heteropolar bonds (ionic linkages). Nonpolar (homopolar or electron-pair) bonds involve an "exchange-energy binding," understandable on the basis of quantum mechanics. However, the two types of bonds are not mutually exclusive, and both are operative in most linkages between atoms. Also, there are gradations between. Therefore, although dalapon may be regarded as relatively ionic, hydrophilic, and polar, it becomes permissible to speak also of its more penetrative, lipophilic tendencies when it is in the nondissociated state.

Chemical manipulation also, such as the addition of a suitable surfactant to a polar, aqueous solution of dalapon, may make it more compatible with plant waxes and possibly even with plasma membranes. Another possible factor is that surfactants (amphipatic molecules) may accumulate or become oriented at the plasma membrane and exert a kind of narcotic action. However, considering the broad array of possible solution additives, there is at present no clear-cut relation between surface activity and dalapon toxicity. Little understood but specific cation-competition effects also apparently exist.

Robbins et al. (*127*) stated: "From consideration of the toxicity of hydrocarbons . . . , it is apparent that increase in polarity enhances the inherent reactivity of a molecule whereas increase in its oil-like properties promotes penetration." As the toxicity of herbicidal solutions and their penetration seem to be opposite processes, those authors concluded that "there must be an optimum point in the balance between them, and this in reality represents a compromise between toxicity resulting from polarity of the molecule and compatibility with the cuticle resulting from oil-like properties." This line of reasoning may be helpful in interpreting the penetrating ability of systemic growth regulators such as dalapon. Surfactants are probably important stabilizers at the solution–plant surface interfaces, in effect achieving a more nearly optimum balance between polar and oil-like properties within the same herbicide molecule.

Both passive and active (metabolic) phases are involved in the uptake of dalapon by roots and fronds of *Lemna minor*, a free-floating aquatic plant (*42*). The metabolic rate of uptake could be partially inhibited by the addition of a structurally similar compound, pyruvic acid, or a range of respiratory inhibitors such as dinitrophenol, sodium azide, sodium arsenite, iodoacetic acid, and phenylmercuric nitrate. The uptake mechanism was most sensitive to inhibitors affecting the sulfhydryl groups, and this inhibition was partially reversed by cysteine and glutathione.

A number of growth responses have been ascribed to the chlorinated aliphatic acid herbicides. However, their exact role and biochemical level remains obscure.

Fawcett et al. (*128*) reported that certain concentrations of various chlorinated aliphatic acids stimulated growth in the wheat cylinder and oat coleoptile bioassays, but that the results were not typical of auxin responses. He suggested that they might be due to changes in membrane permeability. Ingle and Rogers (*129*) showed that although the chlorinated aliphatic acids did cause slight elongation in the wheat cylinder tests, they were inactive in the pea stem test and had little effect on oxygen uptake by mitochondria. They concluded that these compounds do not interfere with the production of metabolic energy but rather with its utilization. Wilkinson (*122*) reasoned that since auxin-type growth stimulation seemed to require both a ring structure and an acidic side chain and the chlorinated aliphatic acids are definitely growth regulators but not auxin-type stimulators, the ring portion of auxin-like compounds may be required for stimulation but not for all growth-regulator responses.

The composition of plant parts can be altered by applications of these acids even though no formative effects or growth suppression are necessarily noted. Corns (*130*) and Miller and Corns (*131*) showed that both TCA and dalapon decreased the moisture content of sugar beet seedlings and increased both sugar and dry-matter content, but had no effect on either water-soluble nitrogen or total nitrogen content.

One striking effect was the increased cold resistance of treated seedlings that can be either a direct effect or an indirect result of the changes in leaf composition. In similar tests, isopropyl *N*-(3-chlorophenyl)carbamate, 2,3,6-trichlorobenzoic acid, and sodium chloride had no effect.

Both TCA and dalapon cause a marked reduction in the amount of surface wax produced on the leaves of various plants (*132,133*), but no mechanism for this response was suggested, other than a general interference with the physiology and biochemistry of the plant. The cuticle is actually a complex mixture of products of cellular metabolism that have migrated to, and outward from, the external surfaces of epidermal cells. Disturbed metabolism in some way interferes with the normal deposition of cuticular components. This phenomenon, in turn, apparently exerts important secondary influences as well. In the case of TCA, for example, Dewey et al. (*134*) showed that *Polygonum aviculare* is much more sensitive to postemergence applications of dinitrophenol herbicides if the soil is pretreated with TCA. Further experiments of Pfeiffer et al. (*135*) revealed an inhibiting action of TCA on the formation of a normal cuticle. Any pretreatment which interferes with or alters the deposition of wax or other cuticular components may drastically affect herbicidal effectiveness and selectivity based on differential wetting. Also, loss or alteration of the cuticle by TCA-treated plants could conceivably lead to a higher rate of transpiration and thereby contribute to an earlier death by wilting. Interestingly, Prasad and Blackman (*136*) observed that when *Salvinia natans* is treated with dalapon, a considerable portion of the floating leaves became submerged in the culture solution. This was attributed, at least in part, to a reduced density of epidermal hairs. Judging from the work of Juniper and Bradley (*133*), the waxy component of the cuticle was also probably altered, affecting wettability.

Foy (*32*) concluded that neither penetrability, translocatability, nor metabolic activation appeared to play a major role in determining species specificities in the phytotoxic action of dalapon against cotton and sorghum. The key to its moderate selectivity still seems unquestionably to reside in the protoplasm, i.e., at the biochemical level.

Most studies on the site of action of 2,2-dichloropropionate and other chlorinated aliphatic acids have been done with microorganisms. Ram and Rustagi (*137*) observed recently, for example, that the inhibition of yeast growth on chloro-substituted isobutyric acid, propionic acid, and acetic acids could be protected by an exogenous supply of β-alanine. The conclusions from such research may or may not apply equally well to common soil microorganisms and may or may not be important in interpreting the mechanism(s) of action in higher plants.

Anderson et al. (*30*), studying yellow foxtail and sugar beets, had suggested that an indirect detoxication reaction could be in operation, accounting for selective toxicity. They observed that dalapon caused the degradation of protein to ammonium compounds, and even all the way to ammonia, in both tolerant and susceptible species. It would seem then that the abnormal protein metabolism accompanied by unusual accumulations of metabolites might be the cause of dalapon's toxicity as well as its selectivity. The capability to detoxify the breakdown products of proteins of certain plants could be the basis of their tolerance (138).

As pointed out by Anderson et al. (30), however, a change in nitrogen metabolism as a biochemical expression of herbicide injury is not unqiue with dalapon. For example, Rebstock et al. (139) found more protein (N × 6.25) and arginine in the shoots of wheat growing in soil treated with TCA than in the control plants. Levels of other amino acids were, in general, decreased by the treatment. The significance of these long-term changes in nitrogen metabolism may be somewhat questionable in relation to determining primary sites of action, however. Numerous workers have shown that under a variety of stress conditions with various organisms, free amino acids have a tendency to accumulate.

Although Hilton et al. (140,141) have shown interference with pantothenic acid metabolism in microorganisms, the same phenomenon could not be demonstrated readily in higher plants. Prasad and Blackman (42) were able to offset the dalapon-induced growth inhibition of Lemna minor only partially with calcium pantothenate and then over a narrow range of concentrations only. β-Alanine was completely ineffective. Their results, therefore, do not support a general view that the primary action of dalapon is to interfere with the biosynthesis of coenzyme A. This is largely in agreement with the findings of Ingle and Rogers (129), who observed that inhibition of cucumber root growth by dalapon could be reversed only to a minor extent with pantothenic acid, 1-pantoic acid, and β-alanine. The latter work (129) also suggests that species factors are involved even in higher plant responses to dalapon. They found partial reversal of dalapon inhibition by these metabolites in cucumber but not in corn.

Hilton et al. (142), in their review of herbicidal action, concluded that in higher plants the protective effect of pantothenate and its precursors against the inhibition of growth by dalapon is small and the antagonisms are not readily apparent.

While there is a general agreement that TCA increases the respiration of a number of plant species (143), dalapon has no effect on the oxygen uptake of maize roots or of soybean mitochondria (144). Foy and Penner (145), using isolated cucumber mitochondria, found O_2 uptake inhibited by TCA and dalapon, but only at high (10^{-2} to 10^{-4} M) concentrations. The only pronounced effect of dalapon found by Ingle and Rogers was that of a 50% reduction in the uptake of the phosphate ion ($^{32}PO_4^{3-}$) into corn seedling roots. On the basis of these results, they suggest that dalapon does not interfere with respiration or the production of metabolic energy, but rather with the utilization of the latter.

An extremely interesting effect of certain chlorinated aliphatic acids is their action as somewhat selective gametocides in certain plants (*11,12*). Scott (*146*), working with cotton, reported that both dalapon and 2,3-dichloroisobutyric acid induced nondehiscent anthers when applied at rates of 100 to 500 μg per plant. Plants thus affected were made sterile and readily produced hybrid cottonseed when cross-fertilized. No other effects of treatment were noted, either on the treated plants or in their hybrid progeny. The application of either pantothenic acid or D-ribose partially reversed the effect of the chlorinated acids.

Susceptibility of plants to dalapon may be under partial genetic control, a fact not altogether unexpected in view of its growth-regulating activity in meristematic regions. Scott reported rather widely differing results in his gametocide experiments with several varieties of cotton. Funderburk and Davis (*147*) reported that hybrid varieties of corn differed in their susceptibility to dalapon. Foy (*148*) and Behrens (*149*) also noted a widely different tolerance to dalapon in a number of inbred lines of corn. Obviously a number of plant processes are affected by the chlorinated aliphatic acid herbicides, and it is likely that more than a single pathway is inhibited. The evidence pointed toward multiple pathways and to more than one site of action.

Disturbance of energy metabolism, particularly the utilization of metabolic energy, could logically lead to the observed growth-regulating effects of the chlorinated aliphatic acid. All anatomical and morphological changes in plants are preceded by biochemical changes. As inferred earlier, no clear-cut relationship exists between formative effects and lethality. Attempts to explain mechanisms of action of a substance which produces formative effects must take cognizance of the influence of such compounds upon the normal processes of growth and differentiation, which are themselves incompletely understood. The principal factor responsible for overall inhibition of growth at cell level is apparently a reduction in meristematic activity. Most observed effects reported in the literature—particularly long-term effects—are probably secondary and do not operate directly on cell division (*42*).

Enzymatic studies using relatively simpler biological systems than those of higher plants, conceivably, can be useful in elucidating the biochemical mechanisms of action and selectivity of the chlorinated aliphatic acids. As Foy pointed out (*33*), the specific point of attack of a toxicant might be on the production of an essential substrate, on enzymes that bring about the release of energy from substrate, or on enzymes required in the essential utilization of this energy. Several sites have been suggested. The final toxic result, however, may actually be produced by a complex series of sequential and consequential reactions. This may account for the fact that the mechanism(s) of action is known for so few growth regulators, if indeed any are known with certainty.

Although far from satisfactory as a general explanation of the phytotoxicity of the chlorinated aliphatic acids in higher plants, one of the most plausible areas of biochemical sensitivity in microorganisms seems to revolve around pyruvate metabolism, which occupies a key position in relation to other metabolic crossroads.

Redemann and Meikle (150) studied dalapon as a competitive inhibitor of an enzyme system involving pyruvate as a substrate. The three enzymes selected for their study were pyruvate oxidase from *Streptococcus faecalis*, pyruvate oxidase from *Proteus vulgaris*, and carboxylase from yeast. Interpretation of double reciprocal plots of $1/S$ vs. $1/V$ lead to the conclusion that inhibition of pyruvate oxidase from *S. faecalis* most closely resembled noncompetitive inhibition, while yeast carboxylase and pyruvate oxidase from *P. vulgaris* both appeared to be competitively as well as noncompetitively inhibited. The noncompetitive inhibition occurred only at dalapon concentrations greater than 7×10^{-4} M with pyruvate oxidase from precipitation of the enzyme substrate complex. Based on calculations using expected pyruvate concentrations in plant tissues, these workers concluded that if such an inhibition is not responsible for the herbicidal action of dalapon, it certainly could contribute to the stunting effect following translocation. It should be pointed out, however, that the bacteria selected are known to contain highly active pyruvate–oxidase systems and that depression in oxygen consumption was employed as a measure of interference by dalapon in the presence and absence of pyruvic acid. On the other hand, in higher plant studies, only at very high concentration is the rate of oxygen consumption depressed (42,129,144,145).

Perhaps an equally (or more) important primary site of action, still involving pyruvate indirectly, is the competitive inhibition of pantothenic acid synthesis (137). Hilton (151) and Hilton et al. (140,141) showed that the growth of yeast (*Saccharomyces cerevisiae*) was inhibited by chlorosubstituted isobutyric, propionic, and acetic acids, but this inhibition was partially reversed by exogenous additions of calcium panthothenate. Hilton et al. (141) reasoned that because of the structural similarity of the chlorinated aliphatic acids to propionic and acetic acids, it seemed probable that their phytotoxicity might result, in part, from interference with pantothenic acid synthesis. Such an effect had been demonstrated with the two unchlorinated acids by King and Cheldelin (152) where they used yeast as a test organism. Their results led to the conclusion that "propionate inhibits growth by competing with β-alanine for attachment within the yeast cell, thereby preventing the coupling of the pantothenic acid moieties."

First indications were that dalapon competed with β-alanine, but later results with pure enzyme preparations have suggested that competition is with pantoic acid rather than β-alanine. In using a fresh sample of dalapon that was 99% pure in comparison with propionic acid, Hilton et al. (141) showed that although β-alanine offered some protection against this herbicide, the effect was not so pronounced as that observed with the unchlorinated parent acid. They suggested that chlorination of propionic acid obviously decreased the ability of the molecule to compete with β-alanine. Is chlorine substituted off slowly before the toxic system manifests itself? This agrees with the slowness to react but there is no absolute evidence for this theory. The remote possibility that initial dehalogenation of dalapon in tissue could, instead of constituting a detoxification mechanism, actually tend to increase its potentialities as an inhibitor of pantothenate synthesis has been discussed by Foy (153). This hypothesis is of improbable herbicidal significance, however, in view of the resistance of dalapon to metabolic decomposition in both tolerant and susceptible species.

van Oorschot and Hilton (154) used the pantothenate-synthesizing enzyme and growing cultures of Escherichia coli to study antimetabolite relations involved in inhibitions by salts of aliphatic acids and their chlorine-substituted derivatives. Protection of the enzyme against these inhibitors followed two different patterns. β-Alanine protected the enzyme against inhibition by unchlorinated aliphatic acids, monochloroacetic acid, and β-chloropropionic acid. Pantoate protected the enzyme against inhibition by α-chloropropionic acid and di- or trichloro-substituted acids of the acetic and propionic series. Chloro-substituted compounds in the first group were less inhibitory to the enzyme than the unchlorinated compounds. However, toxicity to the enzyme increased with additional chlorine substitutions on chloro-substituted compounds antagonized by pantoate.

The kinetic data thus suggested that the enzyme has two sites on which pantoate and β-alanine react to yield panthothenate (14). The two sites can be called **A** and **B**, as illustrated in Fig. 8-8. Dalapon or TCA compete with pantoate for site **A** on the enzyme surface. Conversely, acetate or propionate is competitive with β-alanine for site **B** and uncompetitive with pantoate. The uncompetitive relationship implies that propionate inhibits the enzyme pantoate complex (14). Whatever the mechanism, as discussed by Foy (33) and Leasure (6), if dalapon indeed disrupts pyruvate metabolism or competes with either β-alanine or pantoic acid, it is reasonable to assume that the synthesis of pantothenic acid would be disrupted and the supply of functional coenzyme A would be impaired. Figure 8-9 shows the structural relationships of coenzyme A, depicting how dalapon might disturb normal metabolic functions. Competitive inhibition of pantothenic acid synthesis is illustrated by the replacement of either moiety of pantothenate by dalapon.

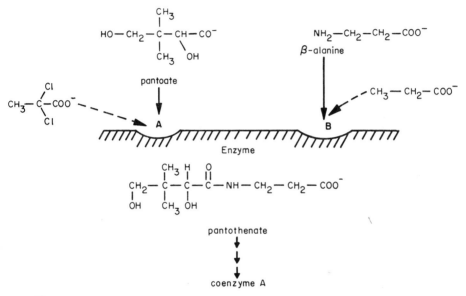

Fig. 8-8. Schematic diagram of pantothenate enzyme surface, showing site **A** where dalapon competes with pantoate and site **B** where propionate competes with β-alanine. [Reprinted by permission from Ref. (*14*), p. 24 courtesy of John Wiley & Sons, Inc.]

Most all the pantothenic acid in animals and microorganisms is reportedly present as coenzyme A, although it is also found in nature in other combined forms such as panthetheine and panthethine. Less is known of its activity and occurrence in higher plants; however, several edible reproductive structures are known sources of the vitamin. It is probably synthesized in the leaves and transported into these storage organs during periods of rapid development. The specific effects of pantothenic acid or coenzyme A upon cell differentiation are little known.

The improper functioning of coenzyme A in plants could lead to drastic changes in plant growth and development. For example, some of the important processes believed to be mediated by coenzyme A are pyruvate oxidation, citrate synthesis, α-keto-glutarate oxidation in the citric acid cycle, fatty acid and steroid synthesis and breakdown, and perhaps auxin action—auxins may act through an ester with coenzyme A (auxinyl coenzyme A). Hence coenzyme A is a key compound in plant metabolism and growth through its control of the energy transfers in carbohydrate, nitrogen, and fat metabolism. Interference of dalapon with the citric acid cycle in any

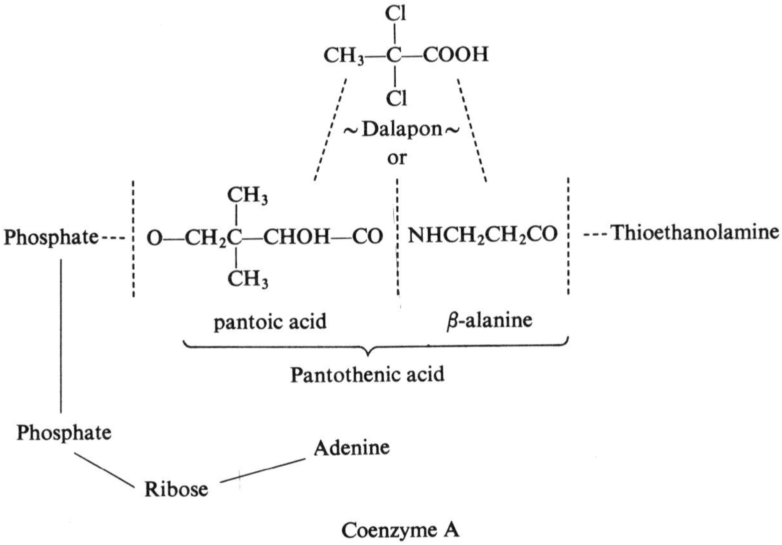

Fig. 8-9. Structural relationships of coenzyme A, depicting how dalapon may disturb normal metabolic functions. Competitive inhibition of pantothenic acid synthesis is illustrated by the replacement of either moiety of pantothenate by dalapon. [Reprinted by permission from Ref. (*153*).]

way, e.g., by competing with pyruvate for enzyme attachment or with β-alanine for attachment to another moiety of pantothenic acid, could indirectly cause disturbances in ancillary processes, such as nitrogen metabolism. (The dark green appearance of dalapon-treated plants, delayed maturation, and prolongation of vegetative growth are characteristic of plants having high levels of available nitrogen.)

It is entirely probable that dalapon exhibits more than one primary site of action. Note that β-alanine yields pyruvic acid on deamination. It is possible that dalapon and related compounds (perhaps increasingly with decreased chlorination) are able to compete with several metabolites that are structurally similar, e.g., β-alanine, pantoic acid, pyruvic acid—variably among plant species.

The low response in roots cannot always be attributed to a lack of accumulation of dalapon, as Foy has shown (33). It seems unlikely that the principal action is in competition with pyruvate, because this substance certainly occurs, albeit fleetingly, in all regions of high respiratory activity, which would include root tips as well as shoot apical meristems. If the principal mechanism is the interference with pantothenic acid synthesis, one possible explanation is that synthesis occurs in the shoots, requiring the products of photosynthesis, and if the process should be altered, the meristematic areas of the shoots (by virtue of their closer proximity) would show the deficiency most readily. Abnormalities can occur in roots under certain conditions, as shown by the work of Grigsby et al. (155) and Prasad and Blackman (124). This suggests the indirect involvement of light, which is consistent with other observations. Also, it seems safe to assume that light (and elevated temperatures) may indirectly exert an effect by causing an increase in accumulation of dalapon in the tops from soil or nutrient solution through an increase in transpiration.

Differences in susceptibility to dalapon among species and among tissues of a given plant are seemingly dependent upon the presence or absence of key enzymes or enzyme precursors. Further experimentation into the mechanisms of herbicidal selectivity of the chlorinated aliphatic acid herbicides should emphasize biochemical distinctions between susceptible and resistant species.

ACKNOWLEDGMENTS

The assistance of Mr. Peter Gous and Mr. Donald Jones in conducting portions of the literature search is gratefully acknowledged.

REFERENCES

1. E. W. Bousquet, U.S. Pat. 2,393,086 (1944).
2. K. C. Barrons, U.S. Pat. 2,642,354 (1951).
3. K. C. Barrons, U.S. Pat. 2,807,530 (1957).
4. B. V. Toornman, U.S. Pat. 2,880,082 (1959).
5. A. G. Norman, C. E. Minarik, and R. L. Weintraub, *Ann. Rev. Plant Physiol.*, **1**, 141 (1950).
6. J. K. Leasure, *J. Agr. Food Chem.*, **12**, 40 (1964).
7. P. W. Zimmerman and A. E. Hitchcock, *Contrib. Boyce Thompson Inst.*, **16**, 209 (1951).

8. G. L. McCall and J. W. Zahnley, *Kansas State Coll. Agr. Expt. Sta. Circ.*, **255** (1949).

9. Dow Chemical Company, *Dalapon Bull. No. 2*, 1953.

10. Pesticides Regulation Division, ARS, USDA, *Summary of Registered Agricultural Pesticide Chemical Uses*, 1967, pp. 206, 732.

11. Rohm and Haas Company, *Progress Report on FW-450 Chemical Gametocide*, 1959.

12. For several pertinent references, see reports of the Cotton Gametocide Symposium, *Proc. Cotton Improvement Conf.*, National Cotton Council, Memphis, Tenn., 1958, pp. 57–101.

13. L. F. Fieser and M. Fieser, *Advanced Organic Chemistry*, Reinhold, New York, 1961, p. 360.

14. P. C. Kearney, C. I. Harris, D. D. Kaufman, and T. J. Sheets, *Advan. Pest Control Res.*, **6**, 1 (1965).

15. V. H. Freed, Mimeograph for Project, 41–47, Oregon State Univ., Corvallis, 1956.

16. V. H. Freed and M. Montgomery, *Res. Progr. Rept., Western Weed Control Conf.*, 1956, p. 98.

17. C. L. Foy, *Hilgardia*, **35**, 125 (1963).

18. C. L. Foy, *Weeds*, **10**, 35 (1962).

19. C. L. Foy, *Weeds*, **10**, 97 (1962).

20. C. L. Foy and L. W. Smith, *Weeds*, **13**, 15 (1965).

21. L. W. Smith, C. L. Foy, and D. E. Bayer, *Weed Res.*, **6**, 233 (1966).

22. L. W. Smith, C. L. Foy, and D. E. Bayer, *Weeds*, **15**, 87 (1967).

23. L. L. Jansen, *Weeds*, **13**, 117 (1965).

24. L. L. Jansen, *J. Agr. Food Chem.*, **12**, 223 (1964).

25. C. G. McWhorter, *Weeds*, **11**, 83 (1963).

26. V. H. Freed, K. McKennon, and M. Montgomery, *Res. Prog. Rept. Western Weed Control Conf.*, 1955, p. 81.

27. V. H. Freed and M. Montgomery, *Res. Progr. Rept., Western Weed Control Conf.*, 1956, p. 96.

28. J. B. Neilands and P. K. Stumpf, *Outlines of Enzyme Chemistry*, Wiley, New York, 2nd ed., 1958, p. 118.

29. American Cyanamid Company, *Tech. Data Experimental Herbicide 6249*, 1955.

30. R. N. Anderson, R. Behrens, and A. J. Linck, *Weeds*, **10**, 4 (1962).

31. F. A. Blanchard, W. W. Muelder, and G. N. Smith, *J. Agr. Food Chem.*, **8**, 124 (1960).

32. C. L. Foy, *Plant Physiol.*, **36**, 688 (1961).

33. C. L. Foy, *Plant Physiol.*, **36**, 698 (1961).

34. G. N. Smith and D. L. Dyer, *J. Agr. Food Chem.*, **9**, 155 (1961).

35. F. A. Blanchard, *Weeds*, **3**, 274 (1954).

36. F. Mayer, *Biochem. Z.*, 328, 433 (1957).

37. K. C. Barrons and R. W. Hummer, *Agr. Chem.*, **6**, 48 (1951).

38. T. W. Tibbetts and L. G. Holm, *Weeds*, **6**, 146 (1954).

39. R. N. Anderson, A. J. Linck, and R. Behrens, *Weeds*, **10**, 1 (1962).

40. A. S. Crafts and C. L. Foy, *Down Earth*, **14**, 1 (1959).

41. C. L. Foy, *Ninth Intern. Botan. Congr. Proc. Abstr.*, **2**, 121 (1959).

42. R. Prasad and G. E. Blackman, *J. Exptl. Botan.*, **16**, 545 (1965).

43. C. L. Foy and J. H. Miller, *Weeds*, **11**, 31 (1963).

44. J. Giovanelli and P. K. Stumpf, *J. Am. Chem. Soc.*, **79**, 2652 (1957).

45. M. M. Schreiber, *J. Agr. Food Chem.*, **7**, 427 (1959).

46. G. I. McIntyre, *Weed Res.*, **2**, 165 (1962).

47. A. H. Kutchinski, *J. Agr. Food Chem.*, **9**, 365 (1961).
48. L. J. Audus, in *Herbicides and the Soil* (E. K. Woodford and G. R. Sagar, eds.), Blackwell, Oxford, 1960, p. 1.
49. W. R. Fennerty, E. Hawtrey, and R. E. Kallis, *Z. Allgem. Mikrobiol.*, **2**, 169 (1962).
50. E. N. Bokova, *Mikrobiologiya*, **23**, 15 (1954).
51. J. N. Ladd, *Australian J. Biol. Sci.*, **9**, 92 (1956).
52. C. E. Zobell, *Advan. Enzymol.*, **10**, 433 (1950).
53. H. L. Jensen, *Can. J. Microbiol.*, **3**, 151 (1957).
54. P. Hirsch and M. Alexander, *Can. J. Microbiol.*, **6**, 241 (1960).
55. D. D. Kaufman, unpublished data, USDA, ARS, CRD, Beltsville, Md., 1963.
56. D. D. Kaufman, *Am. Soc. Agron. Abstr., Soil Sci. Div.*, 1965, p. 85.
57. A. J. Loustalot and R. Ferrer, *Agron. J.*, **42**, 323 (1950).
58. R. E. Ogle and G. F. Warren, *Weeds*, **3**, 257 (1954).
59. B. J. Thiegs, *Down Earth*, **11**, 2 (1955).
60. J. T. Holstun and W. E. Loomis, *Weeds*, **4**, 205 (1956).
61. B. J. Thiegs, *Down Earth*, **18**, 7 (1962).
62. L. A. Magee and A. R. Colmer, *Can. J. Microbiol.*, **5**, 255 (1959).
63. H. L. Jensen, *Nature*, **180**, 1416 (1957).
64. H. L. Jensen, *Soils Fertilizers*, **23**, 60 (1960).
65. H. L. Jensen, *Acta Agr. Scand.*, **10**, 83 (1960).
66. D. D. Kaufman, *Can. J. Microbiol.*, **10**, 843 (1964).
67. H. L. Jensen, *Tidsskr. Planteavl*, **63**, 470 (1959).
68. P. Hirsch and R. Stellmach-Hellwig, *Zentr. Bakteriol. Parasitenk.*, **2**, 683 (1961).
69. H. L. Jensen, *Acta Agr. Scand.*, **13**, 404 (1963).
70. H. Lees and J. H. Quastel, *Biochem J.*, **40**, 803 (1966).
71. A. S. Newman and C. R. Downing, *J. Agr. Food Chem.*, **6**, 352 (1958).
72. R. B. Carroll, *Contrib. Boyce Thompson Inst.*, **16**, 409 (1952).
73. K. C. Barrons, *Down Earth*, **6**, 8 (1951).
74. A. N. McGregor, *J. Gen. Microbiol.*, **30**, 497 (1963).
75. R. B. Carroll, *Proc. Southern Weed Conf.*, **4**, 13 (1951).
76. P. Hirsch, *Weed Soc. Am. Abstr.*, **11**, 547 (1962).
77. H. L. Jensen, *Acta Agr. Scand.*, **9**, 421 (1959).
78. D. D. Kaufman, *Weeds*, **14**, 130 (1966).
79. C. G. Gemmell and H. L. Jensen, *Arch. Mikrobiol.*, **48**, 386 (1964).
80. M. Cohn and J. Monod, *Symp. Soc. Gen. Microbiol.*, **3**, 132 (1953).
81. R. L. Walker and A. S. Newman, *Appl. Microbiol.*, **4**, 201 (1956).
82. P. C. Kearney, D. D. Kaufman, and M. L. Beall, *Biochem. Biophys. Res. Commun.*, **14**, 29 (1964).
83. W. W. Fletcher, in *Herbicides and the Soil* (E. K. Woodford and G. R. Sagar, eds.), Blackwell, Oxford, 1960, p. 20.
84. R. T. Otten, J. E. Dawson, and M. M. Schreiber, *Proc. Northeast. Weed Control Conf.*, **11**, 120 (1957).
85. J. D. Douros, *Dissertation Abstr.*, **19**, 19 (1958).
86. A. D. Worsham and J. Giddens, *Weeds*, **5**, 316 (1957).
87. J. V. Mayeux and A. R. Colmer, *Appl. Microbiol.*, **10**, 206 (1962).
88. A. R. Colmer, *Bacteriol. Proc.*, **53**, 16 (1953).
89. A. R. Colmer, *Appl. Microbiol.*, **1**, 184 (1953).
90. A. R. Colmer, *Proc. Southern Weed Conf.*, **7**, 237 (1954).

252   C. L. FOY

91. L. A. Magee and A. R. Colmer, *Appl. Microbiol.*, **3**, 288 (1955).
92. D. E. Kratochvil, *Weeds*, **1**, 25 (1951).
93. M. E. Hoover and A. R. Colmer, *Proc. Natl. Acad. Sci. U.S.*, **16**, 21 (1953).
94. L. A. Magee, *Dissertation Abstr.*, **19**, 413 (1958).
95. G. H. Elkan, K. W. King., and W. E. C. Moore, *Bacteriol. Proc.*, **58**, 7 (1958).
96. G. H. Elkan and W. E. C. Moore, *Can. J. Microbiol.*, **6**, 339 (1960).
97. M. G. Hale, F. H. Hulcher, and W. E. Chappell, *Weeds*, **5**, 331 (1957).
98. L. T. Richardson, *Can. J. Plant Sci.*, **37**, 196 (1957).
99. L. T. Richardson, *Can. J. Plant Sci.*, **39**, 30 (1959).
100. A. C. Leopold, P. van Schaik, and M. Neal, *Weeds*, **8**, 48 (1960).
101. G. F. Warren, *Proc. N. Central Weed Control Conf.*, **13**, 5 (1956).
102. G. F. Warren, *Proc. N. Central Weed Control Conf.*, **11**, 5 (1954).
103. A. S. Crafts and H. Drever, *Weeds*, **8**, 12 (1960).
104. R. F. Richards, *Proc. Southern Weed Conf.*, **9**, 154 (1956).
105. H. Beinhauer, *Intern. Congr. Plant Protection Proc.*, **1**, 527 (1957).
106. B. E. Day, L. S. Jordan, and R. C. Russell, *Soil Sci.*, **95**, 326 (1963).
107. G. S. Rai and C. L. Hammer, *Weeds*, **2**, 271 (1953).
108. K. C. Barrons and R. W. Hummer, *Proc. Southern Weed Conf.*, **4**, 3 (1951).
109. A. H. Kutschinski, *Down Earth*, **10**, 14 (1954).
110. B. E. Day, *Weed Res.*, **1**, 177 (1961).
111. C. L. Foy, *Hilgardia*, **30**, 153 (1960).
112. M. L. Beall, P. C. Kearney, and D. D. Kaufman, *Weed Soc. Am. Abstr.*, 1964, p. 11.
113. P. C. Kearney, *Advan. Chem. Ser.*, **60**, 257 (1966).
114. P. C. Kearney, D. D. Kaufman, and M. L. Beall, *Weed Soc. Am. Abstr.*, 1964, p. 13.
115. P. C. Kearney, private communication, 1967.
116. P. C. Kearney and D. D. Kaufman, American Chemical Society, 150th Meeting, 1965, p. 16A.
117. M. Alexander, *Advan. Appl. Microbiol.*, **7**, 35 (1965).
118. E. K. Woodford, K. Holly, and C. C. McCready, *Ann. Rev. Plant Physiol.*, **9**, 311 (1958).
119. J. van Overbeek, in *The Physiology and Biochemistry of Herbicides* (L. J. Audus, ed.), Academic Press, New York, 1964, p. 392.
120. C. T. Redemann and J. Hamaker, *Weeds*, **3**, 387 (1954).
121. E. A. Olsson, Jr., M.S. thesis, Colorado State Univ., Fort Collins, 1957.
122. R. E. Wilkinson, Ph.D. thesis, Univ. of California, Davis, 1956.
123. H. Davson and J. F. Danielli, *The Permeability of Natural Membranes*, Macmillan, New York, 1943, p. 361.
124. R. Prasad and G. E. Blackman, *J. Exptl. Botan.*, **15**, 48 (1964).
125. J. van Overbeek and R. Blondeau, *Weeds*, **3**, 55 (1954).
126. F. Daniels, *Outlines of Physical Chemistry*, Wiley, New York, 1953.
127. W. W. Robbins, A. S. Crafts, and R. N. Raynor, *Weed Control*, McGraw-Hill, New York, 2nd ed., 1952.
128. C. H. Fawcett, R. L. Wain, and F. Wightman, *Nature*, **178**, 972 (1958).
129. M. Ingle and B. J. Rogers, *Weeds*, **9**, 264 (1961).
130. W. G. Corns, *Can. J. Botan.*, **34**, 154 (1956).
131. S. R. Miller and W. G. Corns, *Can. J. Microbiol.*, **35**, 5 (1957).
132. B. E. Juniper, *New Phytologist*, **58**, 1 (1959).
133. B. E. Juniper and D. R. Bradley, *Ultrastruct. Res.*, **2**, 16 (1958).

134. O. R. Dewey, P. Gregory, and R. K. Pfeiffer, *Proc. Brit. Weed Control Conf.*, *3rd Blackpool*, **1**, 313, 1956.
135. R. K. Pfeiffer, O. R. Dewey and R. T. Brunskill, *Proc. Intern. Congr. Plant Protection, 4th, Hamburg*, 1957, p. 523.
136. R. Prasad and G. E. Blackman, *J. Exptl. Botan.*, **16**, 86 (1965).
137. H. Y. Ram and P. N. Rustagi, *Sci. Cult. (Calcutta)*, **32**, 286 (1966).
138. T. R. Richmond, *Crop Sci.*, **2**, 58 (1960).
139. T. L. Rebstock, C. L. Hammer, R. W. Luecke, and H. M. Sell, *Plant Physiol.*, **28**, 437 (1953).
140. J. L. Hilton, J. S. Ard, L. L. Jansen, and W. A. Gentner, *Weeds*, **7**, 381 (1959).
141. J. L. Hilton, L. L. Jansen, and W. A. Gentner, *Plant Physiol.*, **33**, 43 (1958).
142. J. L. Hilton, L. L. Jansen, and H. Hull, *Ann. Rev. Plant Physiol.*, **14**, 353 (1963).
143. G. S. Rai and C. L. Hammer, *Quart. Bull. Mich Agr. Expt. Sta.*, **38**, 555 (1956).
144. C. M. Switzer, *Plant Physiol.*, **32**, 42 (1954).
145. C. L. Foy and D. Penner, *Weeds*, **13**, 226 (1965).
146. R. A. Scott, *Plant Physiol.*, **36**, 529 (1961).
147. H. H. Funderburk and D. E. Davis, *Weeds*, **8**, 6 (1960).
148. C. L. Foy, *Res. Progr. Rept.*, *Western Weed Control Conf.*, 1964, p. 108.
149. R. Behrens, in *Summary of 1962 Weed Control Trials in Field Crops*, Minn, Agr. Expt. Sta., 1962.
150. C. T. Redemann and R. W. Meikle, *Arch. Biochem. Biophys.*, **59**, 106 (1955).
151. J. L. Hilton, *Science*, **128**, 1509 (1959).
152. T. E. King and V. H. Cheldelin, *J. Biol. Chem.*, **174**, 273 (1948).
153. C. L. Foy, Ph.D. thesis, Univ. of California, Davis, 1958.
154. J. L. P. van Oorschot, and J. L. Hilton, *Arch. Biochem. Biophys.*, **100**, 289 (1963).
155. B. H. Grigsby, T. M. Tsou, and G. B. Wilson, *Proc. Southern Weed Conf.*, **8**, 279 (1955).
156. K. Holly, in *Plant Physiology and Biochemistry of Herbicides* (L. J. Audus, ed.), Academic Press, New York, 1964, p. 453.

CHAPTER 9

Trifluralin and Related Compounds

G. W. PROBST AND J. B. TEPE

ELI LILLY AND COMPANY
GREENFIELD LABORATORIES
GREENFIELD, INDIANA

9-1. Introduction 255
9-2. Chemical and Physical Properties 256
9-3. Degradation 258
    A. Photodecomposition 259
    B. Aerobic Degradation 261
    C. Anaerobic Degradation 269
9-4. Mode of Action 277
9-5. Summary 279
References 280

9-1. INTRODUCTION

Trifluralin (α,α,α-trifluoro-2,6-dinitro-N,N-dipropyl-p-toluidine) is a prominent member of a new series of selective herbicides. Herbicidal properties and chemical structure suggest they be classified as substituted dinitroanilines. Dinitroanilines have been recognized as dye intermediates for several decades. The fungicidal activity of substituted dinitroanilines has been described ($1,2$). Phytotoxic studies on bean plants were initially reported for 2,4-dinitroaniline in 1955 (3). Their use as herbicides is of recent origin. Of prime interest is the discovery by Alder et al. ($4,5$) that 2,6-dinitroaniline possessed a marked general herbicidal activity as compared to the 2,4-dinitro- or 2,3-dinitroanilines, with the latter being the least active of the three. Selective herbicidal activity was obtained by dialkyl substitution on the amino group of the 2,6-dinitroaniline molecule, with n-propyl the most active dialkyl substitution. Substitution in the 4 position of the ring resulted in herbicidal activity in the following order: $CF_3 > CH_3 > Cl > H$.

255

The usefulness and effectiveness of trifluralin (6,7,8) as a selective, soil-incorporated, preemergent herbicide led to the commercial product. Wide variation in molecular structure of 2,6-dinitroanilines is possible; and as might be expected, other analogs possess herbicidal properties in varying degrees.

9-2. CHEMICAL AND PHYSICAL PROPERTIES

Alder and Bevington (9) demonstrated that both the trifluoromethyl- and methyl-substituted N,N-dipropyl-2,6-dinitroanilines were preemergent herbicides, with trifluralin (1) being more active than dipropalin (2). Dipropalin (2,6-dinitro-N,N-dipropyl-p-toluidine) exhibited some foliar contact phytotoxicity, whereas trifluralin had practically none. This difference in trifluoromethyl and methyl substituents was confirmed by Gentner (10). With both compounds, herbicidal activity was greatest when the alkyl groups on the amino group contained a total of six carbon atoms.

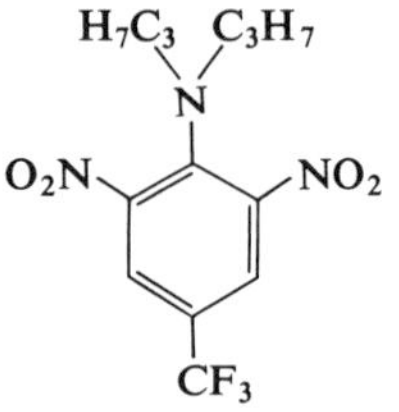

trifluralin
(1)

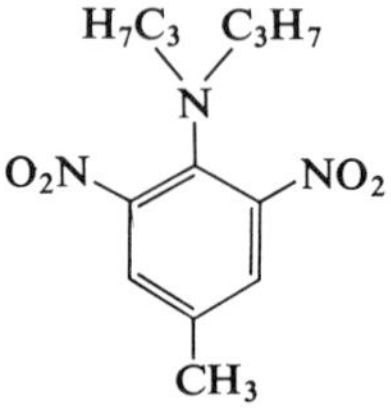

dipropalin
(2)

The successful use of trifluralin for the control of a wide variety of grasses and broadleaf weeds in many agronomic and horticultural crops has spurred interest in other dinitroaniline analogs. Benefin (α,α,α-trifluoro-2,6-dinitro-N-butyl-N-ethyl-p-toluidine) (3) (11) and nitralin (4-methyl-sulfonyl-2,6-dinitro-N,N-dipropylaniline) (4) (12) are two such compounds now in agricultural commerce.

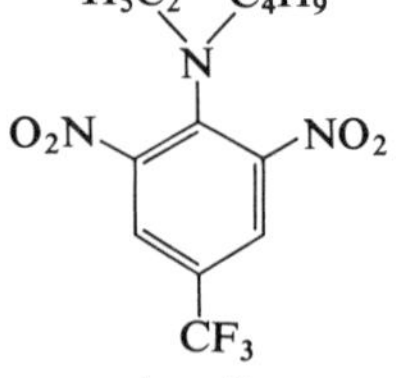

benefin
(3)

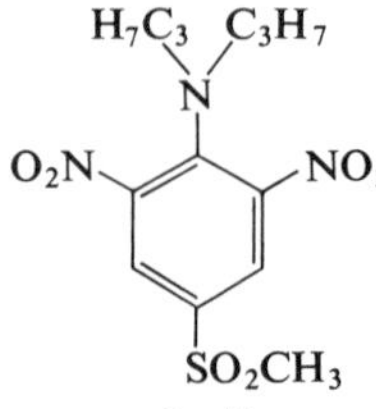

nitralin
(4)

The physicochemical properties of the commercially available herbicides are shown in Table 9-1 (*12,13,14*).

TABLE 9-1

Physicochemical Properties of Trifluralin and Related Compounds

Property	Compound		
	Trifluralin	Benefin	Nitralin
Molecular weight	335.28	335.28	345
Crystal form	Yellow-orange prisms	Yellow-orange prisms	Golden-orange rectangular prisms
Melting range	48.5–49°	65–66.5°	151–152°
Boiling range	96–97° at 0.18 mm Hg	121–122° at 0.5 mm Hg	—
Vapor pressure	1.99×10^{-4} mm Hg at 29.5°	4×10^{-7} mm at 25°	1.5×10^{-6} mm Hg at 25°
Solubility			
Water	< 1 ppm (27°)	< 1 ppm (25°)	0.6 ppm (25°)
Acetone	Soluble	Soluble	Soluble
Ethanol	Slightly soluble	Slightly soluble	Slightly soluble
Xylene	Soluble	Soluble	Slightly soluble

Trifluralin is prepared by reacting 4-chloro-3,5-dinitro-α,α,α-trifluoro-toluene (**5**) with dipropylamine as shown below, whereas benefin (*15*) is prepared with butylethyl amine.

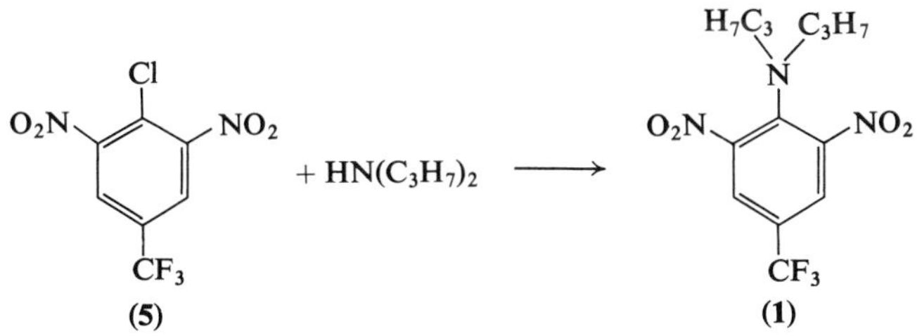

Reacting dipropyl amine with 4-chloro-3,5-dinitrophenylmethylsulfone yields nitralin (*16*).

Extensive toxicological data obtained on trifluralin (*13*) indicate no hazard to man or animals when used as directed. The acute oral LD_0 of trifluralin for adult rats is greater than 10 g/kg. Exposure of rats to a mist containing 2.8 mg of trifluralin per liter caused no adverse effects. No skin irritation was observed in rabbits treated dermally with 2.5 g/kg. Rats were fed 2000 ppm of trifluralin in their diet for a 2-year period without adverse effect and no change in reproduction or fertility through three generations. Trifluralin was given daily to dogs at 1000 ppm in their diet for 2 years without effect.

The LC_{50} of trifluralin as an emulsifiable concentrate in static fish ponds is 0.58, 0.94, and 0.59 ppm for bluegills, fathead minnows, and goldfish, respectively (17). If trifluralin is first sprayed on soil, then added to static water, the LC_{50} value is 2.8 ppm on Princeton fine sand and 13.2 ppm on Brookston silty clay loam for bluegills.

For benefin, the acute oral LD_0 for adult rats is greater than 10 g/kg, and the LD_{50} for newborn rats is 0.8 g/kg (14). The acute oral LD_0 for dog, chicken, and rabbit is greater than 2 g/kg in each species, which is the same value reported for nitralin (12) in mice and rats. Five fresh-water fish species tolerated a suspension of nitralin at 20 ppm for 48 hours.

Application rates for effective weed control are slightly greater for nitralin (12) and benefin (14) than for trifluralin (13). These herbicides are potentially useful for a wide variety of horticultural and agronomic crops. The selective crop tolerance for substituted dinitroanilines is slightly different; for example, the selective action of benefin provides a greater margin of safety with peanuts and tobacco as compared with trifluralin.

9-3. DEGRADATION

The effectiveness of trifluralin as a herbicide stimulated interest in its persistence and degradation in soil (18,19) as well as its metabolism in plants (19,20) and in animals (21–23). Degradation of trifluralin and benefin in soils, plants, and animals apparently proceeds in two distinctive and different patterns. With few exceptions they degrade in a sequence of dealkylation and reduction reactions. Under "aerobic"-type conditions, dealkylation predominates, whereas under "anaerobic"-type conditions, reduction predominates.

Analytical methods used in the investigation of the persistence and mode of degradation of trifluralin were thin-layer chromatography (24), gas chromatography (25), and radiochemical methods including radioauto-graphy and reverse isotope dilution techniques. The investigations were aided by the use of trifluralin synthesized with ^{14}C in different positions (26), namely, in the propyl groups, the trifluoromethyl group, and the benzene-ring portion† of the molecule. Methods were adapted and modified as necessary to permit analysis for degradation products.

A. Photodecomposition

The apparent enhancement of trifluralin herbicidal activity by soil incorporation as compared to surface application (8) suggests possible loss by either volatilization or photodecomposition. The vapor pressure of trifluralin (Table 9-1) suggests that volatility can be a factor under some field conditions. Photochemical decomposition is characteristic of substituted aromatic nitro compounds (27). Wright and Warren (28) exposed trifluralin, as a thin film on glass or sprayed on the soil surface, to sunlight and artificial light from a mercury vapor source. Changes in the absorption spectrum occurred within 2 hours of exposure. Marked alteration in absorbance and a decrease in the inhibitory effect on millet growth were observed after 4 to 6 hours of exposure. Photodecomposition also occurred on the soil surface but to a lesser degree.

Trifluralin and its related compounds in methanol and heptane solutions decomposed extensively when exposed to ultraviolet radiation. Day (29) detected at least 10 trifluralin-related compounds by gas chromatography after exposure of anhydrous methanol solutions containing trifluralin. Two compounds matched reference models, namely, the monodealkylated, product, α,α,α-trifluoro-2,6-dinitro-N-propyl-p-toluidine (6), and α,α,α-trifluoro-2,6-dinitro-p-toluidine (7). The concentration of (6) diminished rapidly after 1 hour, but that of (7) remained at a high level for up to 5 hours. Two other major products were formed in the first hour, but they were not identified. All of these products gradually disappeared after further irradiation.

The model system of the photochemical demethylation of α,α,α-trifluoro-2,6-dinitro-N-methyl-p-toluidine and the N-propyl analog described by McMahon (30) provides insight into the photodecomposition of trifluralin. Irradiation of α,α,α-trifluoro-2,6-dinitro-N-methyl-p-toluidine in n-heptane with an ultraviolet source resulted in the formation of formaldehyde and

† Degradation studies conducted in the Lilly Research Laboratories reveal the purchased ¹⁴C-labeled p-chlorobenzoic acid used in the synthesis of uniformly ring-labeled trifluralin [Marshall et al. (26)] and benefin is a mixture, determined to be 15% uniformly ring-labeled and 85% carboxyl-labeled p-chlorobenzoic acids. The ¹⁴C uniformly ring-labeled trifluralin and benefin referred to in this and previous publications is the mixture described.

α,α,α-trifluoro-6-nitro-2-nitroso-p-toluidine (**8**). Propionaldehyde was identified in a similar irradiation reaction with the N-propyl analog. On the basis of these studies, a portion of the reaction sequence of trifluralin photodecomposition is postulated in Fig. 9-1.

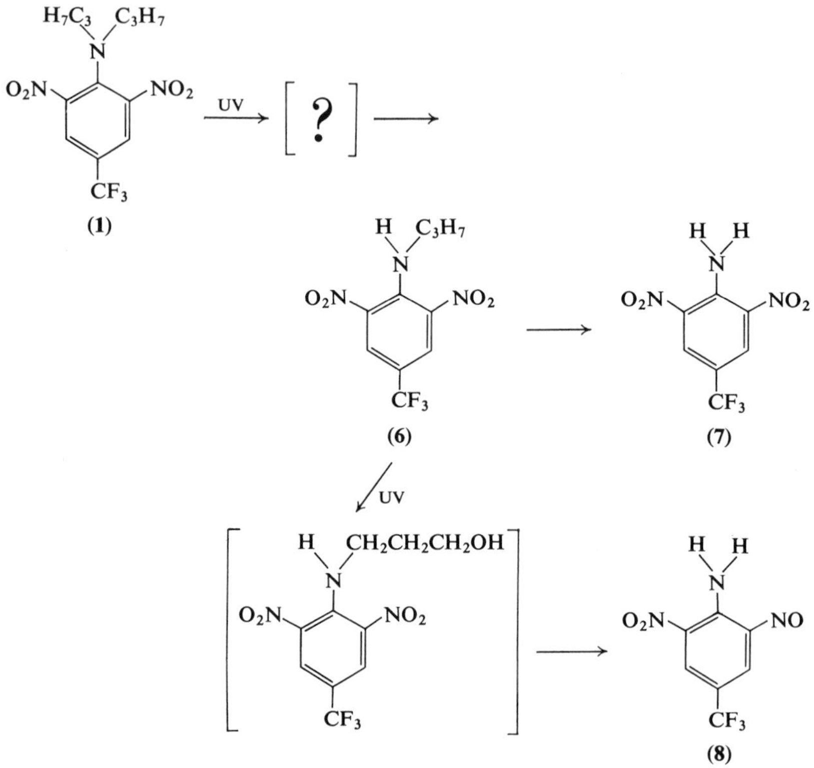

Fig. 9-1. Probable reaction sequence of the photodecomposition of trifluralin based on identified degradation products.

When an ethanol solution of trifluralin was exposed to intense ultra-violet radiation, the absorption maxima shifted from 275 and 376 mμ to 231 and 434 mμ. The latter absorption maxima correspond to those exhibited by compound (**8**) and suggest that it is an intermediate in the photodecomposition sequence. Chemical structure similarity of benefin and nitralin and their instability to light suggest a similar pathway of photodecomposition. The photodecomposition of trifluralin is complex and will require considerable effort to elucidate all the reactions.

B. Aerobic Degradation

1. Soils

Probst et al. (*19*) investigated persistence, leaching, and decomposition under field conditions with radioactive trifluralin. Soybeans were planted in a field plot in which trifluralin labeled with ^{14}C in the trifluoromethyl group was incorporated into the top 2 in. of the soil at a rate of 0.75 lb/acre. The amount of methanol-extractable radioactivity in soil after 29 days was reduced to 39 % of the original and continued to decrease to approximately

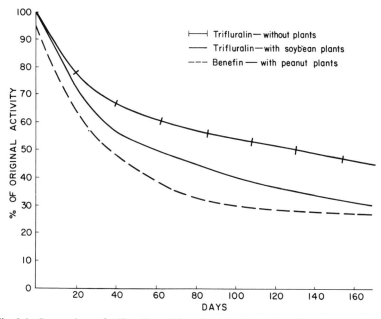

Fig. 9-2. Comparison of trifluralin and benefin degradation in soil under growth-room conditions.

20 % after 43 days. Thereafter, the loss of extractable radioactivity leveled off and gradually decreased during the remainder of the 2-year observation period.

Based on original radioactivity, the amount of trifluralin decreased to less than 10 % as measured by thin-layer chromatography. Thin-layer chromatographic analysis also revealed the presence of trace amounts of α,α,α-trifluoro-2,6-dinitro-*N*-propyl-*p*-toluidine (**6**). A portion of the radioactivity in methanol extracts remained at the origin. This material appears to be a mixture of polar substances resulting from the degradation of trifluralin.

Chemical assays and crabgrass bioassays indicated that trifluralin does not leach or move laterally in soil. It is degraded continuously during the growing season to less than 50 ppb in most soils approximately 160 days after trifluralin application. Repeated applications of trifluralin at recommended rates in soil do not result in a buildup of trifluralin with time, according to Parka and Tepe (*31*).

Persistence under controlled-growth-room conditions has been studied with both trifluralin (*19*) and benefin (*32*). Trifluralin labeled with ^{14}C in the trifluoromethyl group was incorporated in the top 2 in. of soil at 0.75 lb/acre (1.33 ppm). Similarly, ^{14}C-labeled benefin was incorporated at 1.3 lb/acre (2.33 ppm) in soil. Figure 9-2 shows the rate of trifluralin degradation in soil with and without soybean plants and benefin degradation with peanut plants. Disappearance of the herbicides was most rapid during the first 40 days of the experiment, then tended to decline more slowly with time. The initial losses were due, in part, to volatilization of both trifluralin and benefin. The rate changes in the latter stages suggest decomposition of the herbicides. In the case of trifluralin, its disappearance rate was increased slightly in the presence of growing soybean plants. The amount of radioactivity incorporated in the plant does not account for this difference.

Trifluralin degradation rate in the growth room was reduced considerably as compared to that in the field. Small amounts of radioactive carbon dioxide were expired from soil and plants, suggesting a slow but extensive degradation.

To determine if microorganisms play an important role, trifluralin was incorporated in both autoclaved and nonautoclaved soil at 8 ppmw (*19*). This soil was maintained at 75% field moisture capacity and incubated at 80°F. Using crabgrass inhibition as a bioassay, the study revealed that trifluralin degradation proceeds slightly more rapidly in nonautoclaved than in autoclaved soil. Examination of several trifluralin-treated soils failed to show specific microorganisms which caused trifluralin degradation.

Funderburk et al. (*33*) observed that trifluralin was the only radioactive compound present in extracts of ^{14}C-labeled trifluralin-enriched soil. They also examined four species of fungi, *Sclerotium rolfsii*, *Aspergillus niger*, *Fusarium* sp., and *Trichoderma* sp., grown in liquid medium containing trifluralin. Extracts of the solutions, assayed by electron-capture gas chromatography, showed little change in trifluralin concentration. However, the extract from *A. niger*, in addition to trifluralin, contained a small quantity of α,α,α-trifluoro-2,6-dinitro-*N*-propyl-*p*-toluidine (**6**). Thus, in summary, microorganisms may contribute to the destruction of trifluralin to simpler compounds, but there is no evidence that this is the major mode of degradation.

In the previous experiments, soil in a normal environment was defined as an "aerobic"-type condition (19). Extracts of these soils, examined by thin-layer chromatography, radioautography, and gas chromatography, were compared to model compounds. Although intermediates corresponding to the model compounds were detectable only in small amounts, a pathway of aerobic trifluralin degradation can be postulated, as shown in Fig. 9-3.

The material which remains at the origin on thin-layer chromatographic plates in the solvent systems studied has been designated as polar products (19). This mixture could not be resolved into discrete, identifiable substances in a variety of solvent systems. Hydrolysis of the mixture failed to change its chromatographic behavior. Reduction of the polar products with tin and hydrochloric acid yielded a mixture containing α,α,α-trifluorotoluene-3,4,5-triamine (11) as the major constituent. The recovery of the aromatic triamine suggested that polar products could be formed from the condensation of aromatic amines, for example, azo and hydrazo compounds. This assumption is supported by the observations of Bartha and Pramer (34) in which the herbicide 3',4'-dichloropropionanilide decomposes in soil to 3,4-dichloroaniline, which in turn is condensed to form 3,3',4,4'-tetrachloroazobenzene.

The initial aerobic degradation step, the removal of one propyl group to form (6), occurs in field and growth-room soil as well as in photodecomposition. Compound (6) is the apparent intermediate in dual pathways of decomposition. Further dealkylation to form α,α,α-trifluoro-2,6-dinitro-p-toluidine (7) followed by subsequent reduction of one nitro group yielding α,α,α-trifluoro-5-nitrotoluene-3,4-diamine (10) constitutes one pathway. The alternate pathway converts (6) to α,α,α-trifluoro-5-nitro-N-propyl-toluene-3,4-diamine (9) by reduction prior to further dealkylation to form (10). A small amount of trifluralin degradation product with one nitro group reduced was detected by radioautography, indicating an initial reduction step; but under the defined aerobic conditions, the main pathway appears to be dealkylation followed by reduction.

Evidence based only on radioautographs of thin-layer chromatograms of soil extracts from growth-room studies permits a postulated pathway of aerobic benefin degradation, as shown in Fig. 9-4. Model compounds were cochromatographed with the extracts and served as a criterion of identification. The reaction sequence, as with trifluralin, indicated that dealkylation reactions occur prior to reduction. Both the monoethyl (12) and the monobutyl (13) derivatives of benefin (3) were detected. Only the nitro

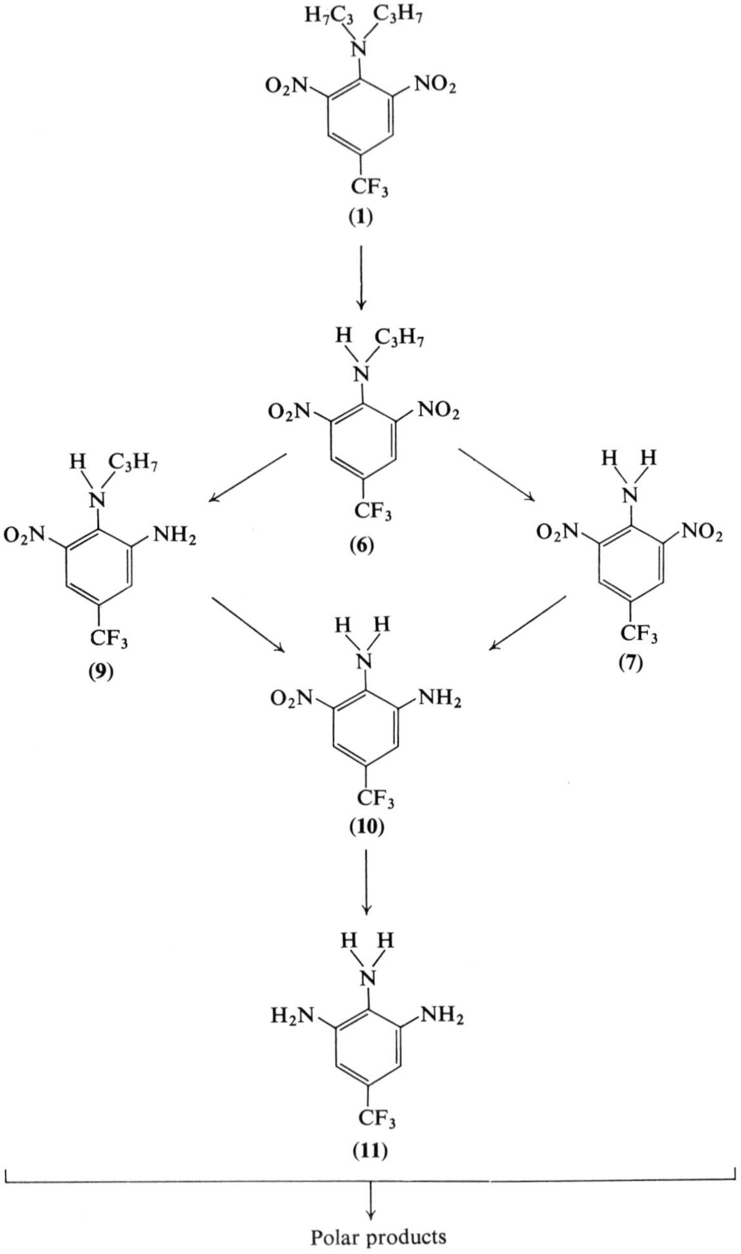

Fig. 9-3. Postulated pathway of aerobic trifluralin degradation in soil.

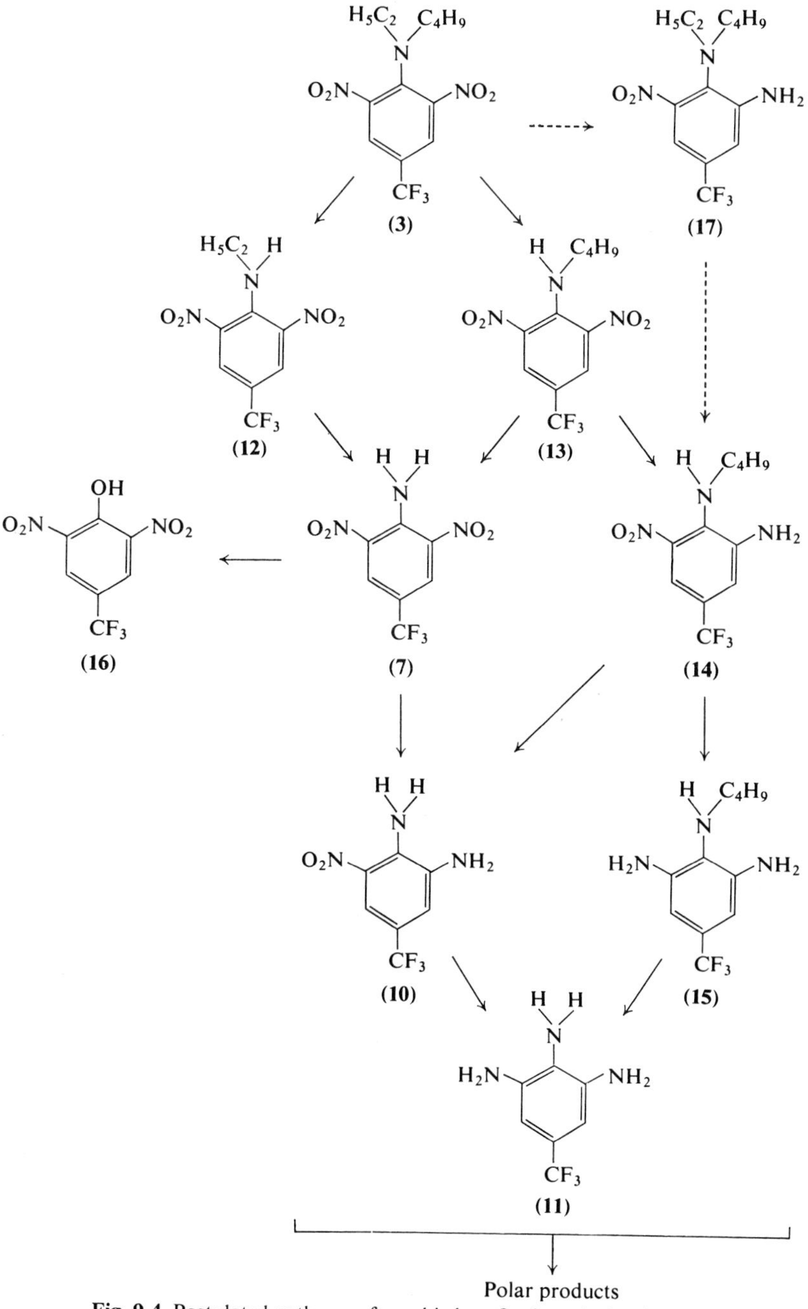

Fig. 9-4. Postulated pathway of aerobic benefin degradation in soil.

groups of the monobutyl compounds were subject to reduction forming α,α,α-trifluoro-N-butyltoluene-3,4,5-triamine (15). If the monoethyl compound (12) was further degraded, it apparently dealkylated to form the corresponding aniline (7). In any event, successive dealkylation or reduction eventually results in the formation of α,α,α-trifluorotoluene-3,4,5-triamine (11). Benefin with one reduced nitro group (17) was detected in trace amounts. Trace quantities of a similar initial reduction product was observed in the aerobic degradation of trifluralin.

Of special interest was the detection of α,α,α-trifluoro-2,6-dinitro-p-cresol, which theoretically could also be derived from trifluralin but has not been detected as a trifluralin degradation product in soils. Existence of compound (16) in benefin-treated soil was further substantiated by detection of the methyl ether on thin-layer chromatograms after methylation of the soil extract (35). In addition to the recognizable degradation products, several unknowns were present on the radioautographs. Polar products are formed during the degradation of both trifluralin and benefin and probably arise through the formation of aromatic amines in the degradations.

2. Plants

Residue analysis with a sensitivity of 5 to 10 ppb indicated that trifluralin and benefin or their degradation products were not incorporated in the leaves, seeds, or fruit of a wide variety of plants. Roots from plants grown in soil containing these herbicides will exhibit a residue, but only in that region of contact with the herbicide. Although no residue has been encountered in most tolerant crops, studies were undertaken to determine the distribution of residual radioactivity in plants grown in soil containing ^{14}C-labeled trifluralin and benefin (19,20,32).

Analyses of soybean and cotton plants grown in soil containing ^{14}C trifluralin labeled in the propyl group or in the trifluoromethyl group revealed the presence of radioactivity in the lipids, glycosides, hydrolysis products, proteins, and cellular fractions. The universal distribution of the radioactivity without definite identification of trifluralin or recognizable metabolites suggests nondescript incorporation.

Residues of trifluralin were found on the outside layer or peel of some root crops. The amount of trifluralin found in carrot root depends upon the age and size of the root as well as the rate and depth of trifluralin incorporation in the soil.

Carrots were grown in soil containing ^{14}C-trifluoromethyl-labeled trifluralin (20). The average total radioactivity found in carrots was 0.65

ppm calculated as trifluralin, which was distributed principally in the peel (69 %) and at the approximate junction of the phloem and the xylem (10 %). Trifluralin constituted 84 % of the radioactivity in the carrot extract, with the major metabolic product (6) representing approximately 4.3 % of the total radioactivity. Trace amounts of α,α,α-trifluoro-5-nitro-N-propyl-toluene-3,4-diamine (9) and 4-(dipropylamino)-3,5-dinitrobenzoic acid (18) were identified by thin-layer chromatography with one trace zone of radio-activity not identified. Less than 5 % of the radioactivity present was in the nonidentified polar product fraction. Figure 9-5 shows the pathway of trifluralin metabolism in carrot root based on identifiable metabolites only.

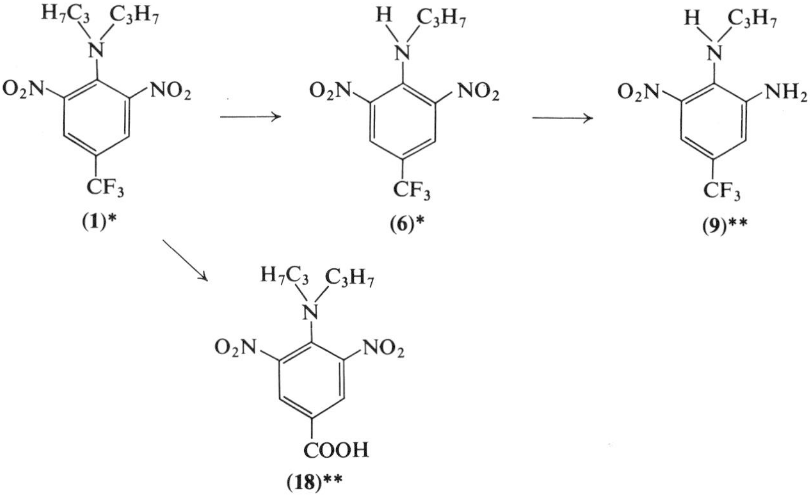

Fig. 9-5. Reactions sequence of trifluralin degradation in carrot root based on identified* and detected** products.

It was not determined if the compounds found in carrot root were the result of degradation in soil or the result of biological conversion by carrot tissue. The presence of model compound (18), in which the trifluoromethyl group had been changed to a carboxyl group, does suggest that this compound was not absorbed from soil, as it has been found only in the plant tissue. A trace amount of trifluralin was the only identifiable product in carrot tops.

Biswas and Hamilton (36) exposed bare-rooted sweet potato and peanut plants to a solution of ^{14}C–trifluoromethyl-labeled trifluralin for up to 72 hours. Based on thin-layer chromatography and infrared analysis of the plant extracts, they suggested trifluralin may have been metabolized by dealkylation, reduction, or the probable formation of a benzoic acid or phenolic derivative.

Herberg et al. (32) investigated the metabolism of ^{14}C-labeled benefin in peanut plants and alfalfa. Mature peanut plants, grown under growth-room conditions, were harvested and divided into leaves, stems, roots, hulls, and meat. The distribution of total radioactivity, benefin, and its metabolites, was determined by radiochemical methods in conjunction with thin-layer chromatographic methods described by Golab (35,37).

A striking feature of the results is a comparison of the total radioactivity incorporated in peanut plant parts and the amount of extractable radioactivity that is associated with recognizable compounds. More than 93% of the radioactivity, like that associated with trifluralin in soybeans and cotton plants, is nondescript and is viewed as extensively degraded benefin. In peanut plant parts, benefin was the principal compound detected and represents 3% of the total radioactivity (equivalent to 0.20 ppm of benefin). Of the total benefin, leaves and stems accounted for < 0.02 ppm and meat < 0.001 ppm. The detectable degradation products, which match the cochromatographed model compounds on radioautographs of thin-layer chromatograms, constitute a smaller amount of radioactivity than that reported for benefin. The maximum concentration of the major degradation product in roots (12) was calculated to be 0.114 ppm. Examination of the degradation products in the various plant parts reveals a similarity of products in roots and hulls with those recognized in soil. In order, stems, leaves, and meats contain fewer products in lesser amounts. These differences suggest that benefin and its degradation products were absorbed from soil and translocated in the plant rather than the adsorption of benefin and its metabolism in the plant tissue. If benefin were metabolized directly in the plant, the recognizable degradation products should be distributed more uniformly. This view is further supported by observations with alfalfa grown in soil treated with labeled benefin at the same rate (32).

Six cuttings of alfalfa were harvested over a period of 227 days. Although the amount of radioactivity found in the different cuttings gradually declines over the experimental period, the mean total radioactivity calculated as benefin was approximately 0.560 ppm. Benefin constituted 1.5% of the total radioactivity in the alfalfa plants. Recognizable degradation products, compounds (10), (11), and (16), were detectable only in trace amounts. Again the majority of radioactivity, approximately 94%, resided in the fractions described as extractable polar products and nonextractable products. The radioactive compounds in the alfalfa plant are similar to the degradation products found in soil but in lesser amounts.

C. Anaerobic Degradation

1. Soil

In the course of investigating trifluralin degradation in soil with moisture contents adjusted to 0, 50, 100, and 200% of field capacity (FC), it was observed that trifluralin in soil at 200% FC was degraded more rapidly as compared to other moisture contents (*18,19*). At 200% FC, 50% of the

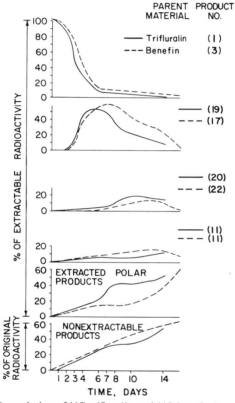

Fig. 9-6. Degradation of ^{14}C-trifluralin and ^{14}C-benefin in soil under water.

added trifluralin disappeared in 10 days and 84% in 24 days. This rapid degradation of trifluralin under this type of "anaerobic" condition was not associated with anaerobic microorganisms or soil type, but it was temperature dependent.

This type of anaerobic state may exist for a short time under conditions of excessive rainfall coupled with poor drainage. This system, soil under water, provided a unique condition for monitoring the degradation of trifluralin and benefin incorporated in soil. Separate experiments were initiated in which both ^{14}C-labeled trifluralin and benefin were incorporated in soil at 4 ppmw; then the respective soils were flooded with water and incubated at 24.5° in the growth room (*19,35*). Figure 9-6 compares the rapid degradation of trifluralin and benefin and the sequential formation of their respective degradation products. In both cases the major reduction product, compounds (**19**) and (**17**) (trifluralin and benefin with one nitro group reduced to an amino group, respectively), appeared maximal on the fifth to the seventh day and then gradually declined. With the decline of compound (**19**), in the trifluralin study, there is a simultaneous rise in compound (**20**), α,α,α-trifluoro-*N,N*-dipropyltoluidine-3,4,5-triamine, as well as extractable polar products. Although the amount of the dealkylated triamine (**11**) steadily increases with time, its formation cannot be considered a major pathway.

As shown in Fig. 9-6, benefin was degraded in a pattern similar to that of trifluralin, with the exception that benefin-extractable polar products formed more slowly. The key reaction in the anaerobic degradation of both trifluralin and benefin is the formation of the first reduction products which serve as the intermediates in the formation of extractable polar products and nonextractable products. The conversion of aromatic amines to polar products is rapid and constitutes the major route of decomposition.

The use of thin-layer chromatography coupled with radioautography provided evidence for the occurrence of lesser metabolites in the soils. Figures 9-7 and 9-8 show the postulated pathways of anaerobic trifluralin and benefin degradation in soil. In the degradation of trifluralin in soil under water (Fig. 9-7), a prominent unknown appeared simultaneously with compound (**20**). This unknown was postulated to be compound (**21**), α,α,α-trifluoro-*N*-propyltoluene-3,4,5-triamine, by its chromatographic behavior. Although compound (**21**) was not available as a reference compound for direct comparison, compound (**15**), α,α,α-trifluoro-*N*-butyltoluene-3,4,5-triamine, a similar analog in the benefin series, was observed in the anaerobic degradation of benefin in soil (Fig. 9-8).

The organic matter in soil would provide a ready source of protons for the reductive degradation of trifluralin-type compounds under the defined anaerobic conditions. However, Golab (*35*) observed that trifluralin degrades more slowly but follows the same anaerobic pathway if Florisil (a commercial magnesium trisilicate) is substituted for soil under the same conditions. The reactions involving Florisil, trifluralin, and water suggest a surface-catalyzed phenomenon, but the source of protons for the reductions

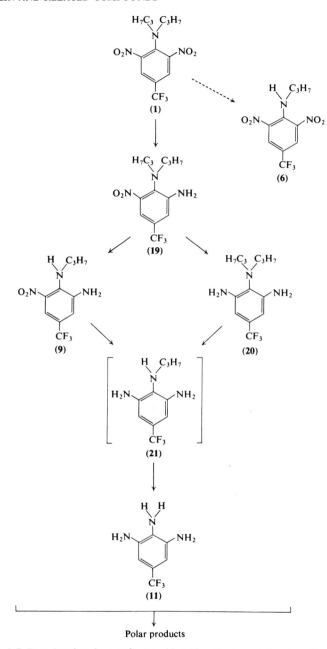

Fig. 9-7. Postulated pathway of anaerobic trifluralin degradation in soil.

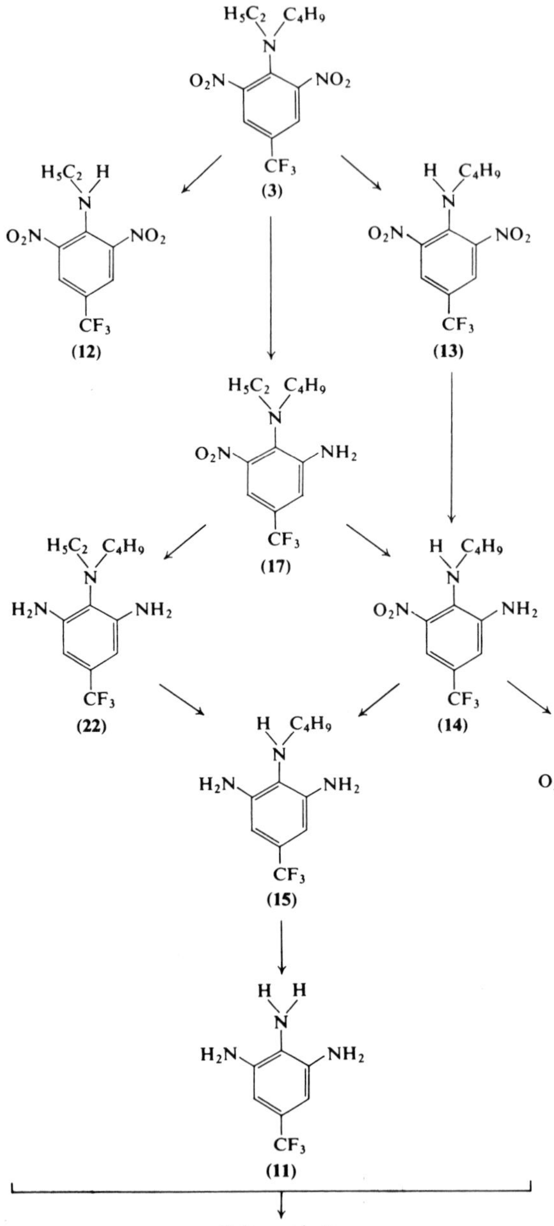

Fig. 9-8. Postulated pathway of anaerobic benefin degradation in soil.

occurring under these conditions is obscure. It is interesting to speculate that the reductive pathway might result from proton donation by the alkyl group produced by an initial oxidative dealkylation. This hypothesis is supported by the fact that during the initial 24 hours of trifluralin degradation in soil under water, the monodealkylated product (6) was detected; however, it subsequently disappeared after 36 hours. In the anaerobic degradation of benefin, both monodealkylated products, compounds (12) and (13), were present as minor constituents. Although these dealkylation reactions were attributed to aerobic conditions existing in the initial stage of the experiment, it seems possible that the alkyl groups could be the source of protons for reduction.

2. Animals

The products identified in the metabolism of trifluralin in animals and artificial rumen fluid indicate a reductive degradation pathway. Emmerson and Anderson (21) administered a single oral dose of ^{14}C–trifluoromethyl-labeled trifluralin to rats. Eighty per cent of the radioactivity was excreted in the feces, while the remaining portion appeared in the urine. Trifluralin and the amino derivative of trifluralin (19) were isolated and identified from feces. Three urinary metabolites were isolated and identified as dealkylated product (7), the diamine (10), and the reduced monodealkylated derivative (9). Other minor metabolites were detected on radioautographs of thin-layer chromatograms. Figure 9-9 shows the dealkylation and reduction pathways of trifluralin degradation in the rats based only on the identified metabolites in urine and feces. The monopropyl derivative (6), shown in the figure with brackets, was apparent in thin-layer chromatography but was not confirmed by other criteria. Trifluralin metabolism in the dog is similar to that observed in the rat.

A lactating cow was fed trifluralin at 1 ppm and also at 1000 ppm in its ration for 39 and 13 days, respectively, to determine the absorption, metabolism, and excretion in ruminant animals. Examination of urine, feces, blood, and milk revealed detectable residues only in feces after the ingestion of trifluralin at 1000 ppm. Trifluralin, (19), and (20), with one and two nitro groups reduced, respectively, were detected in the feces by gas chromatography (22). The results were not adequate to determine the fate of trifluralin in the dairy cow, but indicated it was rapidly metabolized.

Since less than 1 % of the trifluralin administered to the cow could be accounted for, Herberg et al. (22) studied the metabolism of ^{14}C-labeled trifluralin in the goat. A goat was fed nonlabeled trifluralin at 1 ppm in the diet for 11 days, labeled trifluralin for 1 day, and nonlabeled trifluralin

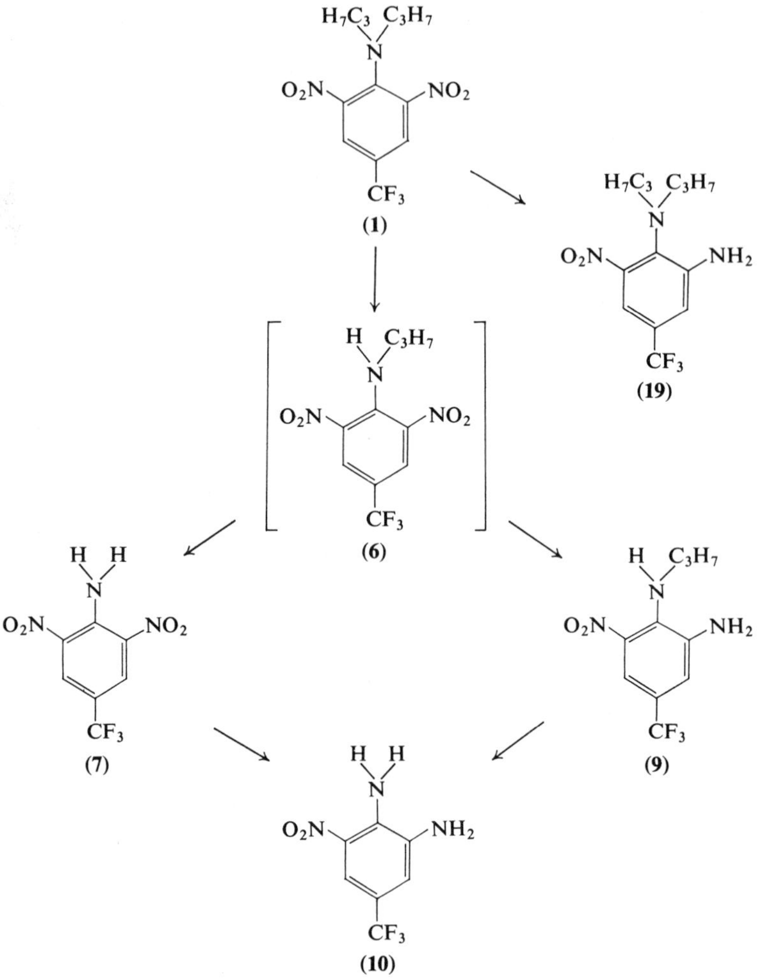

Fig. 9-9. Reaction sequence of trifluralin degradation in the rat based on identified products in fecal material, (1) and (19), and urinary products, (7), (9), and (10).

again for 14 days. Within 6 days, 99% of adminstered radioactivity was accounted for in the urine (17.8%) and feces (81.2%). Radioactivity was present in the urine for 3 days and in the feces for 6 days after adminstration of the labeled compound. No increase in radioactivity above normal level was found in the milk or blood. Of the total radioactivity accounted for in the urine and feces, only 10% was in the form of recognizable compounds.

Neither urine nor feces contained trifluralin. The major metabolite found in the urine and the only one in feces was compound (**20**), trifluralin with both nitro groups reduced. Detection of several other minor metabolites in urine supports a reductive pathway of trifluralin degradation in ruminant animals. Similar studies conducted with ring-labeled benefin revealed the turnover time to be essentially identical with that observed with trifluralin (*32*).

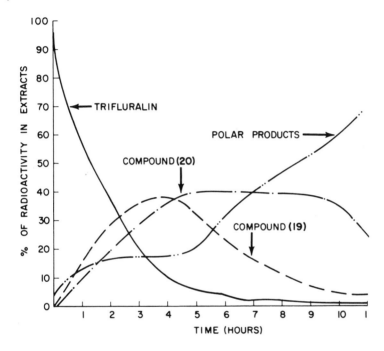

Fig. 9-10. Trifluralin degradation and the formation of degradative products in artificial rumen fluid.

According to Golab et al. (*23,35*), artificial rumen fluid rapidly degrades both trifluralin and benefin. This is a unique medium for observing the rapid formation of degradation products. In separate experiments labeled trifluralin and benefin were introduced into a mixture of rumen fluid and artificial saliva. The mixture was maintained in 1 atm of carbon dioxide and incubated at 37°. Figures 9-10 and 9-11 compare the rapid destruction of trifluralin and benefin as well as the formation of major metabolites.

Trifluralin reduction products, compounds (19) and (20), constitute the major metabolites observed during the course of the reaction (Fig. 9-10). A decline of these metabolites causes an increase in polar products. Radio-autographs of thin-layer chromatograms indicate the presence of compounds (6) and (9) as well as an additional unknown. These latter metabolites are products of dealkylation and represent only 0.1 % of the original trifluralin present in the system. Trifluralin degradation in artificial rumen

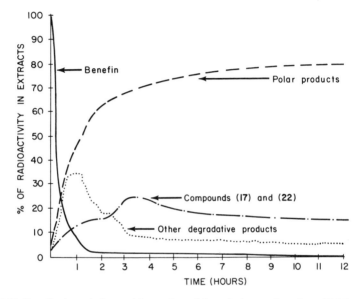

Fig. 9-11. Benefin degradation and formation of degradative products in artificial rumen fluid.

fluid generally follows the pathway outlined for anaerobic degradation in soil shown in Fig. 9-7.

In the artificial rumen fluid system, benefin is degraded more rapidly than trifluralin. Figure 9-11 shows the combined formation of the reduction products, compounds (17) and (22). Other degradation products include the minor metabolites associated with the anaerobic benefin degradation shown in Fig. 9-8. Polar products of benefin accumulate rapidly and constitute 79 % of the extracted radioactivity after 16 hours.

Williams (38) demonstrated that anaerobic growth of *Lachnospira multiparus* and *Bacteroides ruminicola* subsp. *brevis* was not suppressed by trifluralin up to a concentration of 0.5 and 0.1%, respectively. Studies employing ^{14}C–propyl-labeled trifluralin indicated these organisms metabolized trifluralin anaerobically by cleavage of the propyl group and reduction of a nitro group to an amine. Less than 0.03% of the propyl-labeled trifluralin was converted to $^{14}CO_2$. These results are comparable to those observed in artificial rumen fluid.

9-4. MODE OF ACTION

Trifluralin and related compounds exert their herbicidal effect by inhibiting both root and shoot growth and development. Swelling of cotton root terminals, a phenomenon which occurs at the tips of affected roots in most species studied, was first reported by Standifer et al. (39). Fischer (40) observed inhibition of secondary root formation in young cotton plants. The inhibition of root development can be minimized by limiting the depth of soil incorporation of the herbicide. Trifluralin at 0.01–3.0 ppm in nutrient solution had no effect on germination but decreased root length of corn seedlings and cucumber hypocotyls, according to Schultz et al. (41). They also observed that Avena coleoptiles were inhibited by trifluralin in the presence or absence of indoleacetic acid at 10^{-7} M concentration.

The response of 12 plant species to soil-incorporated trifluralin and benefin under greenhouse conditions was explored by Negi and Funderburk (42). The species were grouped on a basis of inhibition of emergence and growth at different rates of application ranging up to 15 ppm. The most tolerant species were mustard, peanuts, soybeans, and cotton. Species intermediate in tolerance were morning glory, corn, cucumber, tomato, and bean. The susceptible group included oats, Johnsongrass, and sorghum. Generally, trifluralin was more toxic to these species than benefin.

Histological examination of root tips grown in the presence of trifluralin provides additional insight into the physiological action of the herbicide. Talbert (43) observed that trifluralin appeared to inhibit cell division in meristematic root tissue of intact soybean roots grown in aerated nutrient solution. A noticeable increase in cell nuclei in the prophase stage of division appeared after 2 hours of treatment as compared to controls. With continued exposure to trifluralin, numerous large polynucleated cells appeared after 24 hours. The cells or corn and cotton root tips, examined by Amato et al. (44), were small and dense; many were multinucleated, with some cells containing up to five nuclei. Normal mitosis was absent. Similar results were obtained by Negi et al. (45). They observed that the epidermis of both roots and shoots of treated corn seedlings were either disorganized or not present. It was suggested that the increase in epidermis cell size could not keep pace with the rate of increase in size of the cortex, which was also irregular in shape.

In summary, morphological and histological evidence demonstrates an effect of trifluralin on plant-cell division. Little information is available on this biological expression in terms of biochemical processes in elucidating the mode of action of trifluralin and related compounds. Schultz and Funderburk (46) have investigated the effect of trifluralin on nucleic acid and protein synthesis in corn roots. Dry weight, total nucleic acids, DNA, RNA, and protein were determined in roots of 3-day-old corn seedlings germinated on paper toweling impregnated with trifluralin. The dry weights of treated and untreated roots were similar, but nucleic acid and protein per milligram of dry weight were reduced in the treated roots. Reduction in total nucleic acid was reflected in the DNA fraction as RNA was increased slightly in the treated plants. Concentrations of 5 and 10 ppm of trifluralin applied to the roots of both sweet potatoes and peanut plants grown in nutrient culture for 72 hours increased both carbohydrates and nucleic acids in the harvested plants, according to Dukes and Biswas (47). The disparity of results in these two investigations in relation to the nucleic acid content possibly can be explained on the differences in the experimental methods employed.

Inhibition of oxygen uptake and oxidative phosphorylation in isolated mitochondria of corn, sorghum, and soybean by both trifluralin and nitralin was investigated by Negi et al. (48). Trifluralin at 10^{-4} M significantly inhibited the oxygen uptake by approximately 25 % in corn and sorghum, with soybean inhibition being about three times greater. At the same concentration the net phosphorus uptake was significantly reduced by more than 50 % in sorghum and corn. The phosphorus uptake in soybean was of the same magnitude, with trifluralin concentration at 10^{-6} M. Results with nitralin were similar, but somewhat more variable. As pointed out by Negi et al., it is not certain that the effect of trifluralin and nitralin on isolated mitochondria takes place in the intact plants, as the active agents must enter the cell and be available to the mitochondria at appropriate concentrations. There is no evidence that trifluralin enters the cell, but inhibition of these processes could be involved in the mode of action of trifluralin. However, the selective herbicidal activity of trifluralin is not explained, as the reduction of oxygen and phosphorus uptake was greater in the resistant species, soybeans, than in the susceptible species, sorghum.

9-5. SUMMARY

Selective herbicidal properties of substituted dinitroanilines may be due to inherent physiological or biochemical characteristics of tolerant and susceptible plants. Physiological tolerance can result from seeds having well-developed embryos and characterized by rapid germination and subsequent growth of both radicle and hypocotyl, thus permitting the root and shoot to grow out of the zone of chemical control. Cotton and soybeans, in addition to having some inherent chemical tolerance, possess these characteristics. On the other hand, mustard and peanuts appear to exhibit greater inherent chemical tolerance in that they survive high concentrations of trifluralin (42).

Although the mode of action of the dinitroaniline herbicides remains obscure, extensive investigation of two representatives, trifluralin and benefin, clearly established which molecular functional groups are modified readily. Studies on the degradation of nitralin have not been reported, but similar pathways of degradation would be expected. The degradation under defined "aerobic" and "anaerobic" conditions favors dealkylation or reduction reactions. The degradation pathways of both herbicides are similar with two notable exceptions: (1) the presence of 4-(dipropylamino)-3,5-dinitrobenzoic acid, trifluralin with the trifluoromethyl group changed to a carboxyl group, in carrot tissue; and (2) the presence of α,α,α-trifluoro-2,6-dinitro-p-cresol in benefin-treated soil under aerobic conditions.

The existence of the benzoic acid derivative is supported by observations with ^{14}C–trifluoromethyl-labeled trifluralin exposed to light in methanol solution. Radioautographs of thin-layer chromatograms of the methanol mixture revealed a radioactive spot which matched the reference compound (35). If light energy can initiate the oxidation of the trifluoromethyl group, it is possible that a similar reaction can occur in carrot tissue. Whether the reaction is enzymatic or nonenzymatic cannot be explained on the basis of present evidence.

Formation of the cresol from either trifluralin or benefin is not universal in all degradation studies as compared to products of dealkylation and reduction. The fact that the cresol was not detected in trifluralin degradation in soil, as contrasted to benefin, may be due to particular experimental conditions or other factors.

The decomposition rate of these herbicides and the accumulation of recognizable degradation products varied markedly in soils, plants, and animals. Microorganisms show great diversity in decomposing organic molecules, but there is little evidence for the microbiological degradation of trifluralin and related compounds. Although small amounts of $^{14}CO_2$ have been demonstrated from both soils and plants in studies with labeled trifluralin, no $^{14}CO_2$ is liberated during the rapid degradation of trifluralin or benefin by artificial rumen fluid. Biological action may be directed to intermediate products resulting from physicochemical decomposition of the parent compound occurring as a function of the environment. Trifluralin is rapidly destroyed by light or in oxygen-deficient aqueous media possessing certain surface characteristics which can be part of an experimental environment. The effects of these physicochemical characteristics may be misinterpreted as an enzyme-catalyzed phenomenon.

Present evidence is inadequate to claim that trifluralin is actively metabolized by plants. On the contrary, the evidence suggests that it is metabolized slowly or not at all. Indeed, the herbicidal property of the substituted dinitroanilines could be due to the inability of plants to metabolize these compounds. The bizarre morphological and histological changes observed in roots exposed to these herbicides suggest that these compounds profoundly affect development of plant cell walls and membranes. Their selective action may be associated with the ability of tolerant plants to develop in spite of the agent or metabolize it at a local site. Further investigation is required to establish the validity of these speculations.

In considering the overall degradation of the substituted dinitroanilines investigated in soils, plants, and animals, the importance of the material referred to as polar products cannot be disregarded. Formation of the unidentified polar mixture from both trifluralin and benefin appears to be the main pathway for the ultimate degradation into carbon dioxide and water.

REFERENCES

1. N. G. Clark and A. F. Hams, *Biochem. J.*, **55**, 839 (1953).
2. R. F. Brookes, N. G. Clark, A. F. Hams, and H. A. Stevenson, Brit. Pat. 845,916 (1960).
3. Plant Regulators, CBCC Positive Data, Series 2, National Research Council, June 1955.
4. Q. F. Soper, E. F. Alder, and W. L. Wright, *Proc. Southern Weed Conf.*, **14**, 86 (1961).
5. E. F. Alder, W. L. Wright, and Q. F. Soper, *Proc. N. Central Weed Control Conf.*, **17**, 23 (1960).
6. S. J. Pieczarka, W. L. Wright, and E. F. Alder, *Weed Soc. Am. Abstr.*, 1961, p. 10.

7. S. J. Pieczarka, W. L. Wright, and E. F. Alder, *Proc. Northeast. Weed Control Conf.*, **16**, 356 (1962).
8. S. J. Pieczarka, W. L. Wright, and E. F. Alder, *Proc. Southern Weed Conf.*, **15**, 92 (1962).
9. E. F. Alder and R. B. Bevington, *Proc. Northeast. Weed Control Conf.*, **16**, 505 (1962).
10. W. A. Gentner, *Weeds*, **14**, 176 (1966).
11. L. Guse, W. Humphreys, J. Hooks, J. V. Gramlich, and W. Arnold, *Proc. Southern Weed Conf.*, **19**, 121 (1966).
12. W. J. Hughes and R. H. Schieferstein, *Proc. Southern Weed Conf.*, **19**, 170 (1966).
13. Technical Report on TREFLAN, Rept. No. EA6103, Elanco Products Company, Indianapolis, Ind., April 1966.
14. Technical Report on BALAN, Rept. No. EA6104, Elanco Products Company, Indianapolis, Ind., May 1966.
15. Q. F. Soper, U.S. Pat. 3,257,190 (1966).
16. S. B. Solaway and K. D. Zwahlen, U.S. Pat. 3,227, 734 (1966).
17. S. J. Parka and H. M. Worth, *Proc. Southern Weed Conf.*, **18**, 469 (1965).
18. S. J. Parka and J. B. Tepe, *Weed Soc. Am. Abstr.*, 1966, p. 40.
19. G. W. Probst, T. Golab, R. J. Herberg, F. J. Holzer, S. J. Parka, C. Van der Schans, and J. B. Tepe, *J. Agr. Food Chem.*, **15**, 592 (1967).
20. T. Golab, R. J. Herberg, S. J. Parka, and J. B. Tepe, *J. Agr. Food Chem.*, **15**, 638 (1967).
21. J. L. Emmerson and R. C. Anderson, *Toxicol. Appl. Pharmacol.*, **9**, 84 (1966).
22. R. J. Herberg, T. Golab, A. P. Raun, and F. J. Holzer, American Chemical Society, 153rd Meeting, Miami Beach, 1967, Abstr. No. 45.
23. T. Golab, E. W. Day, Jr., and G. W. Probst, American Chemical Society, 153rd Meeting, Miami Beach, 1967, Abstr. No. 44.
24. T. Golab, *J. Chromatog.*, **18**, 406 (1965).
25. J. B. Tepe and R. E. Scroggs, *Trifluralin, Analytical Methods for Pesticides, Plant Growth Regulators and Food Additives*, Vol. 5 (Supplemental Volume), (G. Zweig, ed.), Academic Press, New York, 1967, p. 527.
26. F. J. Marshall, R. E. McMahon, and R. G. Jones, *J. Agr. Food Chem.*, **14**, 498 (1966).
27. M. L. Scheinbaum, Ph.D., thesis, Howard Univ., Washington, D.C., 1964.
28. W. L. Wright and G. F. Warren, *Weeds*, **13**, 329 (1965).
29. E. W. Day, Jr., unpublished work, 1963.
30. R. E. McMahon, *Tetrahedron Letters*, **1966**(21), 2307.
31. S. J. Parka and J. B. Tepe, *Weed Soc. Am. Abstr.*, 1968, p. 78.
32. R. J. Herberg, J. V. Gramlich, and T. Golab, unpublished work, 1967.
33. H. H. Funderburk, Jr., D. P. Schultz, N. S. Negi, R. Rodriguez-Kabana, and E. A. Curl, *Proc. Southern Weed Conf.*, **20**, 389 (1967).
34. R. Bartha and D. Pramer, *Science*, **156**, 3782 (1967).
35. T. Golab, unpublished work, 1967.
36. P. K. Biswas and W. Hamilton, Jr., *VIth Intern. Congr. Plant Protection, Abstr.*, Vienna, 1967, p. 388.
37. T. Golab, *J. Chromatog.*, **30**, 253 (1967).
38. P. P. Williams, *Bacteriol. Proc.*, **67**, 8 (1967.)
39. L. C. Standifer, Jr., L. W. Sloane, and M. E. Wright, *Proc. Southern Weed Conf.*, **18**, 92 (1965).
40. B. B. Fischer, *Australian J. Exptl. Agr. Animal Husbandry*, **6**, 214 (1966).
41. D. P. Schultz, H. H. Funderburk, Jr., N. S. Negi, *Weed Soc. Am. Abstr.*, 1966, p. 42.

42. N. S. Negi and H. H. Funderburk, Jr., *Proc. Southern Weed Conf.*, **20**, 369 (1967).
43. R. E. Talbert, *Proc. Southern Weed Conf.*, **18**, 642 (1965).
44. V. A. Amato, R. R. Hoverson, and J. Hacskaylo, *Proc. Assoc. Southern Agr. Workers*, *62nd Ann. Conv.*, 1965, p. 234.
45. N. S. Negi, H. H. Funderburk, Jr., and D. P. Schultz, Agr. Expt. Station, Auburn Univ. Botany and Plant Pathology, Departmental Series No. 2, Auburn, Ala., 1967.
46. D. P. Schultz and H. H. Funderburk, Jr., *Weed Soc. Am. Abstr.*, 1967, p. 58.
47. I. E. Dukes and P. K. Biswas, *Weed. Soc. Am. Abstr.*, 1967, p. 59.
48. N. S. Negi, H. H. Funderburk, Jr., D. P. Schultz, and D. E. Davis, *Weeds*, **11**, 265 (1968).

CHAPTER 10

Diquat and Paraquat

H. H. FUNDERBURK, Jr.

BOTANY AND PLANT PATHOLOGY DEPARTMENT
AUBURN UNIVERSITY AGRICULTURAL EXPERIMENT STATION
AUBURN, ALABAMA

10-1. Introduction 283
A. Chemical and Physical Properties 285
10-2. Degradation 286
A. Degradation of Diquat and Paraquat by Higher Plants . . 286
B. Degradation of Diquat and Paraquat by Microorganisms . 287
C. Photochemical Degradation of Diquat and Paraquat . . 290
D. Fate of Diquat and Paraquat in an Aquatic Environment . . 293
10-3. Mode of Action 294
References 296

10-1. INTRODUCTION

It is not intended that this be a general review on the dipyridyl herbicides, but instead it is a rather thorough treatment of their degradation. For a complete review see Calderbank (*1*). Quaternary ammonium compounds have been used since 1933 as redox indicators under the name of viologens (*2*), but the herbicidal activity of diquat [6,7-dihydrodipyrido(1,2-*a* : 2′,1′-*c*)pyrazidiinium salt] (**1**) was not discovered until early in 1955 (*3*). Michaelis and Hill (*2*) showed that the first step in this reduction involved the addition of one electron to the quaternary salt to form a stable, water-soluble,

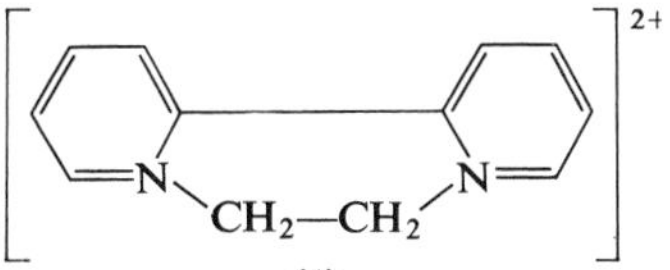

(**1**)

283

intensely colored free radical. Recent work in this general area has been done by Johnson and Gutowsky (4). Since 1955 work has been carried out on the properties and mode of action of this chemical and related compounds and has led to the discovery of paraquat (1,1'-dimethyl-4,4'-bipyridylium salt) (2). Many uses have been found for these chemicals during the last decade (5–14). Unlike most herbicides, the dipyridyls are extremely quick weed killers, causing a top kill of a wide range of plant species at low rates (9,15). Because of this phenomenon, diquat has been used effectively as a desiccant on potatoes (8,9,16,17) and many seed crops including clover, peas, beans, sugar beets, and mangels (18). Diquat has also been used successfully as a defoliant and desiccant for cotton (19). Use of the dipyridyls as desiccants is also spreading to other crops (18).

Pasture renovation is another area where the dipyridyls are being used. Paraquat can be used to kill poor or unwanted grasses in preparation for reseeding with good grass, which under most conditions can be achieved without plowing and with little other preparation (18).

$$\left[CH_3-N \overset{}{\bigcirc}-\overset{}{\bigcirc} N-CH_3 \right]^{2+}$$

(2)

Both diquat and paraquat are effective general weed killers. Their lack of residual activity in most soils limits their use on some industrial sites where long periods of weed control are desirable. However, this rapid inactivation in most soils makes them very suitable for killing weeds before the emergence of the crop (9). The wide spectrum of activity shown by paraquat and diquat limits their use as selective weed killers in growing crops, but there are certain situations in which they can be used without risk of loss. They are not absorbed by brown or older bark and can be used as directed sprays in tree crops, bush fruit, and vines (9). Furthermore, their lack of activity in most soils (20–25) allows their use in susceptible crops, provided that care is taken to avoid contact with the crop plant (9). In addition to selective uses, which depend on avoiding contact with the crop plant, there is a limited selection of crop weed combinations in which there is a sufficient difference in susceptibility to permit the use of one of the dipyridyls as an overall spray. When these herbicides are used in this way, there is usually some damge to the crop, but recovery is rapid and complete (9).

Both diquat and paraquat have been used successfully for the control of various species of aquatic plants. Blackburn and Weldon (7) reported that both chemicals were effective on duckweed (*Lemna minor* L.), azolla (*Azolla carolina* Willd.), and watermeal (*Wolffia columbiana* Karst.). Hiltibran (*26*) reported that diquat was effective on several emergent, submersed, and free-floating plants common in central Illinois ponds. Lawrence (*27*) reported that diquat and paraquat were effective on naiad, parrot feather, elodea, stargrass, eelgrass, duckweed, water hyacinth, needle rush, salvinia, and pithophora.

A. Chemical and Physical Properties

Diquat can be formulated as the dichloride or dibromide salts. The cationic portion of the molecule is the active part. The salts are soluble in water to the extent of 70%. They are also nonvolatile, stable in acid or neutral solution, but form colored complex products in strong alkali (*18,28*). The dibromide salt has a melting point of 320°, and the cation has a molecular weight of 184.

Solutions of diquat turn an intense green color on reduction, due to the formation of a water-soluble, relatively stable, free radical. Reduction is autoxidizable, so that on shaking the solution in air, it becomes colorless again due to the reformation of diquat. Solutions of the free radical exhibit a sharp absorption peak at 378 mμ, and this peak is of a greater intensity than that of unreduced diquat at about 310 mμ (*29*).

Paraquat can be formulated as the di(methyl sulfate) or the dichloride salts, and, like diquat, the cationic portion of the molecule is the active part. The salts are very soluble in water and are nonvolatile, and their stability in acids and bases is very similar to diquat. The molecular weight of the cation is 186.

Solutions of paraquat turn an intense purple color on reduction, due to the formation of a water-soluble, relatively stable, free radical (*30*). Like diquat, the reduction is autoxidizable, so that on shaking the solution in air, it becomes colorless again due to the reoxidation of paraquat. Solutions of the free-radical form absorb at 394 mμ, and the unreduced form absorbs at 260 mμ (*29*).

Concentrated aqueous solutions of paraquat and diquat corrode steel, tinplate, galvanized iron, and aluminum. Therefore, they should be stored only in glass or polyethylene bottles. Formulations for commercial use contain corrosion inhibitors.

Diquat and paraquat are adsorbed on soils by a process of base exchange and held very tenaciously (*18*). In this bound form, it is thought that they are relatively unavailable to various biological systems. This phenomenon will be discussed in detail in Section 10-2.

10-2. DEGRADATION

A. Degradation of Diquat and Paraquat by Higher Plants

Before a chemical can be degraded by a biological system, it usually has to move from the point of application into the living system (31). Some work on absorption and translocation of diquat and paraquat has been done, and the data appear to be quite variable (32–36). Funderburk and Lawrence (33) studied the movement of both chemicals in alligatorweed [Alternanthera philoxeroides (Mart.) Griseb] and found very little translocation of foliar-applied material. Lack of movement could have been due to the desiccating effect that the chemicals had on the leaves. It was further found that very little diquat or paraquat was absorbed and/or adsorbed by the roots of alligatorweed growing in nutrient solution. In most instances it was less than 5% of that applied. However, this amount of uptake was sufficient for subsequent metabolism studies. Funderburk and Lawrence (33) also reported that diquat and paraquat were not very mobile in submersed weeds.

Baldwin (32) has shown that a different situation exists when diquat is applied to the foliage of tomatoes. Under controlled conditions that involved a relatively high humidity, Baldwin treated one leaflet of several plants that had received no light 24 hours prior to treatment. After treatment, one plant was moved into the light after each of the following intervals: 0, 1, 3, and 5 hours. In all plants moved into the light after 1, 3, and 5 hours, death of the tissue was first noted in the treated leaflet after 1 hour and in the whole leaf after 5 hours; and 24 hours after the plants were brought into daylight, they had been completely killed. Baldwin found that in the absence of light no movement of diquat occurred from the treated leaflet to any extent; however, after 5 hours in the light the material was almost completely distributed in every part of the plant. Baldwin suggested that this pattern of movement was compatible with a transport of diquat in the xylem.

Smith and Davies (35) also reported that paraquat showed predominantly xylem translocation, with no apical accumulation and little basal translocation. Thrower et al. (36) studied the movement of diquat in several plants and found that the presence of cuticular wax on leaves interfered with the entry of diquat. Movement of diquat within the plant occurred readily in either light or darkness, and ringing experiments showed that movement took place predominantly in the xylem. Movement in light took place when the relative humidity was near 100% but was markedly less when the humidity was near 50%. Therefore, dipyridyls will move into plants under certain conditions.

After obtaining knowledge concerning the absorption, translocation, and distribution patterns of these chemicals, Funderburk and Lawrence (34) studied their metabolism in bean and alligatorweed. Autoradiographs of electrochromatograms spotted with extracts from alligatorweed indicated that the only ^{14}C-labeled material in the extract was diquat and paraquat. Aqueous extracts of beans treated with ^{14}C-labeled paraquat were extracted with four nonmiscible organic solvents and no radioactivity moved into the organic solvent phase. Aliquots from the aqueous phase were subjected to electrochromatography and autoradiography, and the only spot visible cochromatographed with authentic paraquat. Funderburk and Lawrence (34) also grew beans and alligatorweed that had been treated with ^{14}C-labeled diquat and paraquat in enclosed systems in which CO_2 was trapped, and in no case was there any $^{14}CO_2$ given off.

At the present time there is no indication that either diquat or paraquat is metabolized by higher plants. Slade (37) has reported on the degradation of paraquat applied to plants, but this degradation is physical rather than biological, and it will be discussed under Section 10-2.C.

B. Degradation of Diquat and Paraquat by Microorganisms

Rodriguez-Kabana et al. (38) studied the effect of paraquat on the growth of *Sclerotium rolfsii* Sacc. in liquid culture and in soil. In liquid culture, all concentrations of paraquat (12.5 to 1000 ppm) drastically reduced the mycelial dry weight. This was accompanied by a reduction in glucose, NO_3—N, and inorganic P utilization. Similar data were not taken on paraquat-treated soil, but CO_2 evolution was restricted by all concentrations and greatly reduced only at the high (500 and 1000 ppm) rates. The differences in concentration necessary for significant inhibition in soil and liquid culture were attributed to the strong adsorptive capacity of the soil clay fractions for this compound.

Rodriguez-Kabana et al. (39) also studied the effect of paraquat on *Rhizoctonia solani* Kuhn in liquid culture. The effect on dry weight production was essentially the same as that encountered with *S. rolfsii*.

Bozarth et al. (*40,41*) determined the effect of 0, 10, 100, 500, 1000, and 10,000 ppm of paraquat on the microflora of a sandy loam soil (Cahaba loamy fine sand). The effect of the various concentrations of paraquat on the total number of fungi was determined after 4, 8, and 21 days following treatment. A slight reduction in the number of fungi occurred in some treatments at longer incubation periods; this effect was more evident at the 10,000-ppm paraquat concentration.

In a similar study the total number of bacteria and actinomycetes was determined. At the 4-day incubation period, there was very little difference in numbers among all treatments receiving paraquat. For the 21-day incubation period, there was no appreciable difference in the number of bacteria and actinomycetes among the 0-, 10-, and 100-ppm treatments, but the number of these organisms increased considerably at the higher rates (500, 1000, and 10,000 ppm). The number of bacteria and actinomycetes for the 21-day incubation period was considerably less in all treatments than for the 4- and 8-day incubation periods.

Paraquat-tolerant microorganisms were isolated from Cahaba loamy fine sand that had been enriched with paraquat, serially diluted, and plated on media selected for the particular groups of microorganisms. From these plates a fungus and a bacterium, which grew rather well on high concentrations of paraquat, were selected for additional studies.

The fungus, *Neocosmospora vasinfecta* E. F. Sm., was capable of reducing paraquat to the colored free radical (*42*). This indicated that paraquat accepted electrons from some metabolic process within the fungus. Electrochromatography of the medium containing ^{14}C-labeled paraquat, in which the fungus was cultured, indicated no degradation of the herbicide.

The bacterial isolate (not identified) was also capable of reducing paraquat to the colored free radical. Extracts from the bacterial liquid medium containing 1000 ppm of ^{14}C-labeled paraquat was subjected to electrochromatography after 2, 4, 8, and 16 days. There was no apparent degradation after 2 days, but after 4 days two additional radioactive spots appeared. The 8- and 16-day autoradiographs were similar to the one for the 4-day incubation period. Of the two main spots on the plates other than paraquat, one moved approximately two-thirds the distance of paraquat toward the negative pole. The other spot moved a short distance toward the positive pole, indicating that one of the degradation products had a negative charge. One of the metabolites moved in a manner similar to 1-methyl-4,4′-dipyridinium ion, which has one less positive charge than paraquat (*43*). The other degradation product moved in a manner similar to that of 1-methyl-4-carboxypyridinium ion. Both of these compounds, the degradation product and the 1-methyl-4-carboxypyridinium ion, had a similar type of erratic movement on the thin-layer plates. The erratic movement of this compound can possibly be explained on the basis of its existing as a zwitterion. The pH of the solvent used in these investigations was approximately 4.5, and the buffering capacity of this system was not known. The pH of 4.5 may have been near the isoelectric point for this compound; thus any small change in pH would influence movement of the compound toward either the anode or cathode (43).

These studies suggest that a possible degradation pathway by the bacterial isolate consists of first demethylating the parent molecule, followed by ring

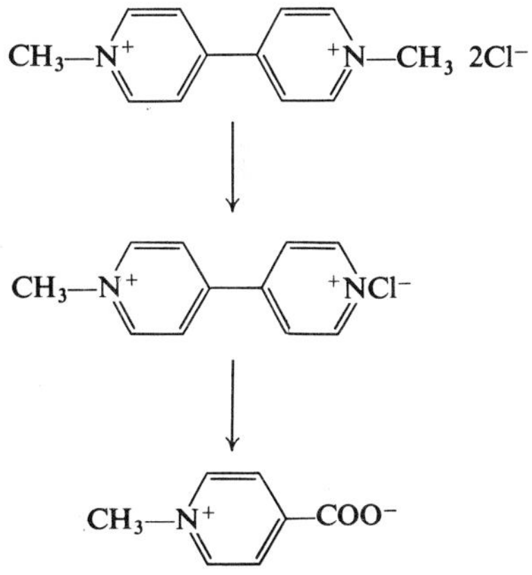

Fig. 10-1. Proposed pathway of degradation by a bacterial isolate. [Reprinted by permission from (43).]

cleavage of one of the heterocyclic rings to eventually form the carboxylated N-methylpyridinium ion (Fig. 10-1). Other intermediate compounds are probably formed during the degradation of paraquat, but none of these has been reported. The fate of the radioactive methyl group, which apparently is cleaved from paraquat, has not been accounted for.

Baldwin et al. (44) have isolated numerous organisms and assessed their ability to use paraquat as a sole source of carbon or nitrogen in synthetic media. Many organisms could grow freely in paraquat media with or without another source of carbon or nitrogen, but they failed to decompose the compound. The ability to utilize paraquat was determined by chemical analysis and by the disappearance of ^{14}C-labeled paraquat from culture solution. *Corynebacterium fascians* (Tilford) Dowson was adapted by serial subculture to tolerate up to 5 % w/v paraquat dichloride in liquid culture.

In cultures containing 10 ppm of paraquat, usually 30–40 % was decomposed in 3 weeks, but the rate and extent of decomposition was variable. Also, an unidentified anaerobic species from soil and *Clostridium pasteurianum* Winogradsky were about as effective as *C. fascians* in decomposing paraquat.

Baldwin et al. (*44*) also isolated a yeast from soils which utilizes paraquat as a sole source of nitrogen. This yeast has been identified as *Lipomyces starkeyi*, and unlike the other organisms described, it decomposed all the 20-ppm paraquat in the cultures and utilized paraquat in preference to nitrate nitrogen. When ^{14}C-labeled paraquat was added to liquid cultures inoculated with this yeast, 95 % of the paraquat was decomposed in 2 weeks, and 82–84 % of the radioactivity was given off as CO_2 during 4-week incubation at 24°. Paper chromatographic analysis of the culture failed to show the presence of intermediate products.

Studies presently underway with *L. starkeyi* in our laboratory support the work of Baldwin (*44*). In addition, we have also shown that this yeast can degrade diquat.

C. Photochemical Degradation of Diquat and Paraquat

Photochemical decomposition in UV light has been studied by Slade (*37, 45,46*) and Funderburk et al. (*29,47*), and it is evident that UV light rapidly degrades both diquat and paraquat (*29*). Funderburk et al. (*29*) reported that 50 % of the ^{14}C from both compounds was lost after 48 hours and more than 75 % after 96 hours. The data for paraquat only are shown in Fig. 10-2. This study measured the effect of UV light on the dipyridyls in the dry form, and apparently both chemicals were degraded to volatile compounds.

When the effect of UV light on dipyridyls was studied in aqueous solutions, no loss of radioactivity from the solutions occurred, but there was considerable degradation. No change occurred in diquat that was stored in the dark (check), and the concentration of diquat decreased with time of exposure to UV light. No diquat was present after 192 hours. Compounds containing ^{14}C, other than diquat, began to appear after only 8 hours of exposure to UV light (Fig. 10-3A).

The concentration of paraquat decreased with increased exposure to UV light, and very little paraquat was present after 48 hours (Fig. 10-3B). The first degradation products appeared after 24 hours, and the concentration of these compounds increased slightly with time of exposure to UV light. One of the degradation products had an R_f of 0.44 and cochromatographed with 1-methyl-4,4'-carboxypyridinium chloride. There were at least two additional degradation products with slightly higher R_f values (*29*).

Slade (*37,45,46*) showed that UV light from a mercury vapor lamp, as well as sunlight, was capable of degrading diquat and paraquat. Two degradation products were identified from paraquat exposed to UV light as 1-methyl-4-carboxypyridinium ion and methylamine hydrochloride and the degradation pathway in Fig. 10-4 was proposed. Slade (*37*) also applied

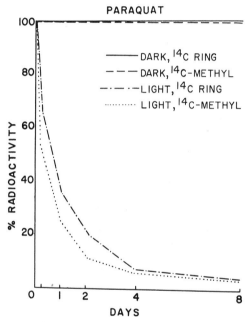

Fig. 10-2. Percentage radioactivity remaining in aluminum planchets containing ^{14}C-ring- and methyl-labeled paraquat after various periods of exposure to UV light. [Reprinted by permission from (*29*).]

paraquat dichloride to maize, tomato, and broad bean plants as droplets of an aqueous solution and analyzed the plants at intervals. In some cases the chemical was injected into plants rather than being applied to the surface. Plants were grown in the open, in the greenhouse, and in darkness. There was no loss of paraquat from plants in the dark, but considerable quantities were lost from plants grown in the open as well as in greenhouses during the summer. Some of the experiments were repeated in winter, but very little paraquat was degraded. The fact that maximum loss of paraquat occurred when the chemical largely remained on the leaf surface suggested that

photochemical degradation induced by UV light from the sun was responsible for the loss (37). Photochemical decomposition in sunlight does not
occur in solution, because the maximum absorption of UV light by aqueous
paraquat occurs as a sharp absorption peak at 257 mμ, whereas the lower
limit of the solar spectrum is 290 mμ. However, when paraquat is adsorbed
on a surface, its wavelength of maximum absorption moves to 275 mμ,

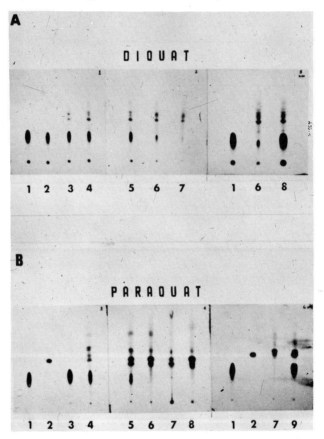

Fig. 10-3. Autoradiographs of thin-layer chromatograms spotted with aliquots from
solutions containing radioactive diquat or paraquat that had been exposed to UV light.
A, 1 = diquat; 2 = check; 3, 4, 5, 6, and 7 = diquat solutions exposed to UV light for 8,
24, 48, 96, and 192 hours, respectively; and 8 = cochromatography of 1 and 6. B, 1 = paraquat; 2 = 1-methyl,4-carboxypyridinium chloride; 3 = check; 4, 5, 6, 7, and 8 = paraquat
solutions exposed to UV light for 8, 24, 48, 96, and 192 hours, respectively; and 9 = cochromatography of 1, 2, and 7. [Reprinted by permission from (29).]

broadening considerably, and sufficient solar radiation at a wavelength greater than 290 mμ is absorbed by it for photochemical degradation (37). Photochemical degradation products isolated from plants sprayed with paraquat were the same as those isolated from paraquat exposed to UV light.

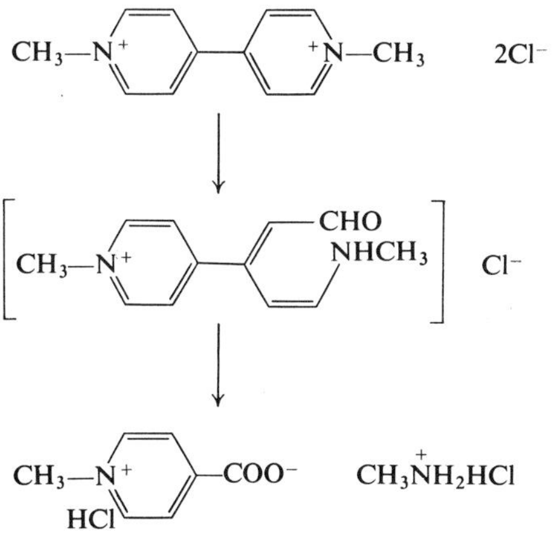

Fig. 10-4. Proposed pathway of paraquat degradation by ultraviolet light (I = 1-methyl-4-carboxypyridinium ion; II = methylamine hydrochloride). [Reprinted by permission from (45).]

Slade (46) has recently shown that UV light as well as sunlight degrades diquat rather rapidly. One principal radioactive decomposition product was isolated and identified as 1,2,3,4-tetrahydro-1-oxo-pyrido-(1,2-a)-5-pyrazinium ion (for additional photochemical studies, see Chapter 12).

D. Fate of Diquat and Paraquat in an Aquatic Environment

The dipyridyls are reported to be very persistent in the bottom mud of pools and ponds (48). In pools to which diquat and paraquat were applied at the rate of 0.3 lb/surface acre in 1962, 1.2 to 7.9 ppm of paraquat and a trace to 1.7 ppm of diquat were found in 1966. The data from this and other studies led Beasley (48) to conclude that paraquat was somewhat more persistent than diquat in the hydrosoils.

Beasley (48,49) also treated goldfish, *Carassius auratus* L., with ^{14}C-labeled diquat and subsequently sacrificed the fish to determine the location and form of the radioactivity. Radioactivity found in most organs increased with time, which suggested that the herbicide (or labeled atom) was distributed throughout the fish by the blood stream; this might be anticipated because of the high water solubility of the herbicide. In all phases of the investigations, maximum radioactivity was detected in the digestive tracts, and autoradiographs of electrochromatograms of plasma from treated fish revealed that only one radioactive compound was present. The relative movement of this compound on TLC plates was the same as for authentic diquat. From these studies one must conclude that diquat is relatively stable in fish.

Beasley (48) also analyzed tissues and organs of channel catfish collected from pools which received single applications of 1 ppm of unlabeled diquat or paraquat and two applications of 1 ppm of diquat or paraquat applied at 3-month intervals. Diquat or paraquat residue was not detected in organs or tissues of fish collected 5 months after a single application or 2 months after the second treatment. Fish from pools treated or retreated with diquat contained 0 to a trace of diquat in the contents of the digestive tract, and fish from pools treated or retreated with paraquat contained in excess of 2 and 6.9 ppm of paraquat, respectively, in the digestive tract contents.

10-3. MODE OF ACTION

Homer et al. (50) assessed the relative herbicidal activity of several of the dipyridyl compounds, and certain trends in activity were apparent. Of the 2,2'-dipyridilium salts studied, only diquat showed a high degree of activity. On examining the quaternary salts derived from 4,4'-dipyridyl, activity was present for a wide range of quaternizing groups, but all phytotoxic properties were lost by substitution of the ring positions adjacent to the interring bond; e.g., the 3,3'-dimethyl derivatives were inactive. The common factor responsible for high activity thus seemed to be that the molecules must be flat or be capable of assuming a planar configuration. This was supported in the case of the 2,2' series by molecular models and spectroscopic data (51).

On examining the herbicidal activity of quaternary salts derived from the remaining isomeric dipyridyls, this criterion alone was not enough to explain activity, since the quaternary salts derived from 2,3'- and 3,3'-dipyridyls were found to be inactive, although capable of a planar configuration. A clue to a further necessary structural requirement was provided by the earlier work of Michaelis and Hill (2), who showed that quaternary salts of 4,4'-dipyridyl were reduced to relatively stable free radicals. The free radical thus formed contains an unpaired electron that can occupy any of the nuclear carbon positions.

Both diquat and paraquat are reduced in a similar way, and from the foregoing studies and others, Homer et al. (52) determined that the ease of reduction and phytotoxicity were related. Furthermore, it seemed a reasonable hypothesis that herbicidal activity depended on the ability of the active compounds to form free radicals by the uptake of one electron.

A number of workers have shown that the dipyridyls are inhibitors of electron transport in photosynthesis (16,34,53–58). Within the system there is an iron-containing electron carrier (ferredoxin) with a redox potential of − 432 mV (59,60,61). It is thus apparent that the reducing potentials of the necessary order of magnitude required for the reduction of the dipyridyl herbicides can be generated in green tissue during photosynthesis (16,62).

Photosynthetic phosphorylation is catalyzed by diquat and paraquat when added to chloroplasts and illuminated in the presence of ADP and inorganic phosphate (57,63). Diquat has been shown to support three types of photophosphorylation by illuminated, isolated chloroplasts from Swiss chard: noncyclic, pseudocyclic, and cyclic photophosphorylation. These experiments show that the dipyridyls are able to act as electron carriers in the system (64).

Black (65,66) has recently pointed out that ferredoxin, one of the electron carriers in photosynthesis, can catalyze the reaction shown in Fig. 10-5. The dipyridyls are thought to fit into this scheme as shown in Fig. 10-6. Upon reduction, the dipyridyl is quickly oxidized in the presence of oxygen to produce hydrogen peroxide; however, Black is of the opinion that hydrogen peroxide is not the toxic agent since catalase as well as peroxidases

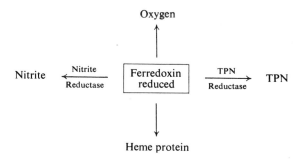

Fig. 10-5. Some reactions catalyzed by reduced spinach ferredoxin. [Reprinted by permission from (66), p. 333.]

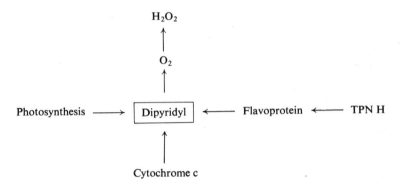

Fig. 10-6. Scheme for the site of action of quaternary dipyridyl salts in photosynthesis. [Reprinted by permission from (*66*), p. 334.]

are common in plant tissue. A simple replacement or short circuiting of the electron transport chain might result in slow death due to a depletion in nutrients and energy loss. It is doubtful whether this mechanism alone would account for the rapid and dramatic death of plants which occurs when they are treated with diquat and paraquat in full sunlight; therefore, it seems more probable that the reactive hydrogen peroxide radicals formed during reoxidation by molecular oxygen accumulate and destroy the plant cells.

In addition to the evidence for a light-induced reduction of diquat and paraquat in photosynthesis, there is evidence that these chemicals can be reduced to free radicals during respiration (*40,41,42*).

REFERENCES

1. A. Calderbank, *Advan. Pest Control Res.*, in press.

2. L. Michaelis and E. S. Hill, *J. Gen. Physiol.*, **16**, 859 (1933).

3. R. C. Brian, *Ann. Appl. Biol.*, **59**, 91 (1967).

4. C. S. Johnson, Jr. and H. S. Gutowsky, *J. Chem. Phys.*, **39**, 58 (1963).

5. H. P. Allen, *Proc. Brit. Weed Control Conf.*, 1960, p. 625.

6. H. J. Amling, J. L. Turner, and T. D. Taylor, *Proc. Southern Weed Conf.*, **16**, 164 (1963).

7. R. D. Blackburn and L. W. Weldon, *Proc. Southern Weed Conf.*, **16**, 365 (1963).

8. A. Calderbank, *Agr. Vet. Chem.*, **1**, 197 (1960).

9. A. Calderbank and S. H. Crowdy, *Ann. Rept. Appl. Chem.*, **47**, 536 (1962).

10. G. E. Coats, H. H. Funderburk, Jr., J. M. Lawrence, and D. E. Davis, *Proc. Southern Weed Conf.*, **18**, 614 (1965).

11. S. R. Colby and G. F. Warren, *Science*, **141**, 362 (1963).

12. J. S. Gunn and P. B. Tatham, *Nature*, **189**, 808 (1961).

13. W. van der Zweep, *Weed Soc. Am. Abstr.*, 1964, p. 107.
14. R. R. Yeo, *Weed Soc. Am. Abstr.*, 1964, p. 107.
15. R. C. Brian, R. F. Homer, and R. L. Jones, *Nature*, **181**, 446 (1956).
16. A. Calderbank, *Proc. Brit. Weed Cont. Conf. 7th*, 1964, p. 312.
17. A. Calderbank, Clare B. Morgan, and S. H. Yuen, *Analyst*, **86**, 569 (1961).
18. A. G. Strickland, *Compt. Rend. J. Etud. Herb.*, EWRC-COLUMA, Paris, 1961, pp. 97–105.
19. W. C. Hall, C. A. Burleson, and C. S. Miller, *Proc. Am. Cotton Defoliation Physiol. Conf. 13th*, 1959, p. 1.
20. G. W. Bailey and J. L. White, *J. Agr. Food Chem.*, **12**, 324 (1964).
21. G. E. Coats, H. H. Funderburk, Jr., J. M. Lawrence, and D. E. Davis, *Weed Res.*, **6**, 58 (1966).
22. G. E. Coats, H. H. Funderburk, Jr., J. M. Lawrence, and D. E. Davis, *Proc. Southern Weed Conf.*, 308 (1964).
23. T. D. Taylor, M.S. thesis, Auburn Univ., Auburn, Ala., 1964.
24. J. B. Weber, P. W. Perry, and R. P. Upchurch, *Soil. Sci. Am. Proc.*, **29**, 678 (1965).
25. J. B. Weber and D. C. Scott, *Science*, **152**, 1400 (1966).
26. R. C. Hiltibran, *Weeds*, **13**, 71 (1965).
27. J. M. Lawrence, *Proc. Southern Weed Conf.*, **18**, 568 (1965).
28. A. Calderbank and S. H. Yuen, *Analyst*, **91**, 625 (1966).
29. H. H. Funderburk, Jr., N. S. Negi, and J. M. Lawrence, *Weeds*, **14**, 240 (1966).
30. A. Calderbank and S. H. Yuen, *Analyst*, **90**, 99 (1965).
31. S. Yamaguchi and A. S. Crafts, *Hilgardia*, **28**, 161 (1958).
32. B. C. Baldwin, *Nature*, **198**, 872 (1963).
33. H. H. Funderburk, Jr. and J. M. Lawrence, *Weed Res.*, **3**, 304 (1963).
34. H. H. Funderburk, Jr. and J. M. Lawrence, *Weeds*, **12**, 259 (1964).
35. L. W. Smith and P. J. Davies, *Weed Res.*, **5**, 343 (1965).
36. S. L. Thrower, N. D. Hallam, and L. B. Thrower, *Ann. Appl. Biol.*, **55**, 253 (1965).
37. P. Slade, *Weed Res.*, **6**, 158 (1966).
38. R. Rodriguez-Kabana, E. A. Curl, and H. H. Funderburk, Jr., *Phytopathology*, **57**, 911 (1967).
39. R. Rodriguez-Kabana, E. A. Curl, and H. H. Funderburk, Jr., *Phytopathology*, **56**, 1332 (1966).
40. G. A. Bozarth, M.S. thesis, Auburn Univ., Auburn, Ala., 1966.
41. G. A. Bozarth, H. H. Funderburk, Jr., and E. A. Curl, *Weed Soc. Am. Abstr.*, 1966, p. 55.
42. G. A. Bozarth, H. H. Funderburk, Jr., E. A. Curl, and D. E. Davis, *Proc. Southern Weed Conf.*, **18**, 615 (1965).
43. H. H. Funderburk, Jr. and G. A. Bozarth, *J. Agr. Food Chem.*, **15**, 563 (1967).
44. B. C. Baldwin, Myrtle F. Bray, and M. J. Geoghegan, *Biochem. J.*, **101**, 15 (1966).
45. P. Slade, *Nature*, **207**, 515 (1965).
46. P. Slade and A. E. Smith, *Nature*, **213**, 919 (1967).
47. H. H. Funderburk, Jr., N. S. Negi, and J. M. Lawrence, *Weed Soc. Am. Abstr.*, 1966, p. 41.
48. P. G. Beasley, Ph.D. thesis, Auburn Univ., Auburn, Ala., 1966.
49. P. G. Beasley, J. M. Lawrence, and H. H. Funderburk, Jr., *Proc. Southern Weed Conf.*, **18**, 581 (1965).
50. R. F. Homer and T. E. Tomlinson, *J. Am. Chem. Soc.*, **504**, 2498 (1960).

51. R. F. Homer and T. E. Tomlinson, *Nature*, **184**, 2012 (1959).

52. R. F. Homer, G. C. Mees, and T. E. Tomlinson, *J. Sci. Food Agr.*, **6**, 309 (1960).

53. T. Kaneshero and G. Zweig, *Appl. Microbiol.*, **13**, 939 (1965).

54. G. C. Mees, *Ann. Appl. Biol.*, **48**, 601 (1960).

55. M. G. Merkle, C. L. Weinweber, and R. W. Bovey, *Plant Physiol.*, **40**, 832 (1965).

56. J. L. P. van Oorschot, *Proc. Brit. Weed Cont. Conf. 7th*, 1964, p. 321–324.

57. G. Zweig, I. Tamas, and E. Greenberg, *Biochim. Biophys. Acta*, **66**, 196 (1963).

58. R. W. Couch and D. E. Davis, *Weeds*, **14**, 251 (1966).

59. M. Calvin, *Rev. Mod. Phys.*, **31**, 147 (1959).

60. M. Calvin, *Rev. Mod. Phys.*, **31**, 157 (1959).

61. B. J. T. Commoner and G. E. Pake, *Nature*, **174**, 689 (1954).

62. R. C. Brian, *Weed Res.*, **4**, 105 (1964).

63. G. Zweig and M. Avron, *Biochem. Biophys. Res. Commun.*, **19**, 397 (1965).

64. G. Zweig, N. Shavit, and M. Avron, *Biochim. Biophys. Acta*, **109**, 332 (1965).

65. C. C. Black, *Science*, **149**, 62 (1965).

66. C. C. Black and L. Meyers, *Weeds*, **146**, 331 (1966).

CHAPTER 11

The Benzoic Acid Herbicides

C. R. SWANSON

CROPS RESEARCH DIVISION
AGRICULTURAL RESEARCH SERVICE, USDA
DELTA BRANCH EXPERIMENT STATION
STONEVILLE, MISSISSIPPI

11-1. Introduction 299
    A. Chemical and Physical Properties 302
11-2. Degradation in Plants and Soils 302
    A. Benzoic Acid 302
    B. Amiben and Dinoben 303
    C. 2,3,6-TBA 309
    D. Dicamba 311
    E. Dichlobenil 313
    F. Ioxynil and Bromoxynil 316
References 317

11-1. INTRODUCTION

The substituted benzoic acids and closely related chemicals have pronounced growth-regulating (1) and phytotoxic (2) properties. Several have found important usage in weed control, and thus their metabolic fate in plants and their behavior in soils is of both practical and theoretical interest. The number of representatives of the benzoic class that are in use as herbicides is much smaller than the number of phenoxyalkanoics, phenylureas, s-triazines, and carbamates. Consequently the amount of literature specifically related to the fate of the benzoics is less extensive. Important studies have been conducted on the major compounds, however, and some pertinent research has been published concerning the metabolism of benzoic acid itself. The following herbicides will be discussed in detail: 3-amino-2,5-dichlorobenzoic acid (amiben) and 3-nitro-2,5-dichlorobenzoic

299

TABLE 11-1

Chemical and Physical Description of Important Benzoic-Related Herbicides

Common name	Structural formula	Empirical formula	Molecular weight	Appearance	Solubility (H$_2$O)	Melting point, °C	Comments	Ref.
Amiben	**(1)**	C$_7$H$_5$Cl$_2$NO$_2$	206.03	White, crystalline	700 ppm	200–201	Stable to oxidation and heat	*10,11,12*
2,3,6-TBA	**(2)**	C$_7$H$_3$Cl$_3$O$_2$	225.47	White, powdery solid	Readily soluble		Stable to m.p. and in H$_2$O	*13*

Dicamba	(3)	$C_8H_6Cl_2O_3$	221.05	White, crystalline	?	114–116	Stable to oxidation and hydrolysis	*14*
Dichlobenil	(4)	$C_7H_3Cl_2N$	172.02	White, crystalline	25 ppm at 25°	114	VP = 5.5×10^{-4} mm Hg at 25°C	*15*
Ioxynil	(5)	$C_7H_3I_2NO$	370.9	White, crystalline solid	1.8 ppm at 25°	212–213.5	Nonvolatile in steam	*16*

acid (dinoben); 2,6-dichlorobenzonitrile (dichlobenil) and 2,6-dichloro-
thiobenzamide (chlorthiamid); 2-methoxy-3,6-dichlorobenzoic acid (dicamba); 3,5-diiodo-4-hydroxybenzonitrile (ioxynil) and 3,5-dibromo-4-
hydroxybenzonitrile (bromoxynil); and 2,3,6-trichlorobenzoic acid (TBA).

A. Chemical and Physical Properties

Physical and chemical characteristics of representative major benzoic
herbicides discussed are presented in Table 11-1.

11-2. DEGRADATION IN PLANTS AND SOILS

A. Benzoic Acid

Benzoic acid is the basic ring structure for the herbicides to be discussed,
but relatively little research has been done on its degradation in plants or
soils (3). Plants readily absorb and translocate benzoic acid or its salts (4),
but evidence for its degradation is lacking. Benzoic acid is metabolized,
however, to a variety of products that most frequently involve hydroxylation
of the ring or complexing with natural plant products.

Specifically, large amounts of benzoylaspartic acid (**6**), along with small
amounts of benzamide (**7**), are found in pea epicotyl tissue incubated with
benzoic acid (5). Other complexes also form in other tissues. Benzoylasparagine (**8**) and the glucose ester of benzoic acid accumulate in relatively large
amounts in wheat, and the benzoyl-glucoside occurs in *Helianthus* hypocotyl
tissue treated with benzoic acid (6–8).

(**6**)   (**7**)   (**8**)

(**9**)   (**10**)   (**11**)

Although wheat coleoptile tissue apparently does not ortho-hydroxylate the benzoic acid ring structure (8), leaf tissue from *Gaultheria procumbens* and *Primula acaulis* does. When incubated with benzoic acid–[14]COOH in the dark, disks from young *Gaultheria* leaves converted 64% of the absorbed chemical to such products as salicylic (9), *o*-pyrocatechuic (10), and *p*-hydroxybenzoic acids (11). In mature leaves less benzoic acid was altered and in old leaves most of the metabolic products were unidentified (9).

Thus the major fate of benzoic acid in higher plants appears to be complexing with sugars or amino acids through the carboxyl group of the benzoic acid. Ring hydroxylation occurs and *O*-glucosides could be expected to be the further products of metabolism. Lack of degradation of the ring indicates persistence of the modified chemical. This pattern of largely nondegradative metabolism will be seen repeatedly as we explore the fate of the several herbicides that are closely related to benzoic acid.

B. Amiben and Dinoben

The discovery of the selective preemergence herbicidal activity of 3-amino-2,5-dichlorobenzoic acid (amiben) (1) was made in 1958 (17). Amiben is a selective herbicide for certain annual grasses and broadleaf weeds, particularly in soybeans, and a notable degree of selectivity exists in sweet potatoes, squash, tomatoes, and other crops (18). The closely related 3-nitro-2,5-dichlorobenzoic acid (dinoben) has similar herbicidal properties but soybeans are more tolerant to amiben (82).

1. Movement and Degradation in Plants

Amiben is readily absorbed by germinating seedlings, and by roots of established plants (19–34). The herbicide is also absorbed by leaves of soybean (29,30,35), barley (29), cucumber, and squash (21) plants, but because its primary use is as a soil-applied herbicide, the majority of research on the fate of amiben has been devoted to its uptake and metabolism by roots. Roots of resistant species such as soybean absorb large amounts of amiben, but translocate very little of it to the above-ground plant organs (27–29,31,33,36). Carboxyl-labeled amiben–[14]C applied to roots of snap beans and soybeans results in little radioactivity in the shoots, but significant amounts of ^{14}C are found in barley leaves after root application (29).

Much of the work on absorption, translocation, and metabolism of amiben has been conducted with carboxyl-labeled amiben–[14]C. Whether reliance can be placed on translocation data derived from movement of ^{14}C depends heavily upon whether or not degradation of the compound occurs. If amiben were decarboxylated and the liberated $^{14}CO_2$ fixed within the plant, measurement of radioactivity in the leaves could give an entirely erroneous impression of translocation of the herbicide. However, evidence from numerous studies of the fate of amiben generally support the assumption that detection of ^{14}C activity from carboxyl-labeled amiben indicates the presence of undegraded amiben. Details of studies concerning translocation of amiben can be obtained by reference to the indicated literature. For the present purposes, it may be stated that amiben is poorly translocated in most species and that where amiben does occur in shoots following root application, it may be due to overloading of the binding mechanism in the roots (24).

In general, there appears to be little or no net loss of amiben by degradation in treated plants. The herbicide is rapidly complexed by many species, with little or no subsequent alteration in most species (24,33).

The existence of a complex was recognized in the first studies on the fate of amiben in plants (30). Complexes account for most of the amiben absorbed by plant tissue, and they appear to be very stable in the plant (33). The early work on amiben indicated a decline in amiben content with time in treated plants (30), and loss of $^{14}CO_2$ from soybean plants treated with amiben–$^{14}COOH$ (26). More recently, it has been shown that with soybeans grown in soil containing amiben–$^{14}COOH$ there was no evolution of $^{14}CO_2$ (32) and in carrots only 4% of the radioactivity was released as $^{14}CO_2$ (20). Presumably, in both of these cases, amiben complexes were involved.

Because the formation of a complex is the major fate of amiben in most plants, considerable attention has been paid to its characterization. A complex has been found in soybeans (22–24,28,30,34,36,37), carrots (20), cucumber (21), squash (21,24), morning glory (24), tomato (25), barley (23), sugar beet and pea (33), and other species (24). The only species thus far evaluated where amiben exists only in the free form is Johnson grass (24).

The major metabolite of amiben is a glycoside of unaltered amiben (22, 34,36,38). Its structure was suggested by comparison with postulated products (22,36) and conclusively identified by critical analysis of the components of acid hydrolysis of the isolated metabolite (34). The metabolite is N-(3-carboxy-2,5-dichlorophenyl)glucosylamine or N-glucosyl amiben (34).

A minor metabolite consistently observed (34) is probably an isomer or rearrangement product of N-glucosyl amiben formed during extraction.

A useful technique for the study of N-glucosyl amiben, and of other N-arylglucosylamines, has been suggested by Kadunce (39). He successfully conducted gas chromatographic analysis of the intact glucoside by first forming the trimethylsilyl derivative and then methylating the product, followed by gas chromatographic analysis.

Surprisingly, Swan and Slife (40) found no amiben complex in treated soybean plants. Although the N-glucosyl amiben has reasonably high stability, it may be that at some stage of plant handling, killing, or extraction, there may have been hydrolysis of what is now known to be the predominant form of amiben in the plant. It has been suggested that lowering the pH to 2.2 at one stage may have hydrolyzed any glucoside present (24).

Intact plants are not required for N-glucosyl amiben formation. Segments of soybean hypocotyl tissue incubated with amiben form the metabolite in vitro (41). The ability of soybean hypocotyl tissue to form N-glucosyl amiben is strongly inhibited by heating at 50° for 10 min and by freezing and thawing. Formation of the metabolite is proportional to the fresh weight of hypocotyl tissue up to 1.0 g when incubated with 2 μM of amiben. Maximum rate of formation is achieved when 1 μM of amiben is incubated with 1 g of tissue, and the reaction is linear with time for at least 10 hours. Inhibition of the reaction by fluoride, N-ethyl maleimide, and $HgCl_2$ suggests that enzymatic activity is involved. Sugar beet seedlings also have a high specific activity (μg of N-glucosyl amiben formed per mg of protein per hr). Tomato seedlings, cucumber roots, and barley roots have intermediate specific activity. Barley shoots, cucumber cotyledons and hypocotyl tissue, and soybean leaves have a low specific activity (41).

Thus there are distinct tissue differences as well as species differences in ability to form the N-glucoside of amiben. The rapidity of formation of the metabolite in treated plants and its relative stability in the tissue where it is produced are noteworthy. It is reasonable to assume that the virtually quantitative conversion of amiben to N-glucosyl amiben by most species limits the degradation of the herbicide.

Partial purification and characterization of an amiben-metabolizing enzyme from soybean has been achieved. Frear (42) studied a soluble enzyme from soybean acetone powder that catalyzes the synthesis of N-glucosyl amiben (12) and other N-glucosyl arylamines. The enzyme (N-arylamine glycosyl-transferase) is specific for uridine diphosphate-5′-glucose (UDP-glucose) (42).

Limited information is available on the influence of environment upon amiben metabolism. Plants that are previously held in the dark to induce starvation form more N-glucoside when the plants are illuminated during amiben treatment than when the plants are kept in the dark during treatment. Dark-treated plants also absorb less amiben (33). Cucumber and soybeans absorb more ^{14}C from solution culture containing amiben–^{14}C at 80°F than at 70°F, but the proportion of absorbed amiben that is retained in the roots is independent of either temperature or atmospheric humidity (27).

Environmental influence seems limited but species do differ in the proportion of amiben complexed. In controlled environment studies, soybean and cucumber converted 98 and 95% of the absorbed amiben to N-glucosyl amiben, but barley transformed only 45% of its amiben to the glucoside (27).

Study of the metabolism of dinoben in plants has been limited, but soybeans do convert dinoben to a metabolite that chromatographs identically with N-glycosyl amiben (23). The hydroxypropyl ester of dinoben is metabolized to dinoben in corn seedlings. The dinoben that is released is reduced to amiben and complexed to N-glycosylamiben (24).

2. Degradation and Movement in Soil

Application of a herbicide to a soil surface exposes the compound to a wide variety of physical, chemical, and biological environmental influences which will modify the persistence of the compound as well as its structural integrity. One of the first factors that might be anticipated to influence the life and behavior of amiben in the soil is photochemical degradation. This has been studied under model conditions in the laboratory employing artificial ultraviolet radiation (43,44) or in normal sunlight (44). Photodecomposition of amiben occurs in methanol (43) or in water solution (44) irradiated with sunlamps. When the amiben acid is compared with the triethylamine salt of amiben in aqueous solution, the acid is the more rapidly decomposed by irradiation. Several products of decomposition are detectable by paper chromatography (44) or gas chromatography (43). In the presence of bisulfite in water solution, amiben is converted to one major product by ultraviolet irradiation. If this product is then methylated, it appears to be the same as the product derived from irradiation of the methyl ester of amiben in methanol (45). The extent to which photochemical degradation occurs on a soil surface under natural conditions has not been evaluated, but it has been suggested that loss can be anticipated and that it may be advisable to transport amiben to the field in light-excluding containers (44). Whether this would be worthwhile depends upon the events occurring at the soil surface immediately after application (see Chapter 12).

Adsorption of amiben to soil constituents does occur (35,46–49), but the extent and strength of adsorption is considerably less than that of many other herbicides (49). Organic matter is the most important soil factor in the adsorption of amiben (35,46). In one instance, under controlled laboratory conditions, a muck soil adsorbed 29% of the applied amiben, while a silty clay loam adsorbed only 9% (48). Clays are much less adsorptive than is organic matter for amiben (46). Kaolinite adsorbs significant amounts, but bentonite, illite, and vermiculite adsorb very little of the herbicide (48). Desorption of amiben from the actively adsorbing muck soils is low. Only about half of the amiben initially adsorbed on a Houghton muck could be desorbed by four successive extractions with distilled water (47). The strong adsorption to organic matter is also reflected in the decreasing phytotoxicity of amiben in the soil as the per cent organic matter in the soil increases (46).

Persistence of amiben in the soil depends upon a number of factors in addition to adsorption. Volatilization could be a significant fate of a herbicide applied to a soil surface where the potential for such loss would be high. But volatilization of amiben could not be demonstrated over a 4-week period at temperatures ranging from 15 to 35° at relative humidities from 0 to 100% (48).

Microbial degradation in the soil is an important route of dissipation for many herbicides. In liquid cultures inoculated with soil, amiben degradation is hardly noticeable (48). But when incubated with nonsterile soil, evidence of amiben degradation does exist (17,19,35,46,50–53). Greatest loss of amiben activity is experienced in soils high in organic matter (46,52) and degradation by microorganisms in such soils exerts a marked effect (53). Evolution of $^{14}CO_2$ from nonsterile soils (19,51) suggests that some microbial degradation does occur. Amiben is degraded to a greater extent than

is either 2,3,6-trichlorobenzoic acid (2,3,6-TBA) or 2-methoxy-3,5-dichloro-
benzoic acid (dicamba) (46). The relatively slow rate of degradation is
related to the number of chlorine atoms on the ring (51). Because there is
no pronounced change in the rate of decomposition of amiben with time,
it is assumed that the decomposition detected is nonspecific, whether it be
microbial, chemical, or a combination of the two (19).

Leaching can account for loss of herbicidal activity from the surface
layers of soil in some cases. Movement of amiben through a heavy loam soil
does not occur beyond the surface 0.25 in. to any great extent (17). As might
be expected from the data on adsorption of amiben by soil, loss by leaching
is most pronounced from a sandy soil and progressively less as the clay and
organic complement are increased (52,53). The rate at which amiben moves
through a soil column is related to the rate of water movement, and the
depth to which the herbicide penetrates depends upon the amount of water
applied.

Undoubtedly the net persistence of amiben is a resultant of the several
factors discussed, and the dominant factor will change depending upon the
particular circumstances. There appears to be no influence of soil pH upon
detoxication of amiben (50). Slow detoxication in soils has been demonstrated by bioassay: 128 ppm in 8 weeks (50), 42 % in 11 months (54), 43 %
in 50 days, and 85 % at 141 days (35). In the field, dissipation is frequently
faster than under controlled laboratory conditions. This may be because
of enhanced photodecomposition and leaching in the field (54). Soil
temperature may modify the persistence of amiben. At a low soil temperature the total persistence of amiben is greater than at higher temperatures,
and there is a marked lag phase of several months before loss is apparent.
The suggestion that the lag phase indicates microbial rather than chemical
degradation (54) has not been experimentally confirmed.

Most of the studies on amiben behavior have dealt with the acid or
ammonium salt forms. Reports of investigations with esters and an amide
of amiben (37,55–57) warrant discussion. Their behavior may be expected
to differ on the basis of solubility alone. The solubility of the amiben salts
exceeds 250,000 ppm, that of the amide is approximately 1200 ppm, and
the methyl ester is soluble to the extent of about 120 ppm. Considerably
less water solubility is exhibited by the butoxyethyl and hydroxypropyl
esters of amiben (57). Depth of leaching is more dependent upon the form
of amiben applied than upon the soil type. When 4 in. of water were applied
to soil surfaces treated with amiben, the ammonium salt moved to a depth
of 15 to 25 cm, the aluminum salt to 11 to 21 cm, the amide to 5 to 13 cm,
and the methyl ester to 0 to 6.5 cm, as determined by crabgrass germination

bioassay (55). These depths are reasonably correlated with the respective water solubilities. Lack of difference in depth of penetration in soils varying from 4% clay to 45% clay (55) clearly demonstrates the limited adsorption potential of amiben in most soils and emphasizes the importance of solubility. Thus under heavy rainfall conditions the forms of amiben having lower water solubilities might leach less and thus be more effective under conditions ideal for leaching (37).

The methyl ester of amiben–^{14}C is converted to amiben in 5 days of soil incubation, but the amide is converted to amiben only very slowly if at all (37). The amiben amide is initially inactive and requires activation in nonsterile soil to be herbicidal. Such activation is enhanced by as little as 0.5 in. of rainfall (56). The several esters differ in the time required to reach 50% hydrolysis in soil. For the methyl ester this is reached in 2.9 days; for the hydroxypropyl ester, 7.5 days; and for the butoxyethanol ester, 16 days under moist conditions (57). But when dry soil is used, the methyl ester is not hydrolyzed.

Thus one might expect that amiben persistence would be greatest as the butoxyethanol ester in a dry soil of high organic content and least for an amiben salt in a moist, sandy soil where high rainfall would accelerate leaching.

C. 2,3,6-TBA

2,3,6-Trichlorobenzoic acid (2,3,6-TBA) (2) is not notably selective. Except for perennial weed control in cereal grains, its primary use is for nonselective vegetation control or as a component of mixtures with other herbicides. The compound was evaluated as a herbicide in the field at Jealott's Hill, England, as early as 1948 (58), and was first shown to exhibit strong plant-growth-regulating activity in 1950 (59).

1. Degradation in Plants

Zimmerman and Hitchcock (1) showed that 2,3,6-TBA is readily translocated upward, inducing leaf and stem modifications. The compound is translocated basipetally as well, and it may be exuded from the roots of leaf-treated plants into the surrounding soil or nutrient solution (60).

Uptake of 2,3,6-TBA has been studied critically in stem tissue. In excised stem segments of *Avena sativa*, the uptake is primarily through the cut surfaces. Although rapidly absorbed initially, the rate of 2,3,6-TBA uptake becomes negative after 4 to 6 hours, resulting in a net transfer of the chemical from the tissue to the ambient solution (*61*). This loss is prevented by addition of streptomycin or decamethylene diguanidine dihydrochloride to the medium (*62,63*). Accumulation is enhanced by addition of cetyl-trimethylammonium bromide. This unstable accumulation process may involve adsorption in the cell membrane between the 2,3,6-TBA carboxyl function and the quaternary ammonium group of the choline portion of α-lecithin. Binding of the growth regulator is destroyed by phospholipase-D but is restored by addition of cationic nitrogen compounds that compete with the choline quaternary ammonium group of α-lecithin for the anionic site of phospholipase-D.

Plant species vary from highly susceptible (bean) to moderately resistant (corn). If 2,3,6-TBA is applied to the leaf surface of each, corn translocates the herbicide from the treated leaf much less readily than does bean (*64*). As a consequence, 2,3,6-TBA accumulates to a great extent in actively growing meristematic regions of those species that translocate the chemical.

The first indication of metabolism of the 2,3,6-trichlorobenzaldehyde was reported in 1952 (*65*). It was suggested that the reason the aldehyde had any activity was due to its slight conversion to 2,3,6-TBA in pea stem tissue.

Metabolism of 2,3,6-TBA by plants is slight. Extractable radioactivity partitioned into acidified ether from alkaline ammonium sulfate extracts contain only unmetabolized 2,3,6-TBA–^{3}H (*64*). Similarly, when fed to barley plants through the roots, the only detectable tritium in the guttate fluid from the leaves is unaltered 2,3,6-TBA–^{3}H. The 10% nonextractable radioactivity in Mason's study (*64*) consisted primarily of 2,3,6-TBA associated with protein. This complex released 2,3,6-TBA when denatured with perchloric acid.

When applied to wheat plants through the roots at 5 lb/acre or sprayed on the foliage at $\frac{1}{2}$ and 1 lb/acre, 2,3,6-TBA was found in all cases to be present both in the straw and in the seed heads at harvest (*66*). The analysis in this case was by gas–liquid chromatography and peaks were detected that could have been breakdown products of 2,3,6-TBA. If degradation of this herbicide occurs in plant tissues, the products are not yet established.

2. Degradation in Soil

Persistence of 2,3,6-TBA in treated soil has been noted by a number of investigators (*54,67–72*). Where bean bioassay was used to follow loss from soil in pot tests, there was no material reduction of 2,3,6-TBA in 22 months (*72*). Field studies on North Carolina Coastal Plain soils showed that the herbicide persisted at least 18 months after an 8-lb/acre application (*70*). Its persistence in Midwestern soils has also been documented (*67,71*).

In a sandy clay loam in Nebraska, sufficient 2,3,6-TBA persisted from a 20-lb/acre application to kill soybeans 5 years after treatment. Persistence was less, but still high, in lighter loam soils (67). Under laboratory conditions, persistence of 2,3,6-TBA may be appreciably less than in the same soils in the field due to markedly lower average soil temperature under field conditions (67). This could indicate some degradation by microbial activity in the soil. When incubated with a moist clay soil and subsequently studied by bioassay, reduction of 2,3,6-TBA content could be directly related to conditions favorable for microbial activity. Greater breakdown in an organic soil than in a sandy soil supports this conclusion (69).

Specific information on the degradation products in either plants or soil is lacking. Release of ionic ^{36}Cl from 2,3,6-TBA–^{36}Cl in nonsterile soil demonstrates a dechlorination reaction (68), but the products remain unidentified.

D. Dicamba

The herbicide 2-methoxy-3,6-dichlorobenzoic acid (dicamba) (3) is effective as a weed killer for many annual grasses and broadleaf weeds in grain crops. It differs in structure from the broad-spectrum herbicide, 2,3,6-TBA, only by replacement of a chlorine in the 2 position with a methoxy radical, but this change is sufficient to confer considerable selectivity.

1. Movement and Degradation in Plants

Dicamba is absorbed by plant roots (73–75) and translocated to the shoots in wheat, bluegrass (73), and Canada thistle (75). In these species at least there is little retention of dicamba in the roots after root application.

The mobility of dicamba in treated foliage is marked and rapid. Steam girdling of foliar-treated bean plants prevents transport, indicating phloem translocation (76). In nutsedge (*Cyperus rotundus* L.), the herbicide moves slowly but in appreciable amounts from a treated leaf in both phloem and xylem. Although foliar distribution in this species is general, greatest accumulation occurs in the actively growing parts. Accumulation in below-ground organs is poor (77). In buckwheat, dicamba accumulates in the young growing leaves independent of the site of application (74). The decrease in radioactivity in treated buckwheat and Canada thistle is rapid as contrasted with the longer residence time of dicamba in quackgrass and bluegrass leaves (74).

Dicamba is not only translocated basipetally, but it is significantly excreted from roots into the surrounding soil of nutrient solution (60,75,76,78). The closely related 2,5-dichlorobenzoic acid is translocated from leaf to stem but is not detected in the roots (60). In bean plants, leaf treatment results in excretion of apparently unchanged dicamba to the nutrient solution (78). This excretion is enhanced by a low concentration of dimethyl sulfoxide (DMSO) added to the ambient solution surrounding the roots (76).

The extent to which plants degrade dicamba depends upon the species. Purple nutsedge does not metabolize the herbicide (77), and it is at best slowly metabolized in tartary buckwheat where at least 85% of the dicamba–^{14}C was chromatographically identical with authentic dicamba 6 weeks after treatment (74). Other studies with dicamba applied to bean foliage indicate no metabolism of the herbicide by this species (76,78). On the other hand, in Canada thistle, one-third of the radioactivity from dicamba–^{14}C treatment was in the form of an unidentified metabolite 54 days after treatment, and significant amounts of $^{14}CO_2$ were evolved by the plants (75).

The grasses actively metabolize dicamba (73). Within 2 days after treatment of wheat plants, 84% of the recovered radioactivity from dicamba–$^{14}COOH$ existed as conjugates and 16% as intact dicamba. When hydrolyzed, the conjugated materials consisted of 30% intact dicamba, 58% major metabolite, and 11% minor metabolite. Within 18 days after treatment, 100% of the radioactivity existed as conjugates, and of this only 5% was dicamba. The major metabolite accounted for 90% of the radioactivity and the minor metabolite, 5%. The herbicide was not decarboxylated to a measurable extent. The major conjugated metabolite, after hydrolysis, proved to be 5-hydroxy-2-methoxy-3,5-dichlorobenzoic acid (13), and the minor degradation product was 3,6-dichlorosalicylic acid (14). Both wheat and bluegrass metabolized dicamba in the same way and in the same proportions. Metabolism of dicamba in wheat and bluegrass (73) may be represented as follows:

2. Movement and Degradation in Soil

Dicamba moves slightly behind the forward penetration of added water in a soil column (79) and can move upward in the soil when the soil is subirrigated (80). The adsorption of dicamba to soils high in organic matter is greater than for clay or sandy soils, but adsorption to clays is greatest onto a kaolinite clay (81).

Despite relatively low adsorptive potential, contact of dicamba with a silty clay loam resulted in very little loss by volatilization over a 8-week period. By contrast, nearly half of the radioactivity of dicamba–^{14}C was lost from planchets during an 11-week period at equivalent temperatures and relative humidities (81).

In high organic matter soils, dicamba is detoxified completely at pH 5.3 but is highly persistent at pH 7.5. This differential response to pH is attributed to the more favorable environment for adaptation or growth of micro-organisms capable of degrading the chemical at the lower pH (50). A similar response has been noted in bracken soils where dicamba was degraded rapidly at pH 7.5 (82). The same inhibition of degradation is achieved by steaming the soil, thus implicating vigorous microbial activity in nonsterile soil, high in organic matter and low in pH, for optimum degradation of the herbicide.

Dicamba is quite persistent in soil in comparison to 2,4-D. Detoxication of the latter herbicide applied at 1 lb/acre was essentially complete in loam and a sandy loam after 2 weeks but dicamba at 0.5 lb/acre was highly active after 12 weeks' incubation (79).

Loss of herbicidal activity could conceivably be by microbial decarboxy-lation (76) or other transformation of the molecule. Liberation of chloride ion from dicamba in soil has not been detected (72). Alteration of the methoxy substituent has been suggested but has not been substantiated.

Further study of the nature and identity of persistent forms of dicamba in the soil is needed.

E. Dichlobenil

First synthesis of 2,6-dichlorobenzonitrile (dichlobenil) (4) was reported in 1940 (83), and its herbicidal properties were reported in 1960 (84). Dichlobenil is an active herbicide on germinating seeds of many grasses and broadleaf plants and on aquatic weeds.

1. Movement of Dichlobenil in Plants and Soils

Dichlobenil is readily absorbed by roots from aqueous solution (85–90) and subsequently translocated throughout the plant. However, application to the leaves results in very limited absorption and little basipetal translocation. The longer dichlobenil is in contact with the leaf surface, the greater is the extent of absorption and translocation (*88*). The majority of translocation studies have been done with bean (*87–91*), and they show that most efficient absorption is through the roots and that translocation is with the transpiration stream. Essentially the same conclusions may be reached based on the studies with tomato, cucumber, oat (*91*), and alligator weed (*Alternanthera philoxeroides*) (*87–89*).

Although the translocation pattern of any chemical in a plant is a function of the extent to which the chemical gains access to the conduction system and of the physiological status of the plant at the time, translocation of dichlobenil may also be importantly influenced by the physical and chemical characteristics of the herbicide. These properties have been studied by Massini (*91*) and Pate and co-workers (*92*). Massini (*91*) determined the adsorption or partition coefficient k (ratio of the concentration in the adsorbent to the concentration in the liquid phase) for dichlobenil for plant constituents as well as for plant organs and for several soils. Dichlobenil adsorbs very weakly to cellulose and protein, but very strongly to lignin. Intermediate to high levels of adsorption are found for cacao butter and chloroplasts. Adsorption to whole plant organs such as stems, roots, and seeds is low (*91*). Although dichlobenil moves with the transpiration stream, it moves much more slowly than does the transpiration water. This may be due to the high affinity of the herbicide for several plant substances. Strong accumulation in the leaf parenchyma cells surrounding the main veins may be due also to adsorption to chloroplasts (*91*).

Other properties of dichlobenil that are of importance not only to translocation in plants but also to behavior in soil are its relatively low water solubility and high vapor pressure (*85,86,91,92*). Low water solubility contributes to a partition from solution to plant or soil substances such as lignin or humic substances for which the herbicide has an affinity. Its high volatility increases the rate of loss of dichlobenil from a soil or plant surface. In experimental work with dichlobenil in the greenhouse, transfer of dichlobenil to untreated plants by vaporization and adsorption could introduce experimental error (*93*). Dichlobenil volatilizes as the intact molecule (*92*).

Sandy and organic soils remove dichlobenil from solution virtually completely but there is no retention by sand alone (*91*). Persistence of dichlobenil or closely related degradation products is greater in a clay than in a silty clay loam or loam soil (*94*). In the cranberry bog with high organic matter, dichlobenil was not leached beyond the 4-in. depth despite extensive leaching by rainfall (95). Apparently the herbicide is tightly bound by soil organic matter.

The importance of incorporation to reduce loss from a soil surface by volatilization has been recognized in practice. Contrary to most herbicides, rainfall does not decrease persistence of dichlobenil through leaching but increases persistence due to reduction of loss by volatility (85).

2. Degradation of Dichlobenil in Plants and Soils

There is evidence that dichlobenil is metabolized to some extent in bean seedling tissue (90,91), Steam distillation of freeze-dried, dichlobenil-treated plants extracted only half of the radioactivity of the nitrile–^{14}C-labeled herbicide. Further extraction with HCl in ethanol yielded 90% of the remaining radioactivity. A part of the additional radioactivity was a metabolite of undetermined identity, but apparently not 2,6-dichlorobenzoic acid (91).

However, other studies with bean plants and alligator weed distinctly demonstrate the metabolism of dichlobenil to 2,6-dichlorobenzoic acid as a major metabolite (88). Degradation of dichlobenil to 2,6-dichlorobenzoic acid also was demonstrated in species of *Fusarium, Geotrichum, Penicillium,* and *Trichoderma*. Of these fungi, *Fusarium* was the most active in metabolizing the herbicide (88). In both Massini's study (91) and Pate and Funderburk's investigations (88), extracts of bean plants treated with dichlobenil–^{14}C were chromatographed on thin-layer plates (silica gel G) in 1:1 diethyl ether–petroleum ether in the cold. Massini (91) found radioactivity at R_f 0.50 attributable to dichlobenil, and an unknown at R_f 0.10. When dichlobenil was subjected to the same procedures used in extraction of treated plant tissue, an additional radioactive spot was detected at R_f 0.25. The spot at R_f 0.10 did not correspond to 2,6-dichlorobenzoic acid, but no indication was given of the identity of the spot at R_f 0.25 (91). Pate and Funderburk (88) detected a dichlobenil metabolite at R_f 0.25 that cochromatographed identically with 2,6-dichlorobenzoic acid. Esterification of the aqueous extract produced a radioactive spot at R_f 0.95, the same R_f obtained with authentic methyl-2,6-dichlorobenzoate. Finally, they compared the retention times of the methylated major metabolite and methyl-2,6-dichlorobenzoate. The retention times were identical (89). The amount of 2,6-dichlorobenzoic acid in dichlobenil-treated bean and alligator weed plants increases with time after treatment (88). It appears that the 2,6-dichlorobenzoic acid (15) may be reasonably accepted as a metabolite of dichlobenil (4) in plants.

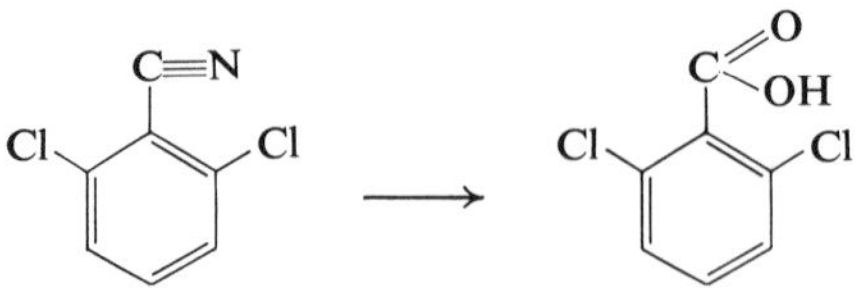

(3)

(4)   (15)

Very little information is available concerning degradation products of dichlobenil in soil. In one study, analysis of soil treated with dichlobenil revealed the presence of approximately equal parts of dichlobenil and 2,6-dichlorobenzoic acid, thus suggesting that the latter is an intermediate of dichlobenil decomposition in soil (94) as well as the major metabolite in plants.

Work on a closely related herbicide, 2,6-dichlorothiobenzamide (chlorthiamid) (16) is pertinent (96–98). This compound is converted in both soil and plants to dichlobenil (4).

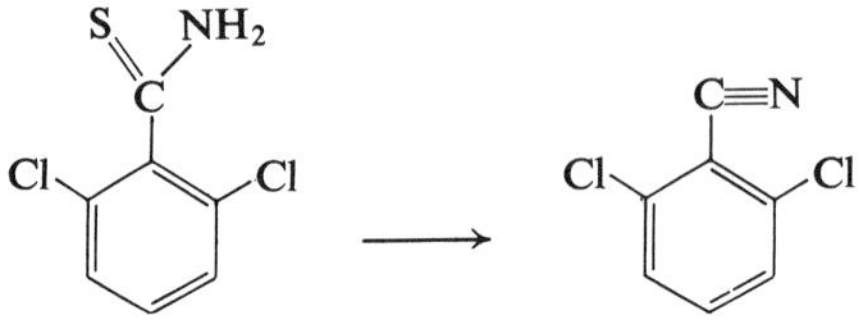

(4)

(16)   (4)

Detailed metabolism studies on chlorthiamid degradation are not yet available, but no evidence has been presented to indicate that subsequent metabolism of the dichlobenil formed from chlorthiamid to 2,6-dichloro-benzoic acid happens in either plants or soils (96–98). It would be instructive to determine whether chlorthiamid could inhibit the degradation of dichlobenil to 2,6-dichlorobenzoic acid.

F. Ioxynil and Bromoxynil

The 3,5-dihalogeno-4-hydroxybenzonitriles are of relatively recent introduction as herbicides. They were reported in 1963 (99,100) as potential postemergence herbicides. They were tested in 1960 by Amchem Products and the high herbicidal activity of 3,5-diiodo-4-hydroxybenzonitrile (ioxynil) (5) and 3,5-dibromo-4-hydroxybenzonitrile (bromoxynil) was discovered (101). They are specifically useful for postemergence application in wheat and barley to control seedling broadleaf weeds, particularly as a fall treatment in fall-planted grains.

Although thought of as contact foliage herbicides, ioxynil and bromo-xynil are absorbed and translocated. Movement of ioxynil from the treated leaf into older and particularly into younger leaves was claimed on the basis of appearance of chlorosis in untreated leaves of *Polygonum lapathifolium.* In wheat there was little chlorosis beyond the point of application on a treated leaf and no necrosis occurred, suggesting that little or no transloca-tion occurs in wheat (*16*).

Ioxynil is subject to degradation under irradiation with ultraviolet light. When irradiated for 20 hours in dry benzene, the chemical is converted to 3,5-diphenyl-4-hydroxybenzonitrile, with the possible involvement of free-radical formation (*102,103*). Paton and Smith (*104*) have postulated the formation of such a free radical that could then interact with sulfhydryls:

(5)

(5)

Whether this reaction is involved in degradation or detoxication of the herbicide is not established. A breakdown of ioxynil in root-treated bean plants to the corresponding benzoic acid and iodide ions has been suggested (*103*), and iodide has also been shown to be present in bean plants treated with ioxynil (*105*).

Acid soils removed more than 78% of the ioxynil in solution when 100 ml of 1000-ppm solution was shaken with 50 g of soil. When limed peat was used, almost 90% was removed. This was attributed to a possible precipita-tion of the herbicide as the relatively insoluble free phenol, rather than removal by adsorption to soil components (*105*). When sterile and nonsterile soil were treated with the herbicide, no breakdown of ioxynil was detectable in the sterile soil, but nearly complete degradation was achieved in 19 days in the nonsterile soil. Microbial degradation of ioxynil in the soil probably produces the corresponding amide and then the acid, with deiodination possible also (*105*).

REFERENCES

1. P. W. Zimmerman and A. E. Hitchcock, *Contrib. Boyce Thompson Inst.*, **16**, 209 (1951).

2. M. L. Sutherland, S. R. McLane, R. D. Hart, and H. L. Raman, *Hormolog*, **3**, 5 (1961).

318 C. R. SWANSON

3. C. R. Swanson, *U.S. Dept. Agr.*, ARS 34–66 (1965).

4. J. E. Pallas, Jr., *Plant Physiol.*, **35**, 575 (1960).

5. W. A. Andreae and N. E. Good, *Plant Physiol.*, **32**, 566 (1957).

6. H. D. Klämbt, *Planta*, **57**, 339 (1961).

7. H. D. Klämbt, *Planta*, **56**, 618 (1961).

8. H. D. Klämbt, *Nature*, **196**, 491 (1962).

9. S. Z. El-Basyouni, D. Chen, R. K. Ibrahim, A. C. Neish, and G. H. N. Towers, *Phytochemistry*, **3**, 485 (1964).

10. Amchem Products, Inc., *Information Sheet IS-32 Herbicide Data*, 1965.

11. Amchem Products, Inc., *Technical Service Data Sheet H-77A*, 1959.

12. Amchem Products, Inc., *Technical Service Data Sheet H-85, Amiben Progr. Rept*, 1960.

13. Amchem Products, Inc., *Information Sheet, Benzac 345 and Benzac 1281*, July 1962.

14. Velsicol Chemical Corp., *Banvel D. Bulletin No. 52I–2*, Nov. 1961.

15. Thompson-Hayward Chem. Co., *Casoron Tech. Information Bull. 3*, Dec. 1962.

16. K. Carpenter, H. J. Cottrell, W. H. DeSilva, B. J. Heywood, W. G. Leeds, K. F. Rivett, and M. L. Soundy, *Weed Res.*, **4**, 175 (1964).

17. M. L. Sutherland, *Proc. Northeast. Weed Control Conf.*, **16**, 546 (1962).

18. S. R. McLane, *Hormolog*, **4**, 3 (1963).

19. R. E. Ascheman, *Dissertation Abstr.*, **24**, 14 (1963).

20. F. M. Ashton, *Weeds*, **14**, 55 (1966).

21. R. S. Baker and G. F. Warren, *Weeds*, **10**, 219 (1962).

22. S. R. Colby, *Science*, **150**, 619 (1965).

23. S. R. Colby, *Weeds*, **14**, 197 (1966).

24. S. R. Colby, *J. Agr. Food Chek.i.*, **16**, in press (1969).

25. S. R. Colby, G. F. Warren, and R. S. Baker, *J. Agr. Food Chem.*, **12**, 320 (1964).

26. V. H. Freed, M. Montgomery, and M. Kief, *Proc. Northeast. Weed Control Conf.*, **15**, 6 (1963).

27. R. H. Hodgson, *Weed Soc. Am. Abstr.*, **7**, 64 (1967).

28. R. H. Hodgson, C. R. Swanson, and H. R. Swanson, *Weed Soc. Am. Abstr.*, **6**, 37 (1966).

29. F. W. Slife, *Hormolog*, **4**, 11 (1963).

30. M. L. Sutherland, Amchem Prod. Inc., June 16, 1961.

31. D. G. Swan and F. W. Slife, *Weed. Soc. Am. Abstr.*, 1964, p. 79.

32. D. G. Swan and F. W. Slife, *Weed Soc. Am. Abstr.*, 1964, p. 74.

33. C. R. Swanson, R. H. Hodgson, R. E. Kadunce, and H. R. Swanson, *Weeds*, **14**, 323 (1966).

34. C. R. Swanson, R. E. Kadunce, R. H. Hodgson, and D. S. Frear, *Weeds*, **14**, 319 (1966).

35. L. C. Warner, Ph.D. thesis, Univ. Minnesota, Minneapolis, 1963.

36. C. R. Swanson, R. H. Hodgson, and D. S. Frear, *Plant Physiol. Suppl.*, **40**, xiv (1965).

37. S. R. Colby, *Proc. Northeast. Weed Control Conf.*, **20**, 619 (1966).

38. S. R. Colby, American Chemical Society, 152nd meeting, New York, 1966.

39. R. E. Kadunce, *J. Chromatog.*, **30**, 204 (1967).

40. D. G. Swan and F. W. Slife, *Weeds*, **13**, 133 (1965).

41. D. S. Frear, C. R. Swanson, and R. E. Kadunce, *Weeds*, **15**, 101 (1967).

42. D. S. Frear, private communication, 1967.

43. J. R. Plimmer, *Weed Soc. Am. Abstr.*, 1967, p. 69.

44. T. J. Sheets, *Weeds*, **11**, 186 (1963).
45. J. R. Plimmer, private communication, 1967.
46. T. W. Donaldson and C. L. Foy, *Weeds.*, **13**, 195 (1965).
47. C. I. Harris and G. F. Warren, *Weeds*, **12**, 120 (1964).
48. K. A. Schliebe, O. C. Burnside, and T. L. Lavy, *Weeds*, **13**, 321 (1965).
49. G. F. Warren, *Hormolog*, **4**, 15 (1963).
50. F. T. Corbin and R. P. Upchurch, *Weeds*, **15**, 370 (1967).
51. I. C. Macrae and M. Alexander, *J. Agr. Food Chem.*, **13**, 72 (1964).
52. W. E. Rauser and C. M. Switzer, *Weeds*, **10**, 62 (1962).
53. W. E. Rauser and C. M. Switzer, *Hormolog*, **4**, 13 (1963).
54. O. C. Burnside, *Weeds*, **13**, 274 (1965).
55. H. R. Baker, R. E. Talbert, and R. E. Frans, *Proc. Southern Weed Conf.*, **19**, 117 (1966).
56. A. R. Cooke, *Mededel. Rijksfaculteit Landbouwwetenschappen, Gent*, **31**, 1165 (1966).
57. S. R. McLane, C. B. Mitchell, and M. D. Parkins, *Proc. Southern Weed Conf.*, **20**, 164 (1967).
58. R. C. Brian, in *The Physiology and Biochemistry of Herbicides* (L. J. Audus, ed.), Academic Press, New York, 1964.
59. J. A. Bentley, *Nature*, **165**, 449 (1950).
60. P. J. Linder, J. W. Mitchell, and G. D. Freeman, *J. Agr. Food Chem.*, **12**, 437 (1964)
61. M. A. Venis and G. E. Blackman, *J. Exptl. Botan.*, **17**, 270 (1966).
62. M. A. Venis and G. E. Blackman, *J. Exptl. Botan.*, **17**, 771 (1966).
63. M. A. Venis and G. E. Blackman, *J. Exptl. Botan.*, **17**, 790 (1966).
64. G. W. Mason, Ph.D. thesis, Univ. California, Davis, 1959.
65. K. V. Thimann, *Plant Physiol.*, **27**, 392 (1952).
66. P. G. Balayannis, M. S. Smith, and R. L. Wain, *Ann. Appl. Biol.*, **55**, 149 (1965).
67. O. C. Burnside, G. A. Wicks, and C. R. Fenster, *Weeds*, **13**, 277 (1965).
68. O. R. Dewey, R. V. Lindsay, and G. S. Hartley, *Nature*, **195**, 1232 (1962).
69. O. R. Dewey and R. K. Pfeiffer, *Mededel. Landbouwhogeschool Opzokingsstats, Staat Gent*, **24**, 899 (1959).
70. C. C. Dowler, P. F. Sand, and E. L. Robinson, *Weeds*, **11**, 276 (1963).
71. W. M. Phillips, *Weeds*, **7**, 284 (1959).
72. T. J. Sheets and D. D. Kaufman, *Proc. Southern Weed Conf.*, **18**, 667 (1965).
73. N. A. Broadhurst, M. L. Montgomery, and V. H. Freed, *J. Agr. Food Chem.*, **14**, 585 (1966).
74. W. H. Vandenborn, *Weed Soc. Am. Abstr.*, 1966, p. 62.
75. W. H. Vandenborn and F. Y. Chang, *Weed Soc. Am. Abstr.*, 1967, p. 40.
76. C. L. Foy and W. Hurtt, *Weed Soc. Am. Abstr.*, **7**, 40 (1967).
77. A. C. Magalhaes and C. L. Foy, *Weed Soc. Am. Abstr.*, **7**, 44 (1967).
78. W. Hurtt and C. L. Foy, *Plant Physiol. Suppl.*, **40**, xlviii (1965).
79. H. A. Friesen, *Weeds*, **13**, 30 (1965).
80. C. I. Harris, *Weeds*, **12**, 112 (1964).
81. O. C. Burnside and T. L. Lavy, *Weeds*, **14**, 211 (1966).
82. C. Parker and G. L. Hodgson, *Proc. Brit. Weed Control Conf., 8th*, 1966, p. 614, in *Weed Abstr.*, **16**, 114 (1967).
83. J. F. Norris and A. J. Klemka, *J. Am. Chem. Soc.*, **62**, 1432 (1940).
84. H. Koopman and J. Daams, *Nature*, **186**, 89 (1960).
85. G. E. Barnsley and P. H. Rosher, *Weed Res.*, **1**, 147 (1961).

86. J. Daams, *Z. Pflanzenkrankh. Pflanzenschutz*, **3**, 139 (1965).
87. D. A. Pate and H. H. Funderburk, Jr., *Symp. Use Isotopes Weed Res., Intern. At. Energy Agency, FAO, Vienna, 1965*, **17** (1966).
88. D. A. Pate and H. H. Funderburk, Jr., *Symp. Use Isotopes Weed Res., Intern. At. Energy Agency, FAO, Vienna, 1965*, **17** (1966).
89. D. A. Pate and H. H. Funderburk, Jr., *Proc. Southern Weed Conf.*, **18**, 605 (1965).
90. A. Verloop and W. B. Nimmo, *Symp. Use Isotopes Weed Res., Intern. At. Energy Agency, FAO, Abstr. SM-69/12*, 1965.
91. P. Massini, *Weed Res.*, **1**, 142 (1961).
92. D. A. Pate, H. H. Funderburk, Jr., D. E. Davis, and J. M. Lawrence, *Proc. Southern Weed Conf.*, **17**, 337 (1964).
93. L. D. Brannock, M. Montgomery, and V. H. Freed, *Bull. Environ. Contam. Toxicol.*, **2**, 178 (1967).
94. J. W. Smith and T. J. Sheets, *Weed Soc. Am. Abstr.*, 1967, p. 76.
95. C. W. Miller, I. E. Demoranville, and A. J. Charig, *Weeds*, **14**, 296 (1966).
96. K. I. Beynon, L. Davies, and K. Elgar, *J. Sci. Food Agr.*, **17**, 156 (1966).
97. K. I. Beyon, L. Davies, K. Elgar, and A. N. Wright, *J. Sci. Food Agr.*, **17**, 151 (1966).
98. K. I. Beynon, L. Davies, K. Elgar, and A. N. Wright, in *Herbicides in British Fruit Growing* (J. E. Fryer, ed.), Blackwell, Oxford, 1966.
99. K. Carpenter and B. J. Heywood, *Nature*, **200**, 28 (1963).
100. R. L. Wain, *Nature*, **200**, 28 (1963).
101. A. R. Cooke, R. D. Hart, and N. E. Achuff, *Proc. Northeast. Weed Control Conf.*, **19**, 321 (1965).
102. E. N. Ugochukwu and R. L. Wain, *Chem. Ind. (London)*, **1965**, 35.
103. R. L. Wain, *Proc. Brit. Weed Control Conf. 7th*, 1964, p. 306.
104. D. Paton and J. E. Smith, *Experientia*, **22**, 734 (1966).
105. M. A. Zaki, Ph.D. thesis, Univ. London, in *Weed Abstr.*, **15**, 232 (1966).

CHAPTER 12

Herbicide Photodecomposition

DONALD G. CROSBY AND MING-YU LI

AGRICULTURAL TOXICOLOGY AND RESIDUE RESEARCH LABORATORY
UNIVERSITY OF CALIFORNIA
DAVIS, CALIFORNIA

12-1. Introduction 321
12-2. Photodecomposition 322
    A. Ultraviolet Light 322
    B. Sunlight 324
    C. Equipment 326
    D. Methods 331
12-3. Photochemistry of Herbicides and Plant-Growth Regulators . . 335
    A. Aliphatic and Phenoxy Acids 336
    B. Aromatic Acids 341
    C. Amides and Anilides 344
    D. Carbamates and Ureas 345
    E. Thiolcarbamates and Dithiocarbamates 348
    F. Phenols and Phenyl Esters 348
    G. Amines 351
    H. Heterocyclic Compounds 353
    I. Miscellaneous Herbicides 356
12-4. Discussion 358
References 360

12-1. INTRODUCTION

Have you ever been sunburned? Most of us have experienced in varying degrees this uncomfortable demonstration of the chemical power of the sun's rays. The burn is not due to heat, of course, but to the ultraviolet component of sunlight; erythema, as it is called, appears most rapidly upon irradiation of the skin at 297 mμ, and the effect declines sharply at longer wavelengths until it is negligible above 320 mμ. As we shall see, radiation within this range may be expected to be very important for other photochemical reactions as well.

Many other results and applications of solar-chemical effects have been observed since ancient times. The bone disease known as rickets has long been associated with a person's lack of exposure to sunshine (the conversion of ergosterol to vitamin D requires ultraviolet light); white cloth has been left in sun to bleach since the days of antiquity; many disease-causing bacteria are killed by sunlight, providing an ancient means of water purification; and the fading of organic dyes employed in the coloring of fabrics led to extensive corrective research, one end result of which has been the development of successful color photography.

The chemical power of the invisible light occurring beyond the violet region of the spectrum was recognized about 1800, and the extensive lore of photochemical transformations which accumulated over the succeeding 140 years has been well reviewed by Ellis (1) and Dhar (2). However, it is only within the past two decades that detailed scientific study of the chemical action of ultraviolet light has flowered into its present state of excitement and rapid advance (3).

12-2. PHOTODECOMPOSITION

A. Ultraviolet Light

Light is electromagnetic in character. Although it may be considered to exist in both particulate and wave form, this energy is measured most commonly in terms of either wavelength (λ) or frequency (ν). The common units of measure of λ are the Angstrom (Å) (10^{-8} cm) and the millimicron (mμ) or nanometer (nm) (10^{-7} cm), whereas ν is measured in vibrations (cycles) per second (Hz) or in wave numbers (cm^{-1}). Although the electromagnetic spectrum open to practical laboratory measurement is very broad (Fig. 12-1), the present discussion will be confined to the rather narrow region known as the ultraviolet (UV).

UV light is considered to include wavelengths between 40 and 4000 Å (4–400 mμ), but most chemical experiments have been restricted to the middle (200–300 mμ) and near (300–400 mμ) UV. According to quantum theory, radiant energy occurs in discrete parcels or quanta. The energy (E) of each quantum in ergs is related to wavelength (in cm) or frequency (sec^{-1}) by

$$E = h\nu = hc/\lambda \qquad (1)$$

where h is Planck's constant (6.62×10^{-27} erg-sec) and c is the velocity of light (3×10^{10} cm/sec). Converted into more familiar terms, the energy available to bring about photochemical transformations amounts to about 143 kcal/mole at 200 mμ, 95 kcal/mole at 300 mμ, and 68 kcal/mole at 420 mμ. The amount of energy required to break the carbon–carbon bond in ethane is about 88 kcal/mole and a carbon–hydrogen bond requires about 98 kcal/mole; the hydrogen–oxygen bond of water requires 119 kcal, the oxygen–oxygen bond in hydrogen peroxide requires 52 kcal/mole, and the hydrogen–oxygen bond in hydrogen peroxide requires 90 kcal/mole (4). Although bond strengths vary widely depending upon the type of molecule, physical state, and reaction mechanism, it is apparent that UV light is sufficiently energetic to bring about many kinds of chemical transformations (Fig. 12-1).

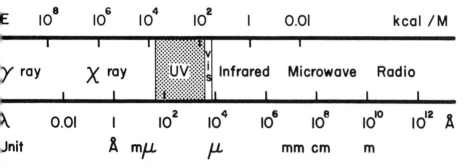

Fig. 12-1. Electromagnetic spectrum.

Quantum energy continues to fall off as wavelength increases. In the comparatively simple types of compounds represented by the large majority of herbicides, light of wavelengths greater than about 450 mμ (blue-violet) representing energies less than 65 kcal/mole would not be expected to bring about chemical changes under most circumstances even if the compounds were able to absorb sufficient energy in this region.

Energy absorption is, of course, the prime requisite for a photochemical reaction. If the amount of energy absorbed at each wavelength is plotted over a wavelength range, the resulting graph is referred to as the absorption spectrum. In the UV region the absorbed energy causes excitation of electrons and may result in the breakage and/or formation of chemical bonds, fluorescence, or merely loss as heat. Energy absorption by complex molecules is dependent in its degree and wavelength upon the chemical structure, and a majority of the aromatic compounds commonly used as herbicides exhibit rather intense absorption in the UV region (i.e., they have UV absorption spectra).

The data of Table 12-1 reveal that most common herbicides exhibit their principal electronic absorption maxima in the region between 220 and 400

TABLE 12-1

UV Absorption Maxima of Selected Herbicides in Water (5)

Common name	Chemical name	Absorption maximum, $m\mu$
Simazine	2-Chloro-4,6-bis(ethylamino)-s-triazine	220
2,4-D	2,4-Dichlorophenoxyacetic acid	220, 230, 283
2,4,5-T	2,4,5-Trichlorophenoxyacetic acid	220, 289
IPC	Isopropyl N-phenylcarbamate	234
Monuron	3-(4'-Chlorophenyl)-1,1-dimethylurea	244
Propanil	3',4'-Dichloropropionanilide	248
Dicryl	3',4'-Dichloro-2-methylacrylanilide	258
Amiben	3-Amino-2,5-dichlorobenzoic acid	297
DNBP	4,6-Dinitro-2-sec-butylphenol	375
Trifluralin	α,α,α-Trifluoro-2,6-dinitro-N,N-di-n-propyl-p-toluidine	376

$m\mu$. The special properties of sensitized reactions will be mentioned later. Energy continues to be absorbed at longer wavelengths—herbicides obviously absorb infrared radiation and provide infrared spectra—but this comparatively low energy is generally sufficient only to increase the amplitude of vibration, rotation, or tumbling of the molecules.

B. Sunlight

Energy from the sun controls such widely varied subjects as the earth's climate, radio transmission, the abundance of commercially important fish, and, of course, through the photosynthetic process of green plants, almost all life on this planet. At the mean solar distance, this energy amounts to about 0.14 W/cm^2, which is equivalent to 1170 W (1.56 hp) on each square yard. However, only about two-thirds of this energy reaches the earth's surface, the rest being absorbed, scattered, or reflected during passage through the atmosphere.

Although the emission spectrum of the sun is very broad indeed, the ozone always present in the atmosphere because of oxygen photolysis effectively absorbs short-wavelength UV light. A wavelength of 286.3 $m\mu$ is the shortest ever recorded at the earth's surface, and solar energy may probably be considered negligible below about 295 mμ. Maximum total energy is found at 540 mμ; Table 12-2 indicates that energy increases rather sharply with increasing wavelength up to this maximum and then falls off slowly.

The data of Table 12-2 also reveal a fact unconsciously recognized by beachgoers for centuries: sunburn may occur even in the shade. Dispersion of UV light in open sky may equal or at times even surpass in energy the

TABLE 12-2

Solar Energy Distribution[a]

Wavelength, mμ	Sunlight energy, μW/cm^2	Skylight energy, μW/cm^4	Total energy μW/cm^2
300	2.6	2.6	5.2
355	144	115	259
400	268	165	433
450	453	216	669
500	525	193	718
550	535	154	689
600	503	118	621
650	459	97	556
700	464	85	549

[a] Midsummer noon in Cleveland, Ohio; 50-Å band. Data from Ref. (6).

direct radiation from the sun. The shorter the wavelength, the greater the dispersion; a clear December day can produce as much as six times more 300–320-mμ energy in skylight than is derived from the sun directly (7).

That long days with high dispersion produce more total light energy than shorter days, despite greater heat and intense direct sunlight, is demonstrated by the total energy measurements published by the U.S. Department of Commerce (8). As shown in Table 12-3, on a late spring day, Washington or Alaska may receive more light energy than Los Angeles or Atlanta; December, of course, provides the opposite extreme.

The intensity of sunlight at any location increases with altitude, with the time of day, and with the clarity of the atmosphere. Interestingly enough, the UV light intensity increases more rapidly with altitude as wavelengths become shorter; the relative proportion of UV is greatest in morning and evening and varies inversely with wavelength; the water vapor or clouds exert relatively little effect on the UV light impinging on the earth's surface.

TABLE 12-3

Average Daily Solar Energy at Various Locations

Station	Solar energy, May 1966, g-cal/cm^2	Solar energy, Dec. 1966, g-cal/cm^2
Davis, California	895	126
Tucson, Arizona	663	277
Prosser, Washington	620	88
Lakeland, Florida	571	303
Barrow, Alaska	564	< 17
Columbia, Missouri	524	151
Atlanta, Georgia	482	203
Los Angeles, California	482	255
New York, New York	455	130

From even this brief description, it may be seen that the amount and intensity of the UV component of sunlight is greater than one might think, and both climatic and geographic factors act to favor the low levels of short-wavelength UV which reach us. Despite the sharp decline in intensity with decreasing wavelength (intensity at 290 mμ is perhaps only one-millionth of that at 320 mμ), examination of the energy equation presented earlier shows that each *quantum* at 300 mμ (95.3 kcal/mole) is almost twice as energetic as a quantum at the 560-mμ maximum intensity of sunlight (51.1 kcal/mole). Photolytic reactions in sunlight essentially are bounded by the UV cutoff of the ozone absorption spectrum (about 290 mμ) on one end and the low-energy limit for the activation of bond breaking at the other. Within this narrow range, however, a wide variety of chemical transformations have been shown to occur.

C. Equipment

Many types of UV light sources have become available commercially during the past decade. These may generally be considered in three categories: (1) incandescent, (2) arc, and (3) fluorescent. Incandescent lamps are familiar to everyone in the form of the household light bulb. These particular lamps employ a tungsten filament in a bulb filled with inert gas. They are, at best, inefficient sources of UV radiation (total UV energy emitted below 380 mμ by a 1000-W photoflood bulb is only about 3 W), but by the use of appropriate filters they may be utilized as very weak sources of long-wavelength UV ("black") light. The "Purple X" lamp produces sufficient UV energy to permit application in the detection of fluorescent minerals, etc.; the possible utility of other incandescent sources is nullified by the very large proportion of heat and visible light which they produce.

The most common arc lamps are those in which an electric discharge is generated in a gaseous element such as neon, xenon, or mercury vapor. Open carbon arcs such as those used in emission spectroscopy have not received extensive application in photochemical experiments.

The mercury vapor arcs, operating under both high and low pressure, have become the standard UV source for most photochemical research. They usually consist of an evacuated quartz envelope containing a small pool of metallic mercury and appropriate electrodes. They are fabricated in a wide variety of forms including spiral, tubular, and bayonet types. These lamps are rich sources of UV light emitted over a broad wavelength

TABLE 12-4

UV Radiation from the 250-W Uviarc[a]

Wavebands, $m\mu$	Principal line, $m\mu$	Radiation, W
< 250		2.20
250–260	253.7	3.00
260–270	265.2	1.99
270–280		0.37
280–290	280.4	1.82
290–300	296.7	1.28
300–310	302.2	2.28
310–320	313.1	4.43
320–360		1.26
360–370	365.4	7.05
370–400		0.48
400–410	404.7	1.74
410–430		0.26
430–440	435.8	4.18
440–540		0.64
540–550	546.1	4.65
550–570		0.29
570–580	578.0	5.05
> 580		1.09

[a] Data from Ref. (9).

range and consisting of a series of sharp spectral lines. A typical high-pressure mercury lamp such as the "Uviarc" produces most of its energy in the UV region at a relatively few principal wavelengths (Table 12-4). The total UV is 26.2 W (10.5% of the lamp input), and total visible light is 17.9 W (or 7.2% of the input). The remainder of the energy, about 80% of the electrical input, is radiated as heat, and prolonged exposure to a Uviarc lamp has caused glassware breakage in our laboratory due to temperature differentials.

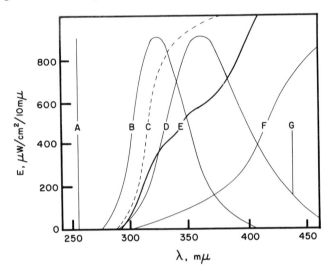

Fig. 12-2. Common sources of UV radiation: the spectral energy distribution of a low-pressure Hg lamp (A); a 40-W fluorescent lamp with filter envelope (B) and without filter (D), showing interference from an unfiltered mercury line G; summer noon sunlight (E); and a daylight-type fluorescent lamp (F). C is the UV absorption curve of ordinary Pyrex glass.

Several types of low-pressure mercury arcs are also available commercially. These intense sources are much cooler and far more efficient producers of UV light than high-pressure lamps, and frequently over 90% of the light is concentrated at 253.7 mμ. The so-called "germicidal lamps," spiral lamps, and Pen-Ray immersible bayonet lamps are of this type. A typical 30-W low-pressure lamp radiates 8.3 W (28% of the electrical input) at 253.7 mμ with a total UV output of 10 W or 33% of the rated power (10).

A common variation of the low-pressure mercury arc is the well-known fluorescent lamp. Here, the lamp envelope is coated with a thin layer of mineral or organic phosphor. The primarily 253.7-mμ radiation within the lamp causes the phosphor to fluoresce, producing a diffuse, even light of somewhat lower intensity than the original arc. Appropriate variation of phosphor composition can provide a wide range of spectral characteristics, but a common feature is the continuous emission of a broad spectral band rather than only of a mercury line spectra. Like other low-pressure mercury lamps, they are cool and efficient, and although they never attain the total power of high-pressure lamps, the UV output approaches that of the common line sources and appears in a much more usable form.

In addition to the usual daylight type of fluorescent lamp, several manufacturers produce lamps which fluoresce in the UV region. Incorporation of mineral filters in the envelopes permits even greater variation in spectral characteristics. Figure 12-2 compares the spectral range and intensity of an unfiltered fluorescent UV lamp [curve (D)] with those of the filtered model (B), a daylight type (F), and the corresponding mercury arc (A). It should be noted that even the ordinary fluorescent lamps used to illuminate many laboratories radiate levels of UV sufficient to cause photochemical changes in especially sensitive compounds.

Many other light sources have been employed in special photochemical applications, including zinc and cadmium resonance lamps, inert-gas resonance lamps, microwave-excited lamps, cathode glow lamps, and superintensity lamps for flash photolysis. Comprehensive discussions of UV sources have been prepared by Koller (7) and Calvert and Pitts (3). It may be of particular interest, however, to mention the value of commercial spectrophotofluorometers as sources of essentially monochromatic light for photochemical experiments. These instruments employ much more intense light sources (such as xenon arcs) than do most spectrophotometers, and irradiation of either solids or solutions at any of the wavelengths important in sunlight is readily accomplished in these versatile instruments.

Reaction vessels vary widely in form and capacity, and their geometry frequently depends primarily on the type of lamp and spectral region under investigation. Glass plates, open dishes and trays, and numerous reactors have been applied in herbicide photolysis (10). Figure 12-3 presents a diagrammatic representation of a comparatively simple reactor which we have found convenient for photochemical studies involving the use of mercury arc light at 254 mμ.

The reaction chamber (A) is enclosed in a jacket (B) through which a tempered fluid may be circulated to permit heating, cooling, or maintenance at a constant temperature. The spiral mercury vapor lamp (C) (Nestor and Faust, Inc., Newark, Delaware) is fitted into a quartz well (D) and although a considerable amount of heat is produced during lengthy experiments, it is not advisable to fill the lamp chamber with fluid. Stirring may be accomplished with a magnetic stirrer or by passing in a stream of air or inert gas through inlet E (from which samples also may be withdrawn at F during irradiation). Gases may escape through outlet G to which a reflux condenser and/or absorption train may be attached.

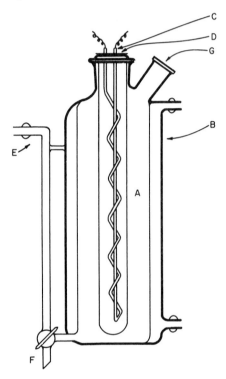

Fig. 12-3. Photochemical reactor for use with bayonet lamps, showing reaction chamber (A), thermal jacket (B), lamp (C), lamp well (D), gas inlet (E), and drain (F).

Another type of reactor in regular use in our laboratory is shown in Fig. 12-4. The light source in this case may be either a germicidal lamp (254 $m\mu$) or a tubular fluorescent lamp. The lamp (B) is inserted through the hollow core of the reactor D, the thin Pyrex wall serving as an effective filter of low-wavelength radiation. When liquids are irradiated, effective agitation is achieved by a stream of air or inert gas introduced through inlet C, and the temperature is measured by a thermocouple in the well at E. The thickness of the liquid light path is restricted to 1 cm, and the outer wall is enclosed in a high-efficiency aluminum reflector. A condenser or absorption apparatus may be attached through joint A.

Various light filters have been employed to select specific spectral bands (3,7), but bandwidth, low transmission, and restriction of area of exposure all present major drawbacks. As mentioned earlier, commercial spectro-photofluorometers (such as the Baird-Atomic Model SF-1) produce sufficient intensities of almost monochromatic light to be very useful for some investigations. The absorptive properties of common "glasses" may also be put to use conveniently in many instances. As shown in curve C of

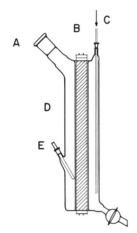

Fig. 12-4. Photochemical reactor for use with fluorescent lamps, showing condenser joint (A), lamp (B), gas inlet (C), reaction chamber (D), and thermocouple well (E).

Fig. 12-2, a 2-mm thickness of Pyrex exhibits a UV transmission cutoff of about 280 mμ; the cutoff for fused quartz is about 180 mμ, while ordinary window glass is essentially opaque below about 310 mμ.

D. Methods

1. Irradiation

Herbicide irradiation has been conducted under many experimental conditions. In fact, almost every investigation has employed methods somewhat different from any others and consequently no uniform tech-niques appear to have emerged. Most experiments have been carried out with herbicides dispersed on solid supports including filter paper, aluminum planchets, soil surfaces, or glass plates. Others have employed solutions or suspensions of the compound in water or benzene. There is no record of herbicide photolysis in the gas phase.

In general, minimum effects are to be expected from irradiation in the solid state. Light is seldom able to penetrate very far into a crystalline deposit, and mixture of the herbicide with solid supports such as the silicic acid of chromatoplates, soil, or filter paper offers so much opportunity for shielding by opaque particles that little photolysis occurs. However, where photodecomposition does occur, it is apparent that the compound under examination either is intrinsically very unstable or its adsorbed state confers instability. It has been estimated that about 98 % of the UV light that enters a crystal is absorbed within a distance of about 10^{-8} cm (1 Å) from the surface (11).

Most herbicides undergo some photodecomposition in the dissolved state. Solvents which themselves do not absorb UV light have received considerable attention in our laboratory. Water, lower alcohols, and hexane provide a range of polarities sufficient to dissolve almost any compound, although the s-triazines present a problem. Acetone and cyclohexane are affected by mercury light, the former yielding methyl and acetyl radicals and the latter apparently undergoing unsaturation and polymerization.

In solution the concentration and thickness of the liquid layer (or degree of agitation) are of prime importance. Thin layers expose relatively more compound to irradiation, and agitation is very important in causing solution to continuously impinge on the light source. If the concentration of a highly absorbing compound in solution is too high, the statistical probability for exposure of an unreacted molecule to a photon is greatly diminished. In fact, the mechanism of the decomposition may differ depending on concentration. For most exploratory purposes, we have found that a concentration range between 50 and 500 mg/liter is generally satisfactory.

Photochemical reactions are not as greatly affected by changes in temperature as are thermally controlled reactions. This is not a surprising observation in view of the free-radical nature of many light-catalyzed processes. However, the duration of irradiation is of singular importance. If only a single product is formed in a photochemical process, then its concentration may be expected to increase with exposure time. Most photolyses generally produce a variety of products, each of which is formed at a rate different from the others and which well may decompose further upon extended irradiation. For this reason, "flash photolysis"—i.e., irradiation with brief burst of high-intensity radiation—has assumed great importance in the study of photochemical reaction mechanisms (12). In conducting the usual type of photochemical experiments with herbicides, in which irradiation with comparatively weak energy sources may require several hours, it is not unusual for reactive intermediates to be lost and only the most stable end products (frequently polymers) to be isolated.

2. Sunlight

Sunlight may be considered to represent a special technique of irradiation. The sun itself provides a light source of ultimate importance in any attempt to investigate the environmental fate of herbicides. Unfortunately, sunlight is unreliable and uncontrollable at best; its intensity varies drastically over a 24-hour period, and useful intensities are available only during about 30 % of a summer day. Heat, air movement, contamination, solvent evaporation, and variable levels of water vapor all act to obscure photochemical results and harass the investigator. Of all the many and often ingenious ways in which the photochemical effects of UV light have been studied, the direct use of the sun as an energy source is scientifically among the least satisfactory.

Probably the greatest technical problems to be encountered in sunlight irradiations, outside of the lack of experimental control, are prevention of contamination by dust, trash, and insects and control of loss through volatilization. These precautions must be effected without undue loss of light intensity, spectral quality, or restriction of air. While thin quartz plates or dishes have been employed to cover open irradiation containers, their cost is generally prohibitive. Glass plates necessarily must be so thin that breakage is a severe problem. We have achieved fairly satisfactory results by covering a low Pyrex crystallizing dish containing the herbicide with a layer of Saran wrap or Mylar film in which a number of small holes have been punched. In this way, air is admitted and condensation on the underside of the film is minimized, while contamination and evaporation are almost completely circumvented. When liquids are irradiated, they should be stirred with a magnetic stirrer and temperature may be controlled by floating the dish in a constant temperature bath.

Many attempts have been made to simulate the wavelength range and intensity of sunlight. This is a very large order, indeed, and has met with only limited success under highly specialized conditions. Each type of light source exhibits its own peculiarities and limitations, for example, mercury arcs are deficient in the red and infrared regions, and even when combined, the several lamps do not appear to be capable of duplicating exactly the natural light of the sun. Recently, several very expensive instruments have been developed which lay claim to solar simulation, but even they prove to have significant variations from nature.

A major part of the problem is the width and complexity of the spectral range which must be represented. For simulation of that part of the solar UV spectrum which is most important to herbicide photolysis, however, several satisfactory variations on the mercury arc are proving to be satisfactory for laboratory investigations. These are fluorescent lamps having the spectral distribution shown by curve D of Fig. 12-2. Comparison with curve F, which represents the spectrum of sunlight, shows that the vital photochemical wavelength region between 290 mμ and 370 mμ is closely simulated by such lamps. Exposure of a series of standard pesticides in solution to sunlight and to an F40BL General Electric lamp in the reactor illustrated in Fig. 12-4 revealed an almost identical array of photodecomposition products from the two types of irradiation, the only significant difference apparently being due to the longer duration of the sunlight experiments.

3. Measurement of Energy

Although it appears that in no instance has the efficiency or quantum yield of herbicide photodecomposition been measured, such information would have both theoretical interest because of the unusual types of compounds involved and practical application in deciding on possible alternative routes of environmental degradation. Intensity measurements at specific wavelengths are of greatest importance in the design and operation of laboratory reactors intended to simulate natural sunlight.

Actinometers, as these measuring devices are called, may be classified as physical, chemical, and biological; the latter have only very limited application at present. Physical actinometers include radiometers (thermopiles, bolometers, and radiometers), photoelectric devices (phototubes, photovoltaic cells, and resistance cells), and ion chambers. These devices are generally used to measure directly the intensity of incident light, although through proper circuitry they may also be arranged to integrate incident energy. Radiometers are essentially wavelength-independent, while the electrical response of the other instruments may vary sharply with changes in wavelength. Devices of this type, suitably calibrated, find their greatest application in the measurement of the light incident on solid surfaces.

Chemical actinometers are generally less convenient in operation than physical actinometers, but they are less expensive, require less calibration, and provide more accurate measurement. Because they integrate intensity, they are very useful in overcoming the errors due to changes in source intensity (particularly in sunlight), and, as solutions, they directly compensate for the peculiarities of the reaction vessel and system. Although a photographic plate may be considered to be a form of chemical actinometer, probably the most common example of this class has been the uranyl oxalate actinometer. This detector is being superseded by the more sensitive ferrioxalate actinometer which operates according to

$$Fe(III)_2(C_2O_4)_3 \rightarrow Fe(II)_2(C_2O_4) + 2CO_2 \tag{2}$$

The ferrous ion so generated is determined spectrophotometrically as its red phenanthroline complex (*13*). Detailed discussion of actinometry have been presented by Calvert and Pitts (*3*), Koller (*7*), and Noyes and Boekel-heide (*14*).

12-3. PHOTOCHEMISTRY OF HERBICIDES AND PLANT-GROWTH REGULATORS

Up to this point our discussion of photochemistry, its equipment, and its methods has been quite general. Even in those instances where the term "herbicide" was used, the discussion could have been applied equally well to almost any organic compound having appropriate absorption character-istics. Despite their present-day application for the practical control of plant processes, this group of organic chemicals represents only a diverse and interesting cross section of structural types from the viewpoint of basic organic chemistry. The photolysis of trichloroacetic acid (*15*) and 2,4-dinitro-6-methylphenol (*16*), for example, was investigated many years before either compound found application as a herbicide.

Throughout the following survey, it is suggested that the examples presented should be viewed especially in terms of their photochemical generality. Although there are relatively few examples to compare, it should be recognized that there are also relatively few major chemical classes of herbicides. Certain common reactions are shared, however, including the replacement of aromatic chlorine atoms by hydroxyl or hydrogen, β-elimination reactions at hetero atoms, etc.

At the present limited state of knowledge, it must be assumed that photochemical reactivity does not necessarily coincide with biochemical reactivity and that herbicide photodecomposition is not immediately related to either metabolism, mode of action, or specific weed-killing applications. In reviewing specific examples of photodecomposition, we have divided the herbicides and plant-growth regulators into arbitrary classes according to a major functional group. Obviously, polyfunctional compounds could belong to several groups. Where pertinent, compound names and type reactions have been cross-referenced.

No attempt has been made to include an exhaustive bibliography; for extensive general coverage of the photochemical literature, the reader is directed to the reviews by Calvert and Pitts (3) and Ellis et al. (1). Generally, brief progress reports and abstracts have not been included here if the work received more extensive coverage in other publications.

A. Aliphatic and Phenoxy Acids

Penfound and Minyard (17) first suggested that light intensity might affect the biological activity of phenoxy herbicides. Water hyacinth plants growing in shade and in sunlight were treated with the butyl ester of 2,4-D at 1000 ppm, and more epinasty and necrosis were observed in the shaded plants. Repetition of the experiment with potted red kidney bean plants revealed that the herbicide produced similar epinasty and necrosis under conditions of direct sunlight, diffuse light, or darkness, except that ultimate survival of the treated plants was more frequent at high light intensities. While these results might be due to the photolysis of the herbicide to less toxic products, the absence of temperature control leaves open the possibility for loss of the 2,4-D ester by volatilization from the relatively warmer leaf surface. In addition, Tutass (18) has suggested that the effect could arise from increased penetration due to reduced stomatal opening under high light intensities.

Despite the ambiguity of results from field experiments, there can be no doubt that 2,4-D (1) and other phenoxy herbicides decompose in aqueous solution under the influence of light. Bell (19) reported that paper chromatography of extracts from 2,4-D solutions irradiated with short-wavelength UV light contained at least five degradation products, some of which were phenolic. Aly and Faust (20) utilized a colorimetric analysis for phenol in their determination of the rate of 2,4-D disappearance in water.

Crosby and Tutass (21) irradiated aqueous solutions of the sodium salt of 2,4-D with UV light at 254 mμ and positively identified the ether-soluble photolysis products. These compounds fitted a sequence shown in Fig. 12-5. The initial photolytic reaction may be either cleavage of the ether bond to form 2,4-dichlorophenol (2) or stepwise replacement of the ring halogens to give 2-chloro-4-hydroxyphenoxyacetic acid (3) or 4-chloro-2-hydroxyphenoxyacetic acid (4). Photolysis proceeds through these two major reactions—ether cleavage and replacement of ring chlorines—to provide 1,2,4-benzenetriol (5), which was isolated as the stable triacetyl derivative.

Aqueous solutions of benzenetriol are unstable to air. This compound was converted via a nonphotochemical oxidation, as rapidly as it was

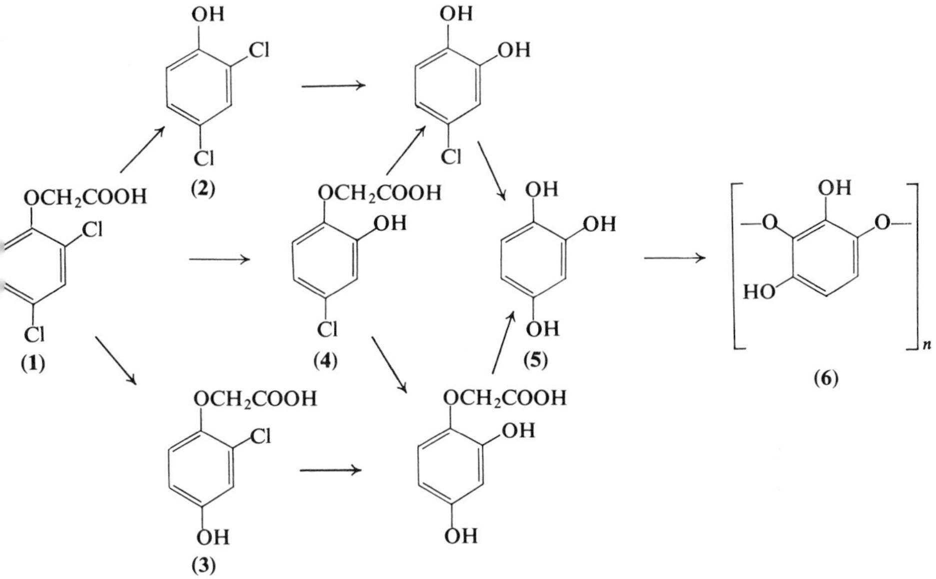

Fig. 12-5. Photolysis pathway for 2,4-D.

formed, to a dark polymer identical in its physical and chemical properties to humic acid (6), a type of polyquinoid found to occur widely in the organic fraction of soil. When desired, air oxidation could be largely circumvented by addition of sodium bisulfite to the reaction mixture. Ether extraction followed by acetylation gave good yields of 1,2,4-triacetoxybenzene in this instance. The formation of humic acid was particularly striking when the 2,4-D photolysis was carried out on wet filter paper. In the laboratory or in outdoor sunlight, filter paper soaked in sodium 2,4-D solution turned black within a few minutes due to polymer formation. Mitchell (22), who examined the UV irradiation of 141 pesticides on filter paper, reported that 2,4-D, MCPA, 2,4,5-T, and silvex were stable under his dry conditions; it appears that an excess of water is necessary for the achievement of appreciable photolysis rates of the phenoxy acids.

Other factors may also play an important part in the rapid photodecomposition of 2,4-D. Hamilton and Aldrich (23), Bell (19), Hansen and Buchholtz (24), and Carrol (25,26) all reported the inactivation of the herbicide by UV or visible light in the presence of riboflavin with the apparent formation of phenolic products. The UV absorption spectrum of sodium 2,4-D (Fig. 12-6) shows that 254-mμ light would be strongly absorbed and could be expected to produce chemical transformations; there is very little absorption above 300 mμ, however, and some activation process appears to be necessary to explain the rapid photolysis of the compound in sunlight or under incandescent lamps. Such a process is known as "sensitization," in which excited molecules of a substance which is an efficient absorber of light energy at some particular wavelength collide with a weak or non-absorber with a subsequent transfer of the energy. The sensitizer is generally

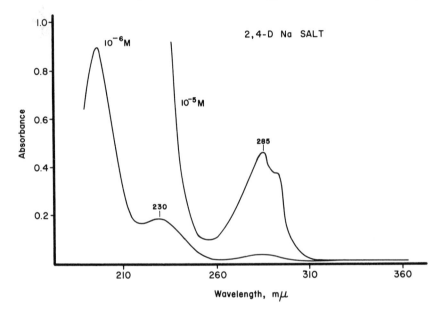

Fig. 12-6. UV absorption spectrum of aqueous solutions of 2,4-D sodium salt.

unchanged and may again absorb a quantum of light energy. Thus sensitization represents a form of catalysis. Alone, sensitizers which have absorbed energy frequently lose it by fluorescence, and many potential sensitizers may be detected in this way. Riboflavin is one such compound; other common sensitizers are zinc oxide, ferric salts, mercury vapor, and eosine.

Despite the negative results of Mitchell (22), Crosby and Tutass (27) have found that 2,4,5-T (2,4,5-trichlorophenoxyacetic acid), silvex [2-(2',4',5'-trichlorophenoxy)propionic acid], 2,4-DB [4-(2',4'-dichlorophenoxy)butyric acid], and the isomeric monochlorophenoxyacetic acids are readily photolyzed as their sodium salts in aqueous solution to provide the corresponding chlorophenols. However, Mitchell did observe the apparent conversion of the butyl, butoxyethyl, butoxyethoxypropyl, isobutyl, 2-ethylhexyl, isooctyl, and isopropyl esters of 2,4-D and the same esters of 2,4,5-T (except isobutyl) to the corresponding phenoxy acids.

Whether or not photolysis represents a significant route for the environmental degradation of phenoxy herbicides still remains in doubt. Although decomposition of 2,4-D to phenols has been demonstrated to occur in artificial ponds under the influence of UV light (20), there appeared to be little photodecomposition under natural conditions (28). Winston and Ritty (29) claim to have shown conclusively that phenoxy compounds are not converted to phenols in a natural watershed area. The dynamic character of photodecomposition and the other environmental forces acting on the chemicals would make the point very difficult to prove, however, particularly when humic acids are likely to be the end products.

As mentioned previously, several investigators have clearly demonstrated the riboflavin-sensitized photolysis of 2,4-D, and the observations that the growth-regulating and herbicidal effects of the compound are counteracted by riboflavin and light are not surprising. However, the careful experiments of Mellor and Salisbury (30) have shown that UV light was effective in preventing epinasty in 2,4-D-treated plants whether irradiation was performed *before or after* herbicide treatment. Carroll (25) also concluded that the apparent photosensitized inactivation of 2,4-D (corn root growth test) was due to an effect of light on the root rather than destruction of the chemical.

(7)

Another type of arylkyl acid herbicide is represented by fenac (2,3,6-trichlorophenylacetic acid) (7). Gas chromatography of the methylated acid, however, showed it to contain significant proportions of other isomeric trichlorophenylacetic acids as well as some di- and tetrachloroacids (31). UV irradiation of fenac (sodium salt) in water resulted in an extremely complex mixture which was not resolved by gas chromatography. Using the three individual monochlorophenylacetic acid isomers as models, Crosby (10) showed that UV irradiation of aqueous solutions of the sodium salts resulted in replacement of aromatic halogens by hydroxyl groups, replacement of halogen by hydrogen to give phenylacetic acid (8), and further degradation of the phenylacetic acid in turn to benzyl alcohol (9), benzaldehyde (10), and benzoic acid (11) (Fig. 12-7). "Humic Acid" represented the end-product of the further photolysis of the hydroxyphenyl-acetic acids as shown in the figure.

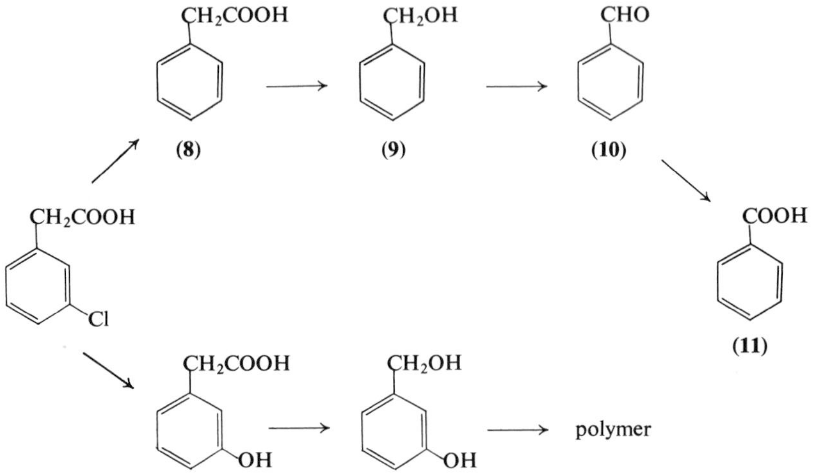

Fig. 12-7. Photolysis pathway for 3-chlorophenylacetic acid in water.

Naphthaleneacetic acid [NAA (12)], as aqueous solution of its sodium salt, is very unstable to UV irradiation (32). A number of photolysis products have been isolated, one of which is 1-naphthylcarbinol (13), analogous to the benzyl alcohol formed from phenylacetic acid.

Although not of commercial importance as a herbicide or plant-growth regulator, mention should be made of the photolysis of indole-3-acetic acid [IAA or auxin (14)]. Because of the presumed significance of IAA to the growth of higher plants and the undisputed destruction of the growth-promoting action of externally applied IAA by light to provide a photo-tropic effect, a relatively large body of data exist on IAA-light interactions. Although the majority of these investigations were only secondarily concerned with the identity of photolysis products, it appears that (a) IAA is very sensitive to UV light; (b) the photolysis is readily sensitized; (c) photodecomposition is oxidative; and (d) 3-methylindole, indole-3-alde-hyde, and indole-3-glycolic acid (15) are among the breakdown products as demonstrated by paper chromatography (33–38).

Several simple chlorinated aliphatic acids have received wide application in weed control. Monochloroacetic acid, trichloroacetic acid (TCA), and

(12)   (13)   (14)   (15)

dalapon [2,2-dichloropropionic acid, (16)] are the most familiar. These compounds are very strong organic acids (TCA is as strong as many common mineral acids) and are applied as their alkali metal salts in aqueous solution. Under the influence of UV light, the hydrolysis rate of mono-chloroacetic acid to glycolic acid (17) was markedly increased (39). TCA, rather than being hydrolyzed, is decarboxylated to chloroform and carbon dioxide (or sodium bicarbonate) (15). No photolysis of dalapon occurred under Mitchell's conditions (22), but its hydrolysis to pyruvic acid (18),

(16)   (17)   (18)   (19)   (20)

dehydrochlorination to 2-chloroacrylic acid (19), or reduction to propionic acid all represent reasonable possibilities if proper experimental conditions were provided.

Mitchell (22) also reported that disodium 3,6-endoxohexahydrophthalate [endothal (20)] remained unaffected by UV light. However, again it would be surprising if conditions could not easily be found under which endothal would photolyze as do other simple aliphatic acids (2).

B. Aromatic Acids

The aromatic acids are characterized by a carboxyl group attached directly to an aromatic nucleus such as benzene or pyridine. Due to their relative insolubility, they are generally applied in aqueous solution in the form of their amine or alkali metal salts or in organic solvents as their aliphatic esters. Benzoic acid (11) is a simple example, although it is not herbicidal. In general, the aromatic acids of the benzene series tend to be quite stable, while pyridinecarboxylic acids are easily decarboxylated.

Unlike results with 2,4-D, riboflavin sensitization failed to bring about photoinactivation of either TIBA [2,3,5-triiodobenzoic acid (21)] or the ethyl ester of trichlorobenzoic acid as measured by the cucumber root growth test (23). As demonstrated with polychlorophenoxyacetic acids and fenac, photolysis of these compounds as well as other polychlorobenzoic acids such as Zobar would be expected to result in very complex mixtures

(21)

of decomposition products. Crosby (10) employed as models the isomeric monochlorobenzoic acids and irradiated them at 254 mμ as their sodium salts in aqueous solution. Analogous with the chlorophenylacetic acids (see Section 12-3.A), ring halogen was replaced by both hydrogen and the hydroxyl group. Irradiation of 4-chlorobenzoic acid (22), for instance, produced benzoic acid itself, 4-hydroxybenzoic acid (23), and several other compounds. Two of these were identified conclusively as terephthalic acid (24) and 4-acetylbenzoic acid (25), the source of which has not been explained.

Amiben [3-amino-2,5-dichlorobenzoic acid (26)] was shown to be rapidly decomposed in aqueous solution in the presence of sunlight or a fluorescent sunlamp (10,40), and even dry amiben was slowly decomposed by the sunlamp. A number of photolysis products could be separated by paper or thin-layer chromatography, and some of them responded to the 4-nitro-benzenediazonium fluoborate test for phenols.

(22)   (23)   (24)   (25)

(26)   (27)   (28)   (29)

Very recently, Plimmer and Hummer (*41*) examined in detail the photolysis of amiben and its methyl ester in aqueous solution. As previously reported, amiben was converted under a Pyrex-filtered mercury lamp to a variety of colored products, some of which appeared to be polymers of the humic acid type. To circumvent nonphotochemical air oxidation, the compounds were also irradiated in the presence of sodium bisulfite, as in the case of 2,4-D (*21*). Under these conditions, amiben was reductively dechlorinated to 3-amino-5-chlorobenzoic acid (**27**, R = H), while amiben methyl ester was converted to the corresponding monochloro ester (**27**, R = CH$_3$). This result is parallel to the 2,4-D case in which the chlorine adjacent to the carboxyl appeared to be more readily replaced than the other one; it is to be expected that other amiben photolysis products will include 3-amino-5-chlorosalicylic acid (**28**), 3-amino-2-chloro-5-hydroxybenzoic acid (**29**), 3-aminobenzoic acid, etc.

Picloram (**30**) is also rapidly photolyzed upon UV or sunlight irradiation in aqueous solution (*42*), although the identity of the isolated photolysis products has not yet been reported. Plimmer and Hummer (*41*) have found that the methyl ester is converted to a single major product by loss of a chlorine atom, and, if the usual parallel is followed, it may be expected that

(30)   (31)   (32)   (33)

(34)   (35)   (36)   (37)

3-hydroxy-4-amino-5,6-dichloro-2-picolinic acid (**31**) and/or 4-amino-5,6-dichloro-2-picolinic acid (**32**) or their esters will be present in the reaction mixture. Also, although Freytag (*43*) demonstrated the apparent stability of several pyridinecarboxylic acids to UV light, the occurrence of decarboxylation products would not be surprising.

Two other important chlorinated benzoic acid derivatives are dacthal (**33**) and dicamba (**34**), but no information is available on their lability in light. From the authors' previous experience, it might be predicted that irradiation of (33) at wavelengths longer than 290 mμ would produce only 2,3,5,6-tetrachloroterephthalic acid, while similar irradiation of dicamba would result in rapid photolysis to give the hydroxylated compounds (35) and (36) and the reduced compound (37) as intermediate products, and humic acid as a major end product.

C. Amides and Anilides

Amides are derivatives of carboxylic acids in which the carbonyl group is bonded to nitrogen. When that nitrogen also bears a phenyl substituent, the compounds are sometimes referred to as anilides. Despite the commercial importance of the amide and anilide herbicides, virtually nothing has been reported on their photodecomposition. Mitchell (22) reported that CDAA (38) was photolyzed to several unidentified products when irradiated on filter paper with 254-mμ light; NPA [N-naphthylphthalamic acid (39)] was partially photolyzed, while Duraset [N-3-tolylphthalamic acid (40)] appeared to be unaffected.

CH$_2$=CHCH$_2$
CH$_2$=CHCH$_2$ NCOCH$_2$Cl

(38)   (39)   (40)

In very recent work, Rosen (44) found that diphenamid (41) was photolyzed in aqueous solution by UV light. A principal product was N-methyl-2,2-diphenylacetamide (42), a demethylation product; benzophenone (43), benzhydrol (44), and benzoic acid represented further degradation products in which the carbonyl-containing side chain was entirely removed. N-Formyl-2,2-diphenylacetamide might also be present, but no 2,2-diphenylacetamide was detected.

(41)   (42)   (43)   (44)

A number of other important herbicides and growth regulators may be classed as amides (B-nine, naphthaleneacetamide) or anilides (Clobber, dicryl, Karsil, solan, propanil). Certain type reactions already described may be expected to operate to some extent; aromatic chlorines will be replaced by hydroxyl or hydrogen, and *N*-alkyl groups will be replaced stepwise by hydrogen. However, the primitive state of knowledge concerning the photochemistry of this type of compound precludes any unequivocal general prediction of photolytic pathways at present.

Simple anilides such as acetanilide were found to rearrange under the influence of UV light (*45*) according to Eq. (3), and, although no extensive investigation of structural parameters was reported, several of the common anilide herbicides might be expected to undergo the reaction. Aniline was also formed as a by-product and, under prolonged irradiation, could be expected to react further with the formation of a complex mixture of products (*1*).

$$2\langle\rangle\text{—NHCOCH}_3 \xrightarrow{\lambda} \langle\rangle\text{—NH}_2 + \text{H}_2\text{N—}\langle\rangle\text{—COCH}_3 \quad (3)$$

D. Carbamates and Ureas

Carbamates and ureas are analogous to the amides and anilides discussed previously; instead of attachment of the carbonyl group to an aromatic or aliphatic carbon atom, it is bonded to oxygen (to form an ester) in carbamates and to nitrogen in the ureas. Isopropyl *N*-(3-chlorophenyl)carbamate [CIPC (**45**)] and fenuron [*N*-phenyl-*N'*,*N'*-dimethylurea (**46**)] are typical examples.

The effectiveness of CIPC as a herbicide was shown by Crabtree (*46*) to be altered by shading, although many other factors interfered with a clear interpretation that photolysis was primarily responsible. Indeed, Mitchell

(**45**)   (**46**)

(22) reported that, while CIPC was somewhat affected by UV irradiation, the unchlorinated analog IPC (47) was unreactive. Crosby (10) found that IPC photolyzed by at least two routes, as shown in Fig. 12-8. By one route the carbamate was decomposed through reversal of the reaction in which it was prepared to provide phenyl isocyanate (48) and 2-propanol. The other elimination reaction resulted in propylene and the carbamic acid, which immediately underwent decarboxylation to aniline (49) and carbon dioxide. Aniline and phenyl isocyanate then reacted to form s-diphenylurea (50).

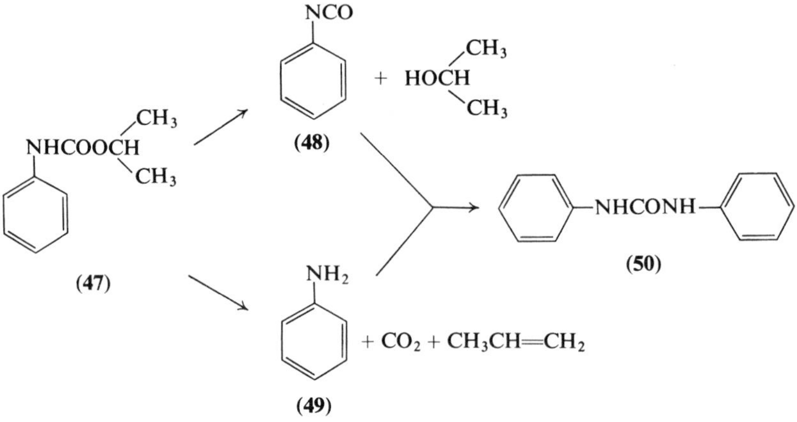

Fig. 12-8. Photolysis of IPC.

Such reactions have been recognized for years in the thermal decomposition of carbamates, and it is interesting that they can take place at or below room temperature when light provides the energy. Similar N-phenylcarbamates such as CIPC, barban and swep may be expected to photolyze in this fashion, at least by formation of the corresponding isocyanate and aliphatic alcohol.

Only a single herbicide representing an O-aryl- instead of an O-alkyl-carbamate has been introduced: Azak (51). Although no information on the photolysis of this compound has been reported to date, it is reasonable to assume that decomposition would occur by elimination of methyl isocyanate, as is the case with other aryl N-methylcarbamates (47), to provide the phenol and/or its further photolysis products.

The facile photolysis of substituted urea herbicides was reported as early as 1955 by Hill et al. (48), although no reaction products were isolated. These authors observed that 83 % of the monuron (52) present as an 88-ppm aqueous solution was decomposed in sunlight over a period of 43 days in a quartz tube. A number of other indications of the photolability of this class have been reported, including changes in UV absorption spectra, reduction in the toxicity to plants, and altered chromatographic behavior (49–56). Among the most common urea herbicides, stability to light decreased in the order neburon, diuron, fenuron, and monuron (55). The reaction may be sensitized by FMN (riboflavin-5′-phosphate) (56). Although no unequivocal examples of the reduction of urea phytotoxicity in the field due to the action of sunlight have been reported, considerable circumstantial

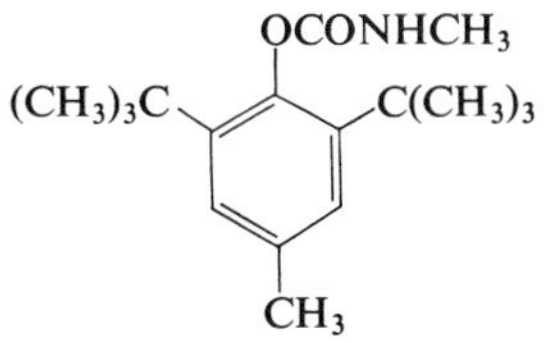

(51)

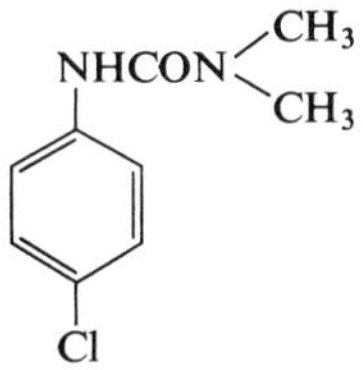

(52)

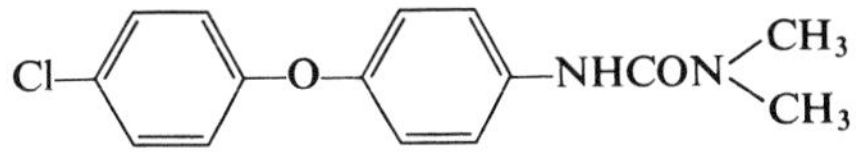

(53)

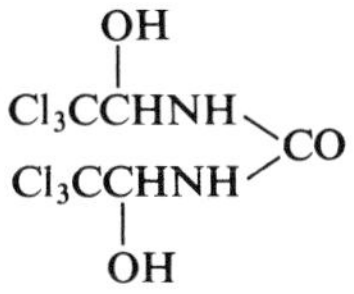

(54)

evidence indicates that, with monuron especially, light represents an important factor in the applicability and environmental fate of these herbicides (58,59). Geissbühler and his associates (49) examined the effect of mercury light on chloroxuron (53) and obtained chromatographic evidence that the compound was demethylated stepwise (see diphenamid, Section 12-3.C). In the current work of our own laboratory, irradiation of monuron in solution results in replacement of the aromatic chlorine by hydroxyl and elimination of dimethylamine to give 4-chlorophenyl isocyanate.

DCU [dichloral urea (54)] has been reported by Mitchell (22) to be stable to UV light on filter paper. In view of the fact that DCU is thermally unstable, however, being reconverted to chloral and urea, it would be entirely reasonable to expect the compound to undergo a similar photodecomposition in solution.

E. Thiolcarbamates and Dithiocarbamates

Just as the carbamates have as their common structural characteristic the attachment of a carbonyl group to nitrogen and to oxygen, thiolcarbamates are characterized by attachment of the carbonyl group to nitrogen and to sulfur. EPTC(S-ethyl N,N-dipropylthiolcarbamate(**55**)] is a typical example.

$$\begin{array}{c} C_3H_7 \\ \diagdown \\ C_3H_7 \diagup \end{array} NCOSC_2H_5$$

(**55**)

The dithiocarbamates, which contain the thiocarbonyl group in place of the carbonyl of the thiolcarbamate, are represented by CDEC (**56**).

No evidence has been offered for the photolysis of thiolcarbamates. However, according to Mitchell (*22*), irradiation of CDEC on filter paper with mercury light resulted in almost complete destruction. Taylorson (*60*) also reported that aqueous suspensions of this compound were altered by relatively brief exposure to UV radiation as shown by changes in gas chromatographic characteristics and bioassays. While photolysis of the cyclic dithiocarbamate DMTT [dazomet (**57**)] has not been reported, the fact that it decomposes spontaneously in moist soil to methylamine, carbon disulfide, and methyl isothiocyanate (**58**) (*61*) suggests strongly that a similar reaction might be expected to occur in light.

$$\begin{array}{c} C_2H_5 \\ \diagdown \\ C_2H_5 \diagup \end{array} NCS-SCH_2\overset{\overset{\displaystyle Cl}{|}}{C}{=}CH_2$$

(**56**)

(**57**)

$$CH_3NCS$$

(**58**)

F. Phenols and Phenyl Esters

Phenols have been employed as soil sterilants for many years, based originally on their efficiency as disinfectants for medicinal use. While crude coaltar cresylic acids (primarily phenol and the isomeric cresols) were first recommended, further investigation in England following World War I disclosed the greatly enhanced herbicidal and fungicidal properties of the nitro- and chlorophenols (*62*).

The effect of UV light on dinitrophenols and 2,4-dinitro-6-methylphenol [DNC, DNOC (**59**)] was reported in 1936 (*16*) and, as with picric acid (**60**),

(59)   (60)   (61)

no reaction of the yellow benzenoid form (low pH) was observed. At alkaline pH, where the red *aci*-nitro quinoid form becomes significant, the reduced amic acid (61) was a major product from picric acid. Esters of nitrophenols were rapidly photolyzed to the parent nitrophenol (63).

Pentachlorophenol [PCP (62)] continues to receive widespread application as a wood preservative, agricultural fungicide, and general-purpose herbicide. The common use of its sodium salt as an aquatic weed killer in Japanese rice fields led to an extensive study of the sunlight photolysis of this compound in aqueous solution (64–66). The principal decomposition products were tetrachlororesorcinol (63), chloranilic acid (64), and compounds (65), (66), and (68). Figure 12-9 provides a sequence by which the presence of these products may be explained. Again we observe the replacement of aromatic chlorines by hydroxyls, followed by the well-known air oxidation to quinones in a manner exactly analogous to the formation of humic acids from 2,4-D.

Hamadmad (67) investigated the effect of UV light on PCP itself in methanol solution. The only detectable product was 2,3,5,6-tetrachlorophenol (69), resulting from reductive dechlorination. When the irradiation was carried out with an aqueous suspension of the phenol, the major product was a humic acid (as shown by infrared spectra). Also, a small quantity of (69) was formed, together with chloranil (70) and chloranilic acid (64), presumably resulting from the stepwise replacement of chlorines by hydroxyls. Although Mitchell (22) reported the partial photolysis of PCP on filter paper by UV light, no products were identified.

(69)   (70)

The dinitrophenols and PCP are unusually strong acids and, in fact, are frequently formulated as solutions of their alkali metal salts. Another type

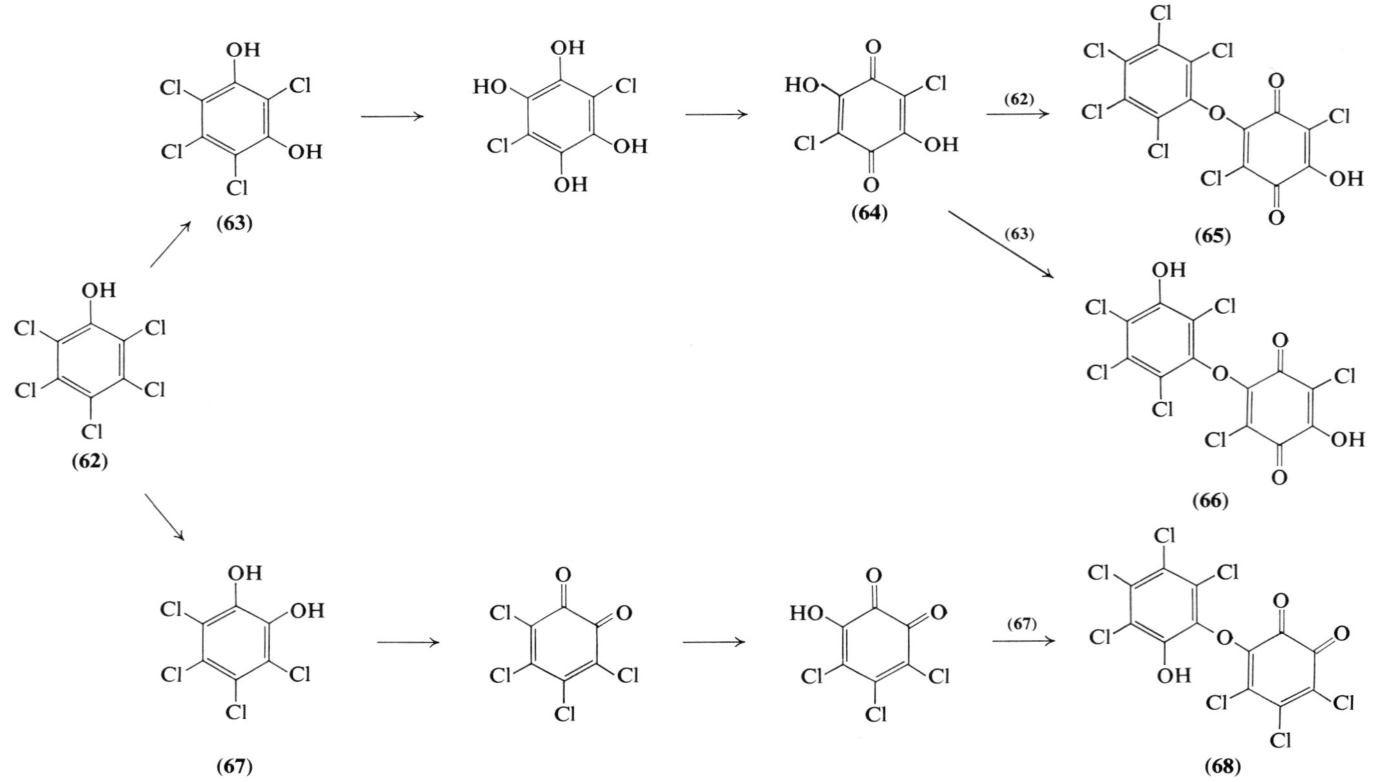

Fig. 12-9. Photolysis of PCP in water.

of strongly acidic phenol, introduced only recently, is represented by 3,5-dibromo-4-cyanophenol [bromoxynil (**71**)] and the corresponding 3,5-diiodo compound [ioxynil (**72**)], generally sold as their acetate or propionate esters. Dilute solutions of ioxynil were found to decompose in sunlight with liberation of iodide ion (*68*), and Ugochukwu and Wain (*69*) reported that irradiation in benzene solution with mercury light resulted in a free-radical reaction to form 3,5-diphenyl-4-cyanophenol (**73**). Likewise, Crosby and Tutass (*27*) found that bromoxynil was photolyzed in aqueous solution to produce polyphenols and the now-familiar humic-acid-type polymers.

An interesting report by Anderson and Reese (*70*) revealed that the UV irradiation of aryl esters in ethanol resulted in a photochemical Fries rearrangement, as shown in Eq. (4). Although esters of none of the phenolic herbicides mentioned here can undergo the reaction, the apparent generality of such orthophotorearrangements makes them something to bear in mind in photochemical investigations.

G. Amines

Amines, whether belonging to the aliphatic or aromatic series, are classed as primary, secondary, or tertiary, depending on whether their trivalent nitrogen atom is mono-, di-, or trisubstituted. Amides, carbamates, thiolcarbamates, etc., are treated as other separate classes, although they contain substituted nitrogens. Heterocyclic compounds containing one or more nitrogens in the ring also are treated as a separate class for the present purposes. This section will be restricted more or less arbitrarily to the several other types of amine herbicides.

3-Amino-1,2,4-triazole [amitrole (**74**)], first introduced to American agriculture in 1954, was introduced to the American public several years

(**74**)

later in the famous "cranberry incident" which focused attention not only on this specific compound but on the entire field of pesticides as well. One of the interesting symptoms of plant intoxication by amitrole is a rapid chlorosis, and the action of light on the herbicide was considered important to an explanation of the mode of action. Despite Mitchell's report (*22*) that amitrol was stable to light, Castelfranco (*71*) found that the compound was rapidly photolyzed in the presence of riboflavin (as a sensitizer) and oxygen. That the degradation was due to a free-radical reaction involving oxygen was shown by the ability of cupric ion, ascorbic acid, and oxygen to replace riboflavin and light in amitrole photolysis (*72*).

Plimmer et al. (*73*) also examined the degradation of amitrole by free-radical-generating systems including Fenton's reagent, UV light, and UV light plus riboflavin. All three systems produced the same result: amitrole was principally converted to carbon dioxide, urea, and cyanamide by ring cleavage and to polymers proposed to be formed through an amine free radical. These authors noted that N-aminoguanidine was also oxidized to cyanamide and urea by Fenton's reagent; as amitrole labeled at C-5 with ^{14}C produced $^{14}CO_2$ but no radioactive urea of cyanamide, it is tempting to speculate that it might decompose via reversal of the route by which it is synthesized from aminoguanidine and formic acid.

Trifluralin [α,α,α-trifluoro-2,6-dinitro-N,N-dipropyl-p-toluidine (**75**)] was observed by Wright and Warren (*74*) to be decomposed both in sunlight and laboratory UV light. Decomposition was paralled by progressive changes in the UV absorption spectrum and loss of herbicidal activity. Although photolysis proceeds on a soil surface, the reaction was much slower than when irradiation was carried out on glass plates. No products were identified.

Photoreduction of one of the nitro groups in DNC to the amine was noted in the preceding section, and partial photoreduction of aromatic nitro compounds to the corresponding nitrosobenzenes has long been known (*1*). Russell (*75*) observed that UV photolysis of dilute aqueous solutions of N-(2,4-dinitrophenyl)-N-methylleucine (**76**) provided 2-nitroso-4-nitro-aniline (**77**) as the major product. Formation of this product is also con-

sistent with the observed photodealkylation of other alkylanilines (76,77).
It may be concluded, then, that photolysis of trifluralin as well as its close
relatives benefin and dipropalin may be expected to produce products which
are reduced and/or dealkylated.

Other amine-containing herbicides discussed here include amiben,
picloram, and the substituted aminotriazines.

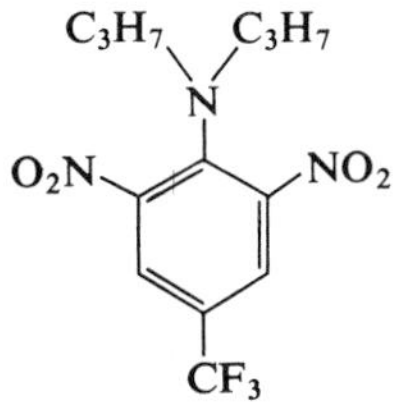

(75) 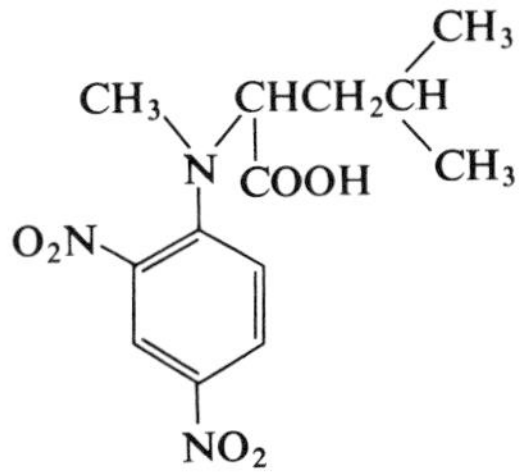   (76) 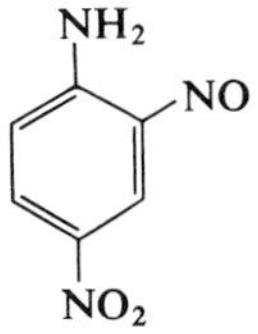   (77)

H. Heterocyclic Compounds

Heterocyclic compounds are characterized by a ring structure, of any
number of members, which contains as a member one or more atoms of an
element other than carbon. Although heterocycles containing oxygen,
sulfur, phosphorus, and other ring atoms are well known, with few exceptions only representatives of the nitrogen heterocycles are now in general
use as herbicides. For example, picloram (30) contains a six-membered
ring with one nitrogen (pyridine); amitrole (74) contains a five membered
ring with three nitrogens (1,2,4-triazole); endothal (20) is a bicyclic compound with an oxygen in the ring; and DMTT [dazomet (57)], a 1,3,5-
thiadiazine, contains two nitrogens and a sulfur.

A number of commercially and scientifically important herbicides belong
to the 1,3,5-triazine series (six-membered ring, with three nitrogen atoms).
Considering that the herbicidal properties of these compounds are due to

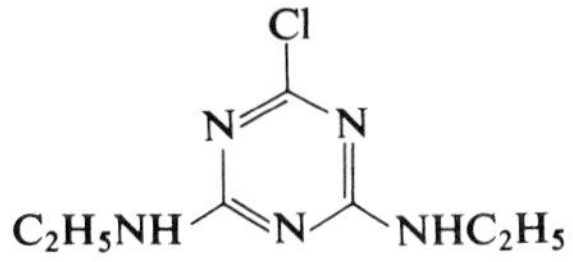

(78) 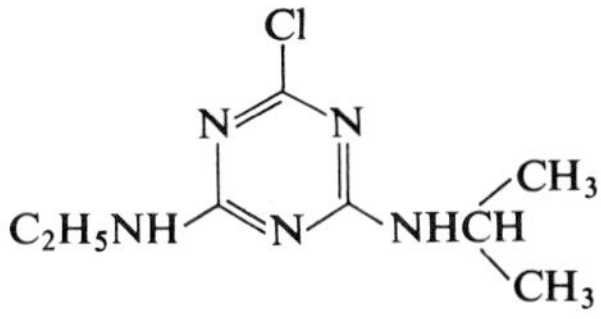   (79)

their inhibition of plant photosynthesis, it seems surprising that there has not been more attention given to the effects of light on the chemicals themselves. Both Dewey (*78*) and Sheets and Danielson (*79*) reported in 1960 the apparent inactivation of simazine (**78**) in sunlight, an effect later observed with both simazine and atrazine (**79**) by many other investigators (*52,55,56, 80–83*). In no instance was the presumed photolysis proved or degradation products isolated.

Simazine was subjected to UV irradiation on filter paper by Mitchell (*22*) as part of his extensive study, but the results were inconclusive. Several years later, Jordan and co-workers (*84*) conducted a very similar experiment and reported that the compound decomposed under both UV light and sunlight, with, however, different products being formed in the two cases. Again, no isolation or characterizations were attempted.

From previous references to the replacement of aromatic halogens by hydroxyl groups or hydrogens under the influence of UV light, it seems probable that simazine and atrazine are at least converted to the corresponding hydroxy analogs. Likewise, the demonstrated photodealkylation of amines and amides may be expected to apply to the triazine herbicides.

Another type of *N*-heterocycle herbicide represents the pyrimidine series (six-membered ring, two nitrogen atoms), at least superficially related to the triazines. Jordan et al. (*52*) reported that solid films of bromacil (**80**) and isocil (**81**) were decomposed by UV light as measured by changes in the absorption spectra. Although no further data on this photolysis have been reported, a considerable volume of information exists concerning the photochemistry of similar pyrimidines because of their importance to nucleic acid interactions and genetic damage.

(80)   (81)   (82)

(83)   (84)

A common photochemical reaction of uracil (82) and its derivatives is hydration of the 5,6 double bond. 1,3-Dimethyl-5-fluorouracil (83), for instance, was converted reversibly to the unstable hydroxy compound (84) by UV light in the presence of water (85). The hydroxy compound (84) then decomposed upon further irradiation to an unknown product.

Another common reaction is dimerization, as demonstrated by thymine (85). Under a variety of conditions, (85) is dimerized by UV irradiation to give the cyclobutane derivative (86) possessing the *syn-cis* configuration (86). Still another photolytic reaction of thymine and its derivatives is oxidation and *N* dealkylation. 1,3-Dimethylthymine (87) is converted to such products as (88), (89), and (90), together with ammonia, methylamine, acetic and formic acids, and formaldehyde (87).

In the presence of other pyrimidines, 5-bromouracil (91) forms a dimer

(85)   (86)   (87)

(88)   (89)   (90)

and mixed dimer, and in living *E. coli* cultures, dimer, uracil, and four other products are formed (88). It is apparent from the variety of known photochemical transformations of uracil derivatives closely related to the pyrimidine herbicides that the photolysis of bromacil and isocil can be expected to be complex.

(91)   (92)

Maleic hydrazide [MH (**92**)] can be seen to be an isomer of uracil, in this case a pyridazine. Although it appeared to be stable in the dry state on filter paper (*22*), Stoessl (*89*) showed that UV irradiation in aqueous solution led to formation of nitric acid, formic acid, succinic acid, maleic acid, and fumaric acid. It is obvious from the nature of these products that water and air are essential for photolysis, although a slow decomposition occurred in the absence of air.

(93)   (94)   (95)   (96)

Air and water also are involved in the rapid photolysis of paraquat (**93**) and diquat (**94**). The decomposition of these pyridinium compounds in light has been observed in several instances (*90–92*), although they remained stable in the dark. An important intermediate in the photolysis of paraquat was isolated by Slade (*93*) and identified as 1-methylpyridinium-4-carboxylate (**95**), the betaine of *N*-methylisonicotinic acid. Methylamine also was isolated as a salt. Recently, Slade (*94*) also reported the structure of the major photodecomposition product of diquat, the tetrahydropyrido-pyrazinium salt (**96**).

I. Miscellaneous Herbicides

Meager photochemical information is available on a few other types of herbicides; what would any classification be worth if it didn't have a section for "miscellaneous"? Certainly one of the toxicologically interesting examples of miscellany is the organomercury compounds, of which phenylmercuric acetate (PMA) appears to be the only member receiving herbicidal application.

The easy breakdown of mercury compounds in light has been known and used for many years. In addition to their use as sensitizers, they undergo cleavage at the C—Hg bond; dimethyl mercury provides mercury, methane, and ethane with quantum yields of unity (*95*), and irradiation of hydroxyethyl mercury chloride yields mercurous chloride and 1,4-butanediol (*96*).

Mercury salts of organic acids are decomposed with the formation of C—Hg bonds, as shown for the acetate example by (*97*)

$$4Hg(OCOCH_3)_2 \xrightarrow{\lambda} Hg_2(OCOCH_3)_2 + 2CH_3Hg(OCOCH_3) + 4CO_2 + C_2H_6 \quad (5)$$

Recently, Takehara and co-workers (*98*) examined the irradiation of eight organomercury compounds with several UV sources including sunlight. In the case of PMA, only 33–38% remained intact after 40 hours under a mercury lamp, and in another experiment 48% remained after 10 hours of sunlight. Irradiation of an aqueous solution of PMA for 2 hours with a mercury lamp caused complete decomposition, while 75% was recovered after 10 hours in sunlight. The only PMA photolysis product identified was mercurous oxide. Considering Eq. (5), one wonders if phenylmethyl mercury was present at some time.

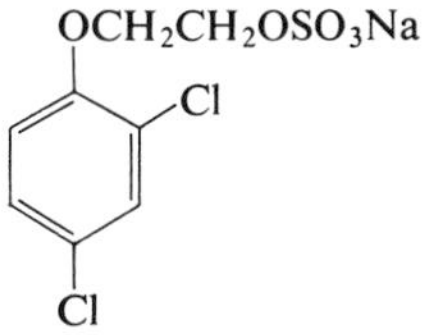
OCH₂CH₂OSO₃Na
Cl
Cl

(97)

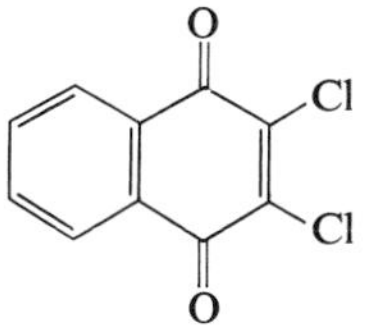
O
Cl
Cl
O

(98)

Another type of herbicide in the miscellaneous category is sesone [sodium 2,4-dichlorophenoxyethyl sulfate (**97**)]. Carroll (*26*) found that growth-regulating activity (cucumber root elongation) was counteracted by riboflavin and light much less effectively than that of 2,4-D under similar treatment. Considering the number of examples appearing in this chapter of the replacement of aromatic halogens by hydroxyl groups and/or hydrogens under photolytic conditions, this seeming stability of sesone appears very unusual.

Solutions of dichlone (**98**) have been observed to bleach upon standing in glass bottles in the light, and the effectiveness of fungicidal seed treatment is greatly reduced upon exposure to the sun.

Although photochemical data on dichlone appear to be lacking, a considerable amount of information is available about quinone photolysis in general (*1*). Reduction to the hydroquinone and dimerization of naphthoquinones to cyclobutane derivatives are known, and replacement of one or both of the chlorines in the reduced dichlone with hydroxyls appears very probable.

12-4. DISCUSSION

From the foregoing survey, it is clear that representatives of most classes of herbicides are decomposed by UV light. Almost all the photolysis experiments mentioned were conducted in the laboratory under artificial conditions, generally with the use of mercury lamps emitting principally at 254 mμ. The majority of herbicides contain aromatic rings which absorb energy strongly at at least one of the mercury line wavelengths (Table 12-4); with the energy available, the basic requirements for photolysis are provided.

Perhaps unfortunately, the irradiation conditions employed in most previous herbicide investigations have been so numerous and varied that only a limited correlation of results is possible. Solutions in a number of solvents and at widely different concentrations; solid films on glass plates and metal planchets; the adsorbed state on silicic acid (acidic conditions), aluminum oxide (alkaline conditions) and soil; crystalline solids; and an undefined state on and in cellulose fibers (filter paper) represent the principal substrates which have been employed.

PCP provides a good example of the importance of irradiation conditions to photolytic pathways. Using a low-pressure mercury lamp at approximately room temperature in each instance, Mitchell (22) reported the PCP remained unchanged when irradiated on filter paper; Hamadmad (67) showed that in hexane solution only 2,3,5,6-tetrachlorophenol was formed, while in water at slightly acidic pH tetrachlorophenol, chloranil, and a large proportion of humic acid polymer appeared. Kuwahara and co-workers (64, 65) found tetrachlororesorcinol, chloranilic acid, and other oxidized products after irradiation in water at slightly alkaline pH.

Sensitization undoubtedly is of greatest significance to irradiation experiments, both in the laboratory and the field, but our knowledge of this phenomenon in the case of herbicidal compounds is virtually nonexistent. Since the early days of photochemistry, it has been recognized that such diverse materials as dyes, natural pigments, zinc oxide, ferric and uranyl salts, cobalt complexes, and elemental iodine can act as efficient catalysts in certain photochemical processes. In laboratory experiments, metal salts are present to some extent in most distilled water, in glass, and in filter paper. Metallic oxides are found in glass and, of course, in chromatographic adsorbents. Even spectral-grade organic solvents contain fluorescent impurities which are potential sensitizers (99). In the field, soil, water, and plant surfaces abound in salts, solid oxides, fluorescent pigments, and doubtless a variety of other substances which can act to sensitize or desensitize photochemical processes.

Other imponderables associated with field studies are the physical state of herbicide residues on plant and soil surfaces; the availability of reducing power (hydrogen-rich organic compounds) and oxidizing or hydroxylating media (primarily water and air); the extent, intensity, and spectral energy distribution of radiation reaching the herbicide; the loss of herbicides and their photolysis products due to volatilization, mechanical removal, and rain; and, in particular, the rate of absorption and metabolism of the photolysis products.

Considering all these factors, it is small wonder that in only a few instances have field experiments been successful in demonstrating herbicide photodecomposition. Several clear instances do exist, however. For example, Slade (100) was able to demonstrate the photolysis of paraquat to 1-methylpyridinium-4-carboxylate on the leaves of a number of crop plant species in sunlight. The photolysis product presents a very low order of mammalian toxicity and, like paraquat itself, is not translocated in the plants to any measurable extent. Kuwahara et al. (101) showed that PCP was decomposed in rice-field water after several days of exposure to sunlight, and the major photolysis products were identified. Rake (102) offered good evidence that sunlight was a major factor in the loss of herbicidal activity of organoborates under arid conditions.

Although numerous other field or practical experiments have been described in which loss of biological activity was attributed to herbicide photodecomposition, in each instance other factors such as volatility, nonphotochemical hydrolysis, leaching, the action of microorganisms, or differential absorption might have strongly influenced the results. It must be concluded that field tests can provide the light intensity, spectral energy distribution, reaction medium, and sensitization sufficient for effective photolysis, but that unequivocal demonstration of the effect appears to be so difficult as to be virtually impossible except under unusual conditions.

It appears both reasonable and probable that in many instances photolysis will provide the same products as metabolism by plants and microorganisms. Hydrolysis of esters and amides, oxidative dealkylation of amines and amides, and reduction of quinones are only a few proved examples in which either light or the chemical energy of living things are directed via UV absorption spectrum and sensitization on the one hand and enzymatic action on the other to provide identical "metabolites." It also should be noted that these hydrolyses, oxidations, and reductions may come about in some instances without the intermediacy of either light or life. Consequently, it may be very difficult indeed to demonstrate clearly that a particular plant metabolite, for example, did not arise from both sources in the field.

For practical purposes, what difference will it make? From the standpoint of possible health hazards due to residues, it probably is not very significant. However, photolysis potentially can "open up" a chemical structure ordinarily resistant to metabolism and so cause accelerated disappearance from the environment. It can also induce chemical transformations entirely separate from the actions of living things, giving rise both to new problems related to pesticide residues and to the possibility of designing herbicides which are either more or less stable than existing types. Photolysis also provides a potential means of great importance for the intentional destruction of pesticide residues in water, soils, and food.

Herbicides decompose under the influence of radiation. Light sources and intensities, physical state, sensitization, and of course the intrinsic chemical and physical properties of the compounds themselves all regulate the nature of the products, the rate of decomposition, and whether or not products are formed at all. However, it is apparent that conditions can be found under which probably all the present-day herbicides and plant-growth regulators will photolyze, and both the problems and positive opportunities offered by this phenomenon are of major importance to agricultural and industrial economics, conservation, and public health.

REFERENCES

1. C. Ellis, A. A. Wells, and F. F. Heyroth, *The Chemical Action of Ultraviolet Rays,* Reinhold, New York, 1941.
2. N. R. Dhar, *The Chemical Action of Light,* Blackie, London, 1931.
3. J. G. Calvert and J. N. Pitts, Jr., *Photochemistry,* Wiley, New York, 1966.
4. J. A. Kerr and A. F. Trotman-Dickenson, in *Handbook of Chemistry and Physics* (R. C. Weast, ed.), Chemical Rubber Co., Cleveland, 46th ed., 1966, p. F-127.
5. G. W. Bailey and J. L. White, *Residue Rev.,* **10,** 97 (1965).
6. M. Luckiesh, *Germicidal, Erythemal, and Infrared Energy,* Van Nostrand, Princeton, N.J., 1946.
7. L. R. Koller, *Ultraviolet Radiation,* Wiley, New York, 2nd ed., 1965, p. 123.
8. U.S. Department of Commerce, *Climatological Data,* Vol. 17, U.S. Govt. Printing Office, Washington, D.C., 1966.
9. General Electric Co., *Lamp Bulletin LD-1,* Lamp Division, Cleveland.

10. D. G. Crosby, American Chemical Society, 152nd Meeting, New York, 1966.
11. J. A. Kitchener, *Sci. J. Roy. Coll. Sci.*, **16**, 1 (1946).
12. G. Porter, in *Technique of Organic Chemistry*, Vol. 8 (A. Weissberger, ed.), Wiley (Interscience), New York, 2nd ed., 1963, p. 1055.
13. C. G. Hatchard and C. A. Parker, *Proc. Roy. Soc. London*, **A235**, 518 (1956).
14. W. A. Noyes, Jr. and V. Boekelheide, in *Technique of Organic Chemistry*, Vol. 2 (A. Weissberger, ed.), Wiley (Interscience), New York, 1948, p. 79.
15. S. N. Banerji and N. R. Dhar, *A. Anorg. Allgem. Chem.*, **134**, 172 (1924).
16. J. Molnar, *Compt. Rend.*, **201**, 1482 (1935).
17. W. T. Penfound and V. Minyard, *Botan. Gaz.*, **109**, 231 (1947).
18. H. O. Tutass, thesis, Univ. of California, Davis, 1966.
19. G. R. Bell, *Botan. Gaz.*, **118**, 133 (1956).
20. O. M. Aly and S. D. Faust, *J. Agr. Food Chem.*, **12**, 541 (1964).
21. D. G. Crosby and H. O. Tutass, *J. Agr. Food Chem.*, **14**, 596 (1966).
22. L. C. Mitchell, *J. Assoc. Offic. Agr. Chemists*, **44**, 643 (1961).
23. R. H. Hamilton and R. J. Aldrich, *Weeds*, **2**, 202 (1953).
24. J. R. Hansen and K. P. Buchholtz, *Weeds*, **1**, 237 (1952).
25. R. B. Carroll, *Am. J. Botany*, **36**, 821 (1949).
26. R. B. Carroll, *Contrib. Boyce Thompson Inst.*, **16**, 409 (1952).
27. D. G. Crosby and H. O. Tutass, unpublished, 1965.
28. O. M. Aly and S. D. Faust, *New Jersey Agr.*, **46**, 12 (1964).
29. A. W. Winston and P. M. Ritty, *Proc. Northeast. Weed Control Conf.*, **15**, 396 (1961).
30. R. S. Mellor and F. B. Salisbury, *Plant Physiol.*, **40**, 506 (1965).
31. H. S. Segal, personal communication, 1966.
32. C. S. Tang and D. G. Crosby, unpublished, 1967.
33. L. Brauner, *Z. Botan.*, **41**, 291 (1953).
34. L. Brauner and M. Brauner, *Z. Botan.*, **42**, 83 (1954).
35. M. G. Ferri, *Nature*, **168**, 334 (1951).
36. A. Fischer, *Planta*, **43**, 288 (1954).
37. A. W. Galston, *Proc. Natl. Acad. Sci.*, **35**, 10 (1949).
38. W. Klingmiller, *Planta*, **55**, 283 (1960).
39. H. Euler, *Ber.*, **49**, 1366 (1916).
40. T. J. Sheets, *Weeds*, **11**, 186 (1963).
41. J. R. Plimmer and B. E. Hummer, personal communication, 1967.
42. C. T. Redemann, personal communication, 1966.
43. H. Freytag, *Ber.*, **69B**, 32 (1936).
44. J. D. Rosen, personal communication, 1967.
45. D. Elad, D. V. Rao, and V. I. Stenberg, *J. Org. Chem.*, **30**, 3252 (1965).
46. G. Crabtree, *Proc. Northeast. Weed Control Conf.*, **12**, 33 (1958).
47. D. G. Crosby, E. Leitis, and W. L. Winterlin, *J. Agr. Food Chem.*, **13**, 204 (1965).
48. G. D. Hill, J. W. McGahen, H. M. Baker, D. W. Finnerty, and C. W. Bingeman, *Agron. J.*, **47**, 93 (1955).
49. H. Geissbühler, C. Haselbach, H. Aebi, and L. Ebner, *Weed Res.*, **3**, 277 (1963).
50. L. S. Jordan, C. W. Coggins, B. E. Day, and W. A. Clerx, *Weeds*, **12**, 1 (1964).
51. W. H. Minshall, *Weeds*, **5**, 29 (1957).
52. L. S. Jordan, J. D. Mann, and B. E. Day, *Weeds*, **13**, 43 (1965).
53. L. W. Weldon and F. L. Timmons, *Weeds*, **9**, 111 (1961).

54. W. V. Welker, Jr., *Dissertation Abstr.*, **23**, 1142 (1962).
55. L. S. Jordan, B. E. Day, and W. A. Clerx, *Proc. Western Weed Control Conf.*, 1963, p. 78.
56. L. S. Jordan, B. E. Day, and W. A. Clerx, *Proc. Western Weed Control Conf.*, 1962, p. 89.
57. P. B. Sweetser, *Biochim. Biophys. Acta*, **66**, 78 (1963).
58. F. M. Ashton, *Weeds*, **13**, 164 (1965).
59. R. D. Comes and F. L. Timmons, *Weeds*, **13**, 81 (1965).
60. R. B. Taylorson, *Weeds*, **14**, 155 (1966).
61. D. E. Munnecke and J. P. Martin, *Phytopathology*, **54**, 941 (1964).
62. A. Matthews, *J. Agr. Sci.*, **14**, 1 (1924).
63. E. Havinga and R. O. de Jongh, *Bull. Soc. Chim. Belges*, **71**, 803 (1962).
64. M. Kuwahara, N. Kato, and K. Munakata, *Agr. Biol. Chem. (Tokyo)*, **30**, 232 (1966).
65. M. Kuwahara, N. Kato, and K. Munakata, *Agr. Biol. Chem. (Tokyo)*, **30**, 239 (1966).
66. C. W. Hiatt, W. T. Haskins, and C. Oliver, *Am. J. Trop. Med. Hyg.*, **9**, 527 (1960).
67. N. Hamadmad, thesis, Univ. California, Davis, 1967.
68. R. L. Wain, *Proc. Brit. Weed Control Conf.*, **7**, 306 (1964).
69. E. N. Ugochukwu and R. L. Wain, *Chem. Ind. (London)*, **1965**, 35.
70. J. C. Anderson and C. B. Reese, *J. Chem. Soc.*, **1963**, 1781.
71. P. A. Castelfranco, A. Oppenheim, and S. Yamaguchi, *Weeds*, **11**, 111 (1963).
72. P. A. Castelfranco and M. S. Brown, *Weeds*, **11**, 116 (1963).
73. J. R. Plimmer, P. C. Kearney, D. D. Kaufman, and F. S. Guardia, *J. Agr. Food Chem.*, **15**, 996 (1967).
74. W. L. Wright and G. F. Warren, *Weeds*, **13**, 329 (1965).
75. D. W. Russell, *J. Chem. Soc.*, **1963**, 894; **1964**, 2829.
76. K. Satake and T. Okuyama, *Bull. Chem. Soc. Japan*, **32**, 526 (1959).
77. G. M. Ide and R. E. Jones, U.S. Pat. 3,196,097 (1965).
78. O. R. Dewey, *Proc. Brit. Weed Control Conf.*, **5**, 91 (1960).
79. T. L. Sheets and L. L. Danielson, *U.S. Dept. Agr. Pub.*, **20–9**, 170 (1960).
80. F. M. Ashton, *Weeds*, **13**, 164 (1965).
81. E. Aelbers and K. Homberg, *Proc. Brit. Weed Control Conf.*, **5**, 91 (1960).
82. R. D. Comes and F. L. Timmons, *Weeds*, **13**, 81 (1965).
83. A. Gast, *Mededel. Landbouwhogeschool, Gent*, **27**, 1252 (1962).
84. L. S. Jordan, B. E. Day, and W. A. Clerx, *Weeds*, **12**, 5 (1964).
85. M. Fikos, K. L. Wierzchowski, and D. Shugar, *Biochem. Biophys. Res. Commun.*, **16**, 478 (1964).
86. G. E. Blackman and R. J. H. Davies, *Chem. Commun.*, **1965**, 215.
87. R. Alcantara and S. Y. Wang, *Photochem. Photobiol.*, **4**, 465, 473 (1965).
88. K. C. Smith, *Photochem. Photobiol.*, **2**, 503 (1963); **3**, 1 (1964).
89. A. Stoessl, *Chem. Ind. (London)*, **1964**, 580.
90. G. E. Coats and H. H. Funderburk, Jr., *Weed Res.*, **6**, 58 (1966).
91. H. H. Funderburk, Jr., N. S. Negi, and J. M. Lawrence, *Weeds*, **14**, 240 (1960).
92. P. Slade, *Weed Res.*, **6**, 158 (1966).
93. P. Slade, *Nature*, **207**, 515 (1965).
94. P. Slade, *Nature*, **213**, 919 (1967).
95. J. W. Linnett and H. W. Thompson, *Trans. Faraday Soc.*, **33**, 501, 874 (1937).
96. V. Weinmayr, *J. Am. Chem. Soc.*, **81**, 3590 (1959).
97. Y. A. Ol'dekop and N. A. Maier, *Zh. Obshch Khim.*, **30**, 303 (1960).

98. H. Takehara, M. Kotakemora, and T. Kajimura, *J. Agr. Chem. Soc. Japan*, **39**, 442 (1965).
99. D. G. Crosby and N. Aharonson, *J. Chromatog.*, **25**, 330 (1966).
100. P. Slade, *Symp. Use Isotopes Weed Res., Intern. At. Energy Agency, Vienna, 1966*, p. 113; *Weed Res.*, **6**, 158 (1966).
101. M. Kuwahara, N. Kato, and K. Munakata, *Agr. Biol. Chem. (Tokyo)*, **29**, 880 (1965).
102. D. W. Rake, *Weed Soc. Am. Abstr.*, 1961, p. 48.

Author Index

Numbers in parentheses are reference numbers and indicate that an author's work is referred to although his name is not cited in the text. Numbers in italics give the page on which the complete reference is listed.

A

Abdel-Wahab, A. M., 132(62, 63), *144*
Abel, A. L., 79(4), 84(4), *108*
Achuff, N. E., 316(101), *320*
Adachi, M., 134(79), 137, 138(80), 140(80), *144*
Aebi, H., 84(20), 85(20, 40), 86(40), 90(73), 91(73), 93(73), 95(73), 96(73), 99(73), *109*, *110*, 163(28), *164*, 347(49), *361*
Aelbers, E., 354(81), *362*
Agundis, O., 63(83), *76*
Aharonson, N., 359(99), *363*
Akamine, E. K., 18(76), *47*
Alcantara, R., 355(87), *362*
Alder, E. F., 255, 256(6–8), 259(8), *280*, *281*
Aldrich, F. D., 188(7), *204*
Aldrich, R. J., 337, 342(23), *361*
Aldridge, M. H., 95(84), 97(84), 100(84), *110*
Aleem, M. I. H., 30(119), 31(119), 38(119), 40, 41(119), *48*
Alexander, M., 19(97–99), 21(97–99), 22(97), 24(97–99), 28(97–99, 115), 29(97–99, 115, 116), 30(119, 120), 31(121–123), 38(119, 120, 145, 146), 39(147, 148), 40(120, 145, 146, 150, 151), 41(120), *48*, *49*, 72(170), *78*, 135(95), 137(95), *144*, 160(22), *164*, 220, 221, 222(54), 223, 224(54), 225(54), 228(54), 232(54), 233, 234, 237, *251*, *252*, 307(51), 308(51), *319*
Allen, H. P., 284(5), *296*
Alt, O., 57(37), *75*
Alverson, R. A., 187(4), *204*

Aly, O. M., 43, *49*, 336, 339(20, 28), *361*
Amato, V. A., 277, *282*
Ames, B. N., 198–201(49), *205*
Amling, H. J., 284(6), *296*
Ammering, J. W., 65(132), 66(132), *77*
Anderson, R. C., 258(21), 273, *281*
Anderson, R. N., 212(30), 213(30, 39), 242, 243, *250*
Andreae, W. A., 11(42), *46*, 131(52), *143*, 302(5), *318*
Appleby, A. P., 149, *164*
Appleman, D., 201(73), *205*
Ard, J. S., 11(46), 42(46), *46*, 243(140), 245(140), *253*
Armstrong, D. E., 61(65, 66), *76*
Arndt, F., 84(24), *109*
Arnold, W., 256(11), *281*
Ascheman, R. E., 303(19), 307(19), 308(19), *318*
Ashton, F. M., 18(65), *47*, 189(25), *204*, 303(20), 304(20), *318*, 347(58), 354(80), *362*
Audus, L. J., 6(14), 18(77, 79, 80), 19(14, 78–82), 21(78, 79, 82), 22(80–82), 23(79–82), 24(81, 82), 26(82), 27, 28(82), 30(81, 82, 117), 44(165), *46–49*, 56(9), *74*, 93, *110*, 227, *251*
Avron, M., 295(63, 64), *298*
Axelrod, J., 105(93), *110*

B

Bach, M. K., 13(52–55), 14, 17(52–54), *47*
Bache, C. A., 36(135), *49*
Badiei, A. A., 15(62), 18(64), *47*

365

Baer, F., 69(163), 72(163), *78*
Bagdasarian, G., 199(55), 200(55), *205*
Bagley, W. P., 120(76), 133(76), 139(76), 140(76), *144*, 198(47), *205*
Bailey, G. W., 284(20), *297*, 324(5), *360*
Baird, D. D., 166(2), *185*
Baker, H. M., 90(71), 91(71), 93(71), 94(71), *110*, 346(48), *361*
Baker, H. R., 308(55), 309(55), *319*
Baker, R. S., 303(21, 25), 304(21), *318*
Bakke, J. E., 66(140, 141), 71(141), *78*
Balayannis, P. G., 36(134), *49*, 310(66), *319*
Baldwin, B. C., 286(32), 289, 290, *297*
Banerji, S. N., 335(15), 341(15), *361*
Barba, R. C., 67(160), 69(160), *78*
Bardarenko, D. D., 189(23), *204*
Barnsley, G. E., 56(7), *74*, 313–315(85), *319*
Barrons, K. C., 207, 212, 224(73), 231, *249*, *250*, *252*
Bartels, P. G., 199(58), 200(58), 202(58, 80, 83, 84), 203(83, 84), *205*, *206*
Bartha, R., 93, *110*, 136(96, 96a, 97a), *144*, *145*, 263, *281*
Baskakow, Yu. A., 128(38, 39), 139, *143*
Basler, E., 6–8(25), 15(62), 16(25), 18(64), *46*, *47*
Bayer, D. E., 85(43), 86(43), 87(43, 46), *109*, 191(36), 192(36), 197(36), 198(36), *205*, 211(21, 22), *250*
Beall, M. L., 228(82), 234(112), 235(82), 236(82, 114), *251*, *252*
Beasley, P. G., 293(48), 294, *297*
Beaudoin, R. L., 65(135), 69(135), *78*
Behrens, R., 62(72), 63(72, 83), 64(111), *76*, *77*, 152(6), 153(6), *164*, 187(3), *204*, 212(30), 213(30, 39), 242(30), 243(30), 244, *250*, *253*
Beinhauer, H., 231(105), *252*
Belasco, I. J., 87(45), *109*
Belksma, M., 89(63), *110*
Bell, G. R., 19(90, 91), 21(90, 91), 22(90, 91), 24(90, 91), 26(91), 28, 29, *48*, 336, 337, *361*
Bender, M. L., 121(15), *142*
Bentley, J. A., 309(59), *319*
Berrer, D., 58(43), 59(45, 46), *75*
Berthet, P. L., 166(3), *185*
Berthold, R. V., 120(12), 133(12), *142*

Bevington, R. B., 256, *281*
Beynon, K. I., 316(96–98), *320*
Bingeman, C. W., 90(71), 91(71), 93(71), 94(71), *110*, 346(48), *361*
Birk, L. A., 63(76, 79), *76*
Bisalputra, T., 200(72), *205*
Bishop, N. I., 88(50), 89(58), *109*, *110*
Biswas, P. K., 64(104), 65(129), *77*, 267, 278, *281*, *282*
Black, C. C., 88(57), 89(59), *110*, 295(66), 296(66), *298*
Blackburn, R. D., 284(7), *296*
Blackman, G. E., 213(42), 239(124), 241(42), 242, 243, 244(42), 245(42), 249, *250*, *252*, *253*, 310(61–63), *319*, 355(86), *362*
Blake, J., 189(28), 190(28), *204*
Blanchard, F. A., 212(31, 35), 213(31), 217, 238(31), *250*
Blondeau, R., 240(125), *252*
Bocks, S. M., 19(107), 26(107), *48*
Boehme, C., 69(163), 72(163, 164), *78*, 101, 104, 106(89, 90), 107, *110*
Boekelheide, V., 335, *361*
Bogorad, L., 202(81), 203(85, 91), *206*
Bokova, E. N., 218(50), *251*
Bollag, J.-M., 19(98, 99), 21(98, 99), 24(98, 99), 28(98, 99), 29(98, 99, 116, 118), 30(118), *48*
Borash, A. J., 119(5), *142*
Borck, K., 130(46), *143*
Börner, H., 85(30, 41, 42), 86(42), 90(30), 91, 93, 94(30), 105, *109*
Bounds, H. C., 21(101), 38(101), *48*
Bourke, J. B., 149, 152(7), 156, 163, *164*
Bousquet, E. W., 207, *249*
Bovey, R. W., 295(55), *298*
Bowling, C. C., 138(102), *145*
Bowman, J. S., 66(138, 139), *78*
Boyd, E. L., 119(5), *142*
Boyd, V. F., 93(111), 104, *110*, *111*
Boyland, E., 128, *143*
Boyle, F. P., 6(9), *45*
Bozarth, G. A., 288(42, 43), 289(43), 296(40–42), *297*
Bradley, D. R., 242(133), *252*
Brannaman, B. L., 15(58), 41(58), *47*
Brannock, L. D., 314(93), *320*

Brauner, L., 340(33, 34), *361*
Brauner, M., 340(34), *361*
Bray, H. G., 101, *110*
Bray, M. F., 289(44), 290(44), *297*
Brian, R. C., 6(17), *46*, 283(3), 284(15), 295(62), *296–298*, 309(58), *319*
Broadhurst, N. A., 311(73), 312(73), *319*
Brodie, B. B., 105(94, 100), *110*, *111*, 137(97), *145*
Brookes, R. F., 255(2), *280*
Broquist, H. P., 119(54), *205*
Brown, J. C., 189(20), 198, 199, 201(20), *204*
Brown, J. P., 26(112), *48*
Brown, J. W., 6(10, 11), 7(11), 8(11), 16(11), 18(72), *45–47*
Brown, M. S., 67(154), *78*, 189(21), 190, 192, 199, 201(21), *204*, 352(72), *362*
Brown, T. E., 88(56), *110*
Brunskill, R. T., 242(135), *253*
Bryant, J. B., 63(90), *76*
Bucha, H. C., 79(3), *108*
Buchanan, G. A., 63(77), *76*
Buchholtz, K. P., 337, *361*
Bukovac, M. J., 64(106), *77*
Bull, D. L., 106(103, 104), *111*, 129(42a), 130(47), 131(47), *143*
Burger, K., 30(120), 31(120), 38(120), 40(120), 41(120), *48*
Burk, J., 130(46), *143*
Burke, J., 188(9), *204*
Burleson, C. A., 284(19), *297*
Burnside, O. C., 6(30), 8(30), 15(30), 16(30), 18(30), 31(30), *46*, 62(72), 63(72), *76*, 307(48), 308(54), 310(54, 67), 311(67), 313(81), *319*
Burschel, P., 63(75), *76*, 134(82), *144*
Butts, J. S., 7(33), 12(47, 48), 13(51), 14, 17(47, 51), 18(48, 51), *46*, *47*
Byrde, R. J. W., 19(103), 26(103), 38(103), 39(103), *48*

C

Calandra, J. C., 65(136), *78*
Calderbank, A., 283, 284(8, 9, 16, 17), 285(28, 30), 295(16), *296*, *297*
Calvert, J. C., 322(3), 329, 331(3), 335, 336, *360*
Calvin, M., 295(59, 60), *298*

Canny, M. J., 6–8(27), 15(27), 18(27), *46*
Carmichael, J. F., 11(46), 42(46, 158), *46*, *49*
Carpenter, K., 301(16), 316(99), 317(16), *318*, *320*
Carroll, R. B., 44(166), *49*, 224(72, 75), 225(75), 232(72, 75), *251*, 337, 339, 357, *361*
Carter, M. C., 189(20), 191(34, 40), 192(40, 44), 197(34, 40, 44), 198, 199(60), 201(20), 203(34, 90), *204–206*
Casida, J. E., 105(97, 98), 106(97, 98, 102), *111*, 113(1), 119(1), 123(1), 124(1, 19, 20), 125(21–23), 126(19), 128(19, 21–23, 42), 129(23), 131(19), 132(1, 62, 63), 133(20, 75), 135(19), 138, *142–144*
Castelfranco, P. A., 58(38), 65(120), 67(120, 148, 154), 73(120), *75*, *77*, *78*, 189(19, 21), 190(19), 192, 199, 200(72), 201(21, 75), *204*, *205*, 352(71, 72), *362*
Chandler, H., 87(48), *109*
Chang, F. Y., 311(75), 312(75), *319*
Chapman, F. H., 6(31), 15(31), 18(31), *46*
Chappell, W. E., 229(97), *252*
Charig, A. J., 315(95), *320*
Charpentier, M., 63(86, 87, 89), *76*
Cheldelin, V. H., 246, *253*
Chen, D., 303(9), *318*
Chesters, G., 61(66), *76*
Chidsey, C., 126(34), 127(34), 136(34), *143*
Chin, W. T., 133(73), 134(73), 139(73), *144*
Chkanikov, D. I., 8, *46*
Chow, P. N., 6(30), 8(30), 15(30), 16(30), 18(30), 31(30), *46*
Clagett, C. O., 41(154), *49*
Clark, N. G., 255(1, 2), *280*
Clayton, J. W., 104(112), *111*
Clerx, W. A., 62(69), *76*, 347(50, 55, 56), 354(55, 56, 84), *361*, *362*
Clifford, D. R., 19(106), 26(106), *48*
Coats, G. E., 284(10, 21, 22), *296*, *297*, 356(90), *362*
Coffee, D. R., 85(39), 95(39), *109*
Coggins, C. W., 15(58), 41(58), *47*, 85(26), *109*, 347(50), *361*
Cohn, M., 227, *251*

Colby, S. R., 284(11), *296*, 303(22–25), 304(22–25, 37, 38), 305(24), 306(23, 24), 308(37), 309(37), *318*

Collins, C., 130(46), *143*

Colmer, A. R., 21(101), 38(101), *48*, 221, 224(62), 229(88–91), 233, *251, 252*

Comes, R. D., 62(74), *76*, 89(69), *110*, 347(59), 354(82), *362*

Commoner, B. J. T., 295(61), *298*

Cooke, A. R., 88(52), *109*, 308(56), 309(56), 316(101), *319, 320*

Coppedge, J. R., 130(47), 131(47), *143*

Corbett, J. R., 14(56), *47*

Corbin, F. T., 307(50), 308(50), 313(50), *319*

Corns, W. G., 241, *252*

Cos, S. T., 199(61), *205*

Cottrell, H. J., 301(16), 317(16), *318*

Couch, R. W., 63(91, 97), 67(97), 70(97), 72(97), *77*, 295(58), *298*

Cowart, L. E., 83(10), *109*

Crabtree, G., 345, *361*

Crafts, A. S., 6(18, 29), 7(29), 11(29), 15–18(29), 41(152), *46, 49*, 56(10), 64(98), 70(98), *74, 77*, 83(8, 9), 84(17), 85(17, 26, 27, 35–38), 90(17), *108, 109*, 213(40), 230(103), 231(103), 240(127), *250, 252*, 286(31), *297*

Crogan, C. O., 67(158), *78*

Crosby, D. G., 11, 15, *46*, 328(10), 329(10), 336, 338, 339, 340(32), 342(10), 343(21), 346(47), 351, 359(99), *361, 363*

Crowdy, S. H., 284(9), *296*

Cruzado, H. J., 83(11), 85(33), 86(33), 90(11, 33), *109*

Cullen, T. E., 133(73), 134(73), 139(73), *144*

Cupery, H. E., 79(2), *108*

Curl, E. A., 262(33), *281*, 287(38, 39), 288(41, 42), 296(41, 42), *297*

D

Daams, J., 313(84, 86), 314(86), *319, 320*

Dallyn, S., 83(12), *109*

Dalton, R. L., 92, 94(79), *110*, 163(27), *164*

Daly, J. W., 126(31–34), 127(33, 34), 136(34), *143*

Danielli, J. F., 239(123), *252*

Daniels, F., 240, *252*

Danielson, L. L., 62(71), *76*, 135(88), *144*, 158, 160, *164*, 354, *362*

Davies, J. J., 26(114), 28(114), *48*

Davies, L., 316(96–98), *320*

Davies, P. J., 286(35), *297*

Davies, R. J. H., 355(86), *362*

Davis, D. E., 63(82, 91, 97), 64(109), 65(113, 114, 116, 127), 67(97, 116, 127, 155), 70(97), 71(155), 72(97), 73(109, 113), *76–78*, 244, *253*, 278(48), *282*, 284(10, 21, 22), 288(42), 295(58), 296(42), *296–298*, 314(92), *320*

Davson, H., 239(123), *252*

Dawson, J. E., 29(118), 30(118), *48*, 229(84), *251*

Day, B. E., 62(68, 69), *76*, 89(70), *110*, 183(13), *185*, 231, 232, *252*, 347(50, 52, 55, 56), 354(52, 55, 56, 84), *361, 362*

Day, E. W., Jr., 258(23), 259, 275(23), *281*

de Jongh, R. O., 349(63), *362*

Delley, R., 56(11), 59(47), *74, 75*

Deming, J. M., 173, *185*

Demoranville, I. E., 315(95), *320*

De Rose, H. R., 18(68, 71), *47*, 135(84a), *144*

De Silva, W. H., 301(16), 317(16), *318*

Deutsch, D. B., 58(38), 67(148), *75, 78*

Dewey, O. R., 62(70), 63(70), *76*, 242(135), *253*, 310(68, 69), 311(68, 69), *319*, 354, *362*

Dhar, N. R., 322, 335(15), 341(2, 15), *360, 361*

Dittert, L. W., 121–123(14), *142*

Donaldson, T. W., 307(46), 308(46), *319*

Donnalley, W. F., 197, *205*

Donoso, J., 68(161), *78*

Dorough, H. W., 105(98), 106(98), *111*, 124(20), 130(47), 131(47), 133(20), *142, 143*

Douros, J. D., 229, *251*

Dowler, C. C., 310(70), *319*

Downing, C. R., 134(83), *144*, 222, *251*

Downs, W. L., 104(112), *111*

Drake, T. F., 11(44, 45), 42(44, 45, 157, 158), *46, 49*

Drever, H. R., 64(98), 70(98), 77, 85(27), 87(46), *109*, 230(103), 231(103), *252*
Dubrovin, K. P., 135(89), *144*
Duff, R. B., 38(141–143), 39(141–143), *49*
Duke, W. B., 63(80), *76*, 183, 184, *185*
Dukes, I. E., 278, *282*
Dunnill, P. M., 197(45), *205*
Dyer, D. L., 212(34), 213(34), 215(34), 217, *250*

E

Eagon, R. G., 199(61), *205*
Ebner, L., 85(31, 40), 86(40), 90(73), 91(73), 93(73), 94(31), 95(73), 96(73), 99(73), *109*, *110*, 163(28), *164*, 347(49), *361*
Edgerton, L. J., 6–8(21), 15(21), 16(21), *46*
Elad, D., 345(45), *361*
El-Basyouni, S. Z., 303(9), *318*
Elgar, K., 316(96–98), *320*
Elkan, G. H., 229, *252*
Ellis, C., 322, 336, 345(1), 352(1), 357(1), *360*
Emmerson, J. L., 258(21), 273, *281*
Ercegovich, C. D., 61(67), 65(125), 67(125), *76*, *77*, 189(22, 26), 190(26), *204*
Erickson, E. A., 15, 41(58), *47*
Ernst, W., 101, 104, 106(89, 90), 107, *110*
Eshel, Y., 134(78), 139(78), *144*, *145*
Euler, H., 341(39), *361*
Evans, A. W., 92(75), *110*, 163(27), *164*
Evans, D. M., 166(3), *185*
Evans, H. J., 203(86), *206*
Evans, S. A., 4(1), 5(1), *45*
Evans, W. C., 19(83), 20(84–86), 24(84), 25(83, 86), 26(83, 85, 102, 114), 28(83), 29(85), *47*, *48*

F

Fahmy, M. A. H., 123(16), *142*
Fallin, E., 152(10), 163(30), *164*
Fang, S. C., 7, 12(48–50), 13(51), 14, 17(50, 51), 18(48, 51), *46*, *47*, 84(14), 85(39), 95, *109*, 148, 149(5), 152(7–10), 153(2), 156, 158(14), 163(29, 30), *164*
Farmer, V. C., 38(141–143), 39(141–143), *49*

Faulkner, J. K., 11(40), 19(40, 104, 105), 26(40, 104, 105), *46*, *48*
Faust, S. D., 43, *49*, 336, 339(20, 28), *361*
Fawcett, C. H., 5(3, 4), 9, 16(4), 31(3, 4, 124), 32(124), 33(3, 4, 124), 34(4), 35(4), 36(3, 4), 37(124), 38(4), 39(4), 42(45), 43(3, 159), *45*, *46*, *48*, *49*, 241, *252*
Feil, V. J., 66(140), *78*
Feinstein, R. N., 200, *205*
Fellig, J., 13(52, 54, 55), 17(52, 54), *47*
Fennerty, W. R., 218(49), *251*
Fenster, C. R., 310(67), 311(67), *319*
Ferguson, C. E., Jr., 132(66), 133(66), *144*
Fernley, H. N., 20(85), 26(85), 28(85), 29(85), *48*
Ferrer, R., 221, 231(57), *251*
Ferri, M. F., 340(35), *361*
Fertig, S. N., 36(137), *49*
Fields, M., 6(10, 11), 7(11, 32), 8(11), 14(32), 16(11), *45*, *46*
Fieser, L. F., 209(13), *250*
Fieser, M., 209(13), *250*
Fikos, M., 355(85), *362*
Finn, T. P., 5(8), 44(8), *45*
Finnerty, D. W., 90(71), 91(71), 93(71), 94(71), *110*, 346(48), *361*
Fischer, A., 79(5), *108*, 340(36), *361*
Fischer, B. B., 277, *281*
Fites, R. C., 15(61), 18(61), *47*
Fletchall, O. H., 63(81), *76*
Fletcher, W. W., 228(83), 229(83), *251*
Fogleman, R. W., 104, *110*
Fontaine, T. D., 11(43–45), 17(43), 42(43–45), *46*
Fowden, L., 197(45), 199, *205*
Foy, C. L., 64(100, 101, 105), 65(120), 67(120, 148), 73(120, 173, 174), *77*, *78*, 188(13), 191(36), 192(36), 197(36), 198(36), *204*, *205*, 209(33), 211(17–22), 212(32, 33), 213(18, 32, 33, 40, 41, 43), 214(33), 215(32, 33), 216(33), 217(33, 41), 222(33), 223(153), 232, 233(33, 41, 111), 239(17, 32), 242–244, 245(145), 246, 248(153), 249, *250*, *252*, *253*, 307(46), 308(46), 311(76–78), 312(76–78), 313(76), *319*
Frank, P. A., 85(29), *109*

Frans, R. E., 308(55), 309(55), *319*
Frear, D. E. H., 189(26), 190(26), *204*
Frear, D. S., 71(167), *78*, 132(57a, 60), 137, 138, *143–145*, 303(34, 36), 304(34, 36), 305(41, 42), *318*
Fredricks, J. F., 191(33, 37, 39), *204*, *205*
Freed, V. H., 6(16, 26), 7(26, 33), 8(26), 12(49), 14(26), 16(26), 18(26, 66), 19(16), 31(26), 36(136), *46*, *47*, *49*, 56(12, 24), 65(12, 24, 121, 122), 67(24, 146), 69(24), 73(24, 121, 122), 74(24), *75*, *77*, *78*, 84(13, 14), 85(39), 95(39, 80), *109*, *110*, 132(64, 65), 134(82), 135(64), *144*, 158(14), 160(20), 163(29), *164*, 189, *204*, 209(15), 210(16), 211, 212(26, 27), 238(16), *250*, 303(26), 304(26), 311(73), 312(73), 314(93), *318–320*
Freeman, F. W., 64(106), *77*
Freeman, G. D., 309(60), 311(60), 312(60), *319*
Frehse, H., 131(48), *143*
Freytag, H., 343, *361*
Friedman, A. R., 126(30), 133(30), *143*
Friedrich, K., 56(11, 28), *74*, *75*
Friesen, G., 119, *142*
Friesen, H. A., 313(79), *319*
Fukuto, T. R., 120(7), 123(7, 16), 130(46), 138(99, 100), 139(13a, 100), *142*, *143*, *145*
Funderburk, H. H., Jr., 63(91, 97), 64(102, 103, 109), 65(113, 114, 116, 127), 67(97, 116, 127, 155), 70(97), 71(155), 72(97), 73(109, 113), *77*, *78*, 85(86), 96(86), 97(86), 99, *110*, 244, *253*, 262, 277(41), 278(45, 48), 279(42), *281*, *282*, 284(10, 21, 22), 285(29), 286(33, 34), 287(38, 39), 288(41–43), 289(43), 290, 291(29), 292(29), 293(49), 295(34), 296(41, 42), *296*, *297*, 313(87–89), 314(87–89, 92), 315(88, 89), *320*, 356(90), *362*
Furtick, W. R., 61(64), *76*, 149(5), *164*

G

Gabbott, P. A., 56(7), *74*
Gaffron, H., 83(6), 89, *108*, *110*

Gale, E. F., 161, *164*
Galston, A. W., 340(37), *361*
Gamborg, O. L., 125(29), *142*
Gard, L. N., 132(66), 133(66), *144*
Gast, A., 51(1, 2), 58(39), 62(73), 64(73), *74–76*, 354(83), *362*
Gaudette, L. E., 105(100), *111*
Gaunt, J. K., 26(102, 114), 28(114), *48*
Geissbühler, H., 84(20, 25), 85(20, 25, 31, 40), 86(40, 44), 90(73), 91, 93(73, 76), 94(31), 95(73, 76), 96, 97(44), 98(76), 99, 101, 106(76), *109*, *110*, 163(28), *164*, 347(49), *361*
Gemmell, C. G., 222(79), *251*
Gentile, A. C., 191(33, 37, 39), 198(52), *204*, *205*
Gentner, W. A., 36, 37(138), *49*, 158(17), 160(17), *164*, 243(140, 141), 245(140, 141), 246(141), *253*, 256, *281*
Geoghegan, M. J., 289(44), 290(44), *297*
George, M., 149, 153, 163(29), *164*
Gertsuskii, D. F., 8(34), *46*
Giddens, J., 229, *251*
Gillette, J. R., 105(94), *110*, 137(97), *145*
Gilmour, C. M., 61(64), *76*
Gingras, G., 88(53, 54), *109*
Giovanelli, J., 217, *250*
Glenn, R. K., 65(118), *77*
Golab, T., 129(44), 130(44), *143*, 258(19, 20, 22–24), 261(19), 262(19, 32), 263(19), 266(19, 20, 32, 35), 268(32), 269(19), 270(19, 35), 273(22), 275(32, 35), 279(35), *281*
Gold, H., 61(55, 56), *76*
Good, N. E., 11(42), *46*, 131(52), *143*, 302(5), *318*
Gramlich, J. V., 63(91, 97), 64(109), 67(97), 70(97), 72(97), 73(109), *77*, 256(11), 262(32), 266(32), 268(32), 275(32), *281*
Gray, R. A., 158(15, 16), 160(15), *164*
Greenberg, E., 295(57), *298*
Gregory, P., 242(134), *253*
Grigsby, B. H., 249, *253*
Gross, D., 93(76), 95(76), 98(76), 99(76), 106(76), *110*
Grundmann, C., 61(57), *76*

Guardia, F. S., 189(28), 190(28, 30), 201(30), *204*, 352(73), *362*
Guillemat, J., 63(85, 86), *76*
Gunn, J. F., 284(12), *296*
Guroff, G., 126(31–34), 127(33, 34), 136(34), *143*
Guse, L., 256(11), *281*
Gutenmann, W. H., 36(137), 39, *49*
Guth, J. A., 93(111), *111*
Gutowsky, H. S., 284, *296*
Gysin, H., 51(1, 2), 56(13–17), 64(15), 65(15), 67(15), 68(15), 69(17), 74, *74, 75*, 120(9), *142*
Gyurko, P., 63(92), *77*

H

Hacskaylo, J., 277(44), *282*
Hagen, C. E., 41(154), *49*
Hagin, R. D., 37(139, 140), *49*
Hale, M. G., 229, *252*
Hall, W. C., 6–8(24), 14(24), 16(24), 17(24), *46*, 187(2), 188, 191(14), 192(14), 197(14), 201(76), 202(2, 76), 203(14), *204, 205*, 284(19), *297*
Hallam, N. D., 286(36), *297*
Hamadmad, N., 349, 358, *362*
Hamaker, J., 238(120), *252*
Hamilton, R. H., 65(126), 67(126, 147, 156, 157), 68(156), 72(126), 73(126), *77, 78*, 337, 342(23), *361*
Hamilton, W., Jr., 267, *281*
Hamm, P. C., 166(1), *185*
Hammer, C. L., 231(107), 243(139, 143), *252, 253*
Hams, A. F., 255(1, 2), *280*
Hance, R. J., 84(22, 23), 85(22), *109*
Hand, D. B., 6(9), *45*
Hansen, J. R., 120(11), *142*, 337, *361*
Hanson, J. B., 6(28), 7(28), 15(61), 16(28), 18(61), *46, 47*, 183(15), 184(15), *185*, 188(12), *204*
Hantsch, A., 61(60), *76*
Harborne, J. B., 131(49), *143*
Harris, C. I., 56(18, 27), 58(41), 61(41), 63(27), 64(41), 67(41, 143), *75, 78*, 84(21), *109*, 209–211(14), 219(14),

220(14), 222(14), 224(14), 227–230(14), 232–236(14), 246(14), 247(14), *250*, 307(47), 313(80), *319*
Harris, R. F., 61(66), *76*
Hart, R. D., 299(2), 316(101), *317, 320*
Hartley, G. S., 89(67), *110*, 310(68), 311(68), *319*
Haselbach, C., 84(20), 85(20, 40), 86(40), 90(73), 91(73), 93(73), 95(73), 96(73), 99(73), *109, 110*, 163(28), *164*, 347(49), *361*
Haskins, W. T., 349(66), *362*
Hassan, A., 133(74), *144*
Hatchard, C. G., 335(13), *361*
Haubein, A. H., 120(10, 11), 133(10), *142*
Haun, J. R., 85(34), *109*
Havinga, E., 349(63), *362*
Hawtrey, E., 218(49), *251*
Heath, D. F., 106(101), *111*
Heim, W. G., 201(73), *205*
Helgesen, E. A., 41(154), *49*
Helling, C. S., 19(99), 21(99), 24(99), 28(99), 29(99, 116), 30(118), *48*
Hemphill, D. D., 65(129), *77*
Herberg, R. J., 129(44), 130(44), *143*, 258(19, 20, 22), 261(19), 262(19, 32), 263(19), 266(19, 20, 32), 268(32), 269(19), 270(19), 273(22), 275(32), *281*
Hernandez, T. P., 18(73), *47*
Herrett, R. A., 120(12, 13, 76), 133(12, 76), 135(87), 139(76), 140(76), *142, 144*, 191(35), 192(35), 197(35), 198(35, 47, 48), *204, 205*
Hersh, R. T., 88(55), *109*
Heyroth, F. F., 322(1), 336(1), 345(1), 352(1), 357(1), *360*
Heywood, B. J., 301(16), 316(99), 317(16), *318, 320*
Hiatt, C. W., 349(66), *362*
Hietala, P. K., 67(150, 152), *78*
Higuchi, T., 121–123(14), *142*
Hill, E. S., 283(2), 294, *296*
Hill, G. D., 87(45), 90(71), 91, 93, 94(71), *109, 110*, 346, *361*
Hiltbold, A. E., 72(171), *78*
Hiltibran, R. C., 285, *297*
Hilton, H. W., 65(130), *77*, 84(18, 19), 85(18, 19), *109*

372

Hilton, J. L., 6(13, 15), 42(15), *46*, 189, 190(18), 198(49, 51, 56, 57), 199(49, 57), 200(49, 56), 201(49), 202(56), 203, *204–206*, 243, 245, 246, *253*

Hirsch, P., 220, 221, 222(54, 68), 223, 224(54, 68, 76), 225(54), 228(54), 232(54, 68), 233, 234, *251*

Hitchcock, A. E., 208(7), *249*, 299(1), 309, *317*

Hodge, H. C., 104, *111*

Hodgson, E., 105(97), 106(97), *111*, 125(22, 23), 128(22, 23), 129(23), 138, *142*

Hodgson, G. L., 303(82), 313(82), *319*

Hodgson, R. H., 133(71), *144*, 303(27, 28, 33, 34, 36), 304(28, 33, 34, 36), 305(33), 306(27), *318*

Hoffman, M. B., 6–8(21), 15(21), 16(21), *46*

Holley, R. W., 6(9, 12), 9(12), 11, *45*, *46*

Holly, K., 218, 219(156), 238(118), *252*, *253*

Holm, L. G., 212, 213, *250*

Holsing, G. C., 133(73), 134(73), 139(73), *144*

Holstun, J. T., 221(60), 230(60), 231, *251*

Holzer, F. J., 258(19, 22), 262(19), 263(19), 266(19), 269(19), 270(19), 273(22), *281*

Homann, P., 89, *110*

Homberg, K., 354(81), *362*

Homer, R. B., 121(15), *142*

Homer, R. F., 284(15), 294(51), 295, *297*, *298*

Honkanen, E., 67(151), *78*

Hooks, J., 256(11), *281*

Hoover, M. E., 229, *252*

Hopkins, T. R., 132(68), 133(68), 136(68), *144*

Horowitz, M., 158, *164*

Hoverson, R. R., 277(44), *282*

Hudgins, H. R., 138(102), *145*

Hughes, W. J., 256–258(12), *281*

Hulanicka, D., 198(50), *205*

Hulcher, F. H., 229(97), *252*

Hull, H. M., 6(15), 42(15), *46*, 203(92), *206*, 243(142), *253*

Hummer, B. E., 343, *361*

Hummer, R. W., 212, 231, *250*, *252*

Humphreys, W., 256(11), *281*

Hurter, J., 67(159) 71(159, 169), *78*

Hurtt, W., 188(13), *204*, 311(76, 78), 312(76, 78), 313(76), *319*

Husted, R. F., 166(2), *185*

Hutchinson, A., 131(55, 56), *143*

Hutchinson, J. R., 192(42), 193, *205*

I

Ibrahim, R. K., 303(9), *318*

Ide, G. M., 353(77), *362*

Ilnicki, R. D., 95, 99, *110*

Ingle, M., 241, 243(129), 245(129), *252*

Ingram, J. M. A., 31–33(124), 37(124), *48*

Irving, C. C., 128(40), *143*

J

Jacobson, K. H., 139(101), *145*

Jagendorf, A. T., 88(51), *109*

Jansen, L. L., 6(13, 15), 42(15), *46*, 158(17), 160(17), *164*, 203(92), *206*, 211(23), 243(140–142), 245(140, 141), 246(141), *250*, *253*

Jaworski, E. G., 7(33), 12(47, 49), 13, 14, 17(47), *46*, *47*, 158, *164*, 167, 174, 176, 177(11), 182, 184, *185*

Jensen, H. L., 21(95, 96), 24(95, 96), *48*, 219(53), 221, 222(53, 63–65, 67, 69, 79), 223, 224(53, 63, 67), 225(63, 67, 77), 226(65), 227, 228(65), 231(53), 232(53, 65, 67, 69), 233, 234, *251*

Jerina, D. M., 126(33), 127(33), *143*

Johnson, C. S., Jr., 284, *296*

Johnson, D. P., 132(67), 133(67), *144*

Johnson, R. H., 85(39), 95(39), *109*

Johnson, S. P., 187(2), 201(76), 202(2, 76), *204*, *205*

Jones, R. E., 353(77), *362*

Jones, R. G., 258(26), 259(26), *281*

Jones, R. L., 284(15), *297*

Jordan, L. S., 62(68, 69), 76, 89(70), *110*, 183(13), *185*, 231(106), 232(106), *252*, 347(50, 52, 55, 56), 354(52, 55, 56), *361*, *362*

Joshi, B. S., 61(61), *76*

Juniper, B. E., 242(132, 133), *252*

K

Kadunce, R. E., 71(167), *78*, 132(57a), *143*, 303(33, 34), 304(33, 34), 305(33, 41), *318*
Kajimura, T., 357(98), *363*
Kallis, R. E., 218(49), *251*
Kaneshero, T., 295(53), *298*
Karinpaa, A., 137(98), *145*
Karlhuber, B., 56(11), *74*
Kaslander, J., 131(51, 54), *143*
Kato, N., 349(64, 65), 358(64, 65), 359(101), *362*, *363*
Katz, S. E., 95, *110*
Kaufman, D. D., 56(18, 27), 63(27, 93, 95, 96), 70(93, 95, 96, 165), 72(93, 96), *75*, *77*, *78*, 113(2), 119(2), 134(2), 135(2, 90, 92–95), 137(95), 138(94a), *142*, *144*, 160(21), *164*, 189(28), 190(28, 30), 201(30), *204*, 209–211(14), 219(14), 220(14, 56), 222(14, 66), 224(14, 55, 66), 225(55, 66), 227(14), 228(14, 82), 229(14), 230(14), 231(66), 232(14), 233(14), 234(14, 112), 235(14, 82), 236(14, 82, 112, 114, 116), 246(14), *250–252*, 310(72), 313(72), *319*, 352(73), *362*
Kaufman, S., 125(24), 127(36), *142*, *143*
Kay, J. H., 65(136), *78*
Kearney, P. C., 56(18, 19, 27), 63(27, 93, 95, 96), 70(93, 95, 96, 165), 72(93, 96), *75*, *77*, *78*, 123, 124(18), 135(17, 90–92, 94, 95), 137(17, 18, 95), 138(94a), *142*, *144*, 189(28), 190(28–30), 198–200(49), 201(30, 49), *204*, *205*, 209–211(14), 219, 220(14), 222(14), 224(14), 227, 228(82), 229, 230(14), 232(14), 233(14), 234(14, 112), 235(14, 113), 236(14, 112, 115, 116), 246(14), 247(14), *250–252*, 352(73), *362*
Kerr, J. A., 323(4), *360*
Kesner, C. D., 129(43a), 139, *143*
Key, J. L., 6(29), 7(29), 11(29), 15–18(29), *46*
Kief, M., 65(121), 73(121), *77*, 95(80), *110*, 189(15), *204*, 303(26), 304(26), *318*

Kiermayer, O., 202(82), *206*
Kiese, M., 107(110), *111*
Kilchher, H., 56(28), *75*
King, C. C., 15(62), *47*
King, K. W., 229(95), *252*
King, L. J., 5(8), 44(8, 164), *45*, *49*
King, T. E., 246, *253*
Kirshner, N., 127(37), *143*
Kitchener, J. A., 332(11), *361*
Klämbt, H. D., 11(41), 18, *46*, 302(6–8), 303(8), *318*
Klein, W. H., 203(88), *206*
Klemka, A. J., 313(83), *319*
Klingman, G. C., 5(6), 9(35), 16(35), 36(35), 39(35), *45*, *46*
Klingmiller, W., 340(38), *361*
Kloetzer, W., 57(32), *75*
Klopotowski, T., 198(50, 53), 199(55), 200(55), 201(53), *205*
Knoche, H. W., 6(30), 8(30), 15(30), 16(30), 18(30), 31(30), *46*
Knuesli, E., 51(1, 2), 56(13, 15, 16, 20–23), 58(43, 44), 59(46), 60(44), 64(15, 20), 65(15), 67(15, 153), 68(15), 69(21), 74, *74*, *75*, *78*, 120(9), *142*
Koivistoinin, P., 137(98), *145*
Kolbezen, M. J., 120(7), 123(7), *142*
Koller, L. R., 325(7), 329, 331(7), 335, *360*
Kondo, K., 126(31), *143*
Koopman, H., 313(84), *319*
Kotakemora, M., 357(98), *363*
Kozlowski, T. T., 64(99), 70(99), *77*
Kramer, J. A. Jr., 120(76), 133(76), 135(87), 139(76), 140(76), *144*
Kratochvil, D. E., 229, *252*
Kreutzberger, A., 61(58, 59), *76*
Krewson, C. F., 11(44–46), 42(44–46, 157, 158), *46*, *49*
Kries, O. H., 18(70), *47*
Kuhr, R. J., 124(19), 126(19), 128(19), 131(19), 132(62), 135(19), *142*, *144*
Kumin, S., 202, *205*
Kutchinski, A. H., 218(47), 232, *251*, *252*
Kuwahara, M., 349(64, 65), 358, 359, *362*, *363*
Kuzirian, O., 134(81), 137, *144*

L

Ladd, J. N., 218(51), *251*
LaDu, B. N., 105(94), *110*, 137(97), *145*
Lake, H. J., 101(88), *110*
Lambrech, J. A., 5(8), 44(8), *45*
Larsen, M., 56(28), *75*
Lavy, T. L., 6(30), 8(30), 15(30), 16(30), 18(30), 31(30), *46*, 307(48), 313(81), *319*
Lawrence, J. M., 64(102, 103), *77*, 284(10, 21, 22), 285(29), 286(33, 34), 287, 290(29, 47), 291(29), 292(29), 293(49), 295(34), *296*, *297*, 314(92), *320*, 356(91), *362*
Leafe, E. L., 6(22), 7, 8(22), 15(22), 16(22), 31(22), *46*
Leasure, J. K., 207(6), 209(6), 211(6), 212(6), 217, 218, 221(6), 228, 247, *249*
Leeds, W. G., 301(16), 317(16), *318*
Leeling, N. C., 133(75), *144*
Lees, H., 222, *251*
Leete, E., 125(25), 127(35), *142*, *143*
Leinweber, C. L., 187(2), 201(76), 202(2, 76), *204*, *205*
Leitis, E., 346(47), *361*
Lemasson, C., 88(53, 54), *109*
Lemin, A. J., 126(30), 129(43), 133(30), 139, *143*
Leonard, C. A., 65(118), *77*
Leopold, A. C., 230(100), *252*
Levenberg, B., 127(36), *143*
Levin, E. Y., 127(36), *143*
Levine, R., 61(62), *76*
Levitt, M., 126(32), *143*
Lider, L. A., 65(118), *77*
Linck, A. J., 64(112), *77*, 191(35), 192(35), 197(35), 198(35), *204*, 212(30), 213(30, 39), 242(30), 243(30), *250*
Linder, P. J., 309(60), 311(60), 312(60), *319*
Lindley, H., 183, *185*
Lindquist, D. A., 106(103, 104), *111*, 129(42a), 130(47), 131(47), *143*
Lindsay, R. V., 310(68), 311(68), *319*
Lindsay-Smith, J. R., 19(107), 26(107), *48*
Linke, H. A. B., 136(97a), *145*
Linnett, J. W., 357(95), *362*

Linscott, D. L., 15(60), 31, 35(131), 37, *47*, *49*
Linser, H., 202(82), *206*
Lisk, D. J., 36(135, 137), 39(147), *49*, 65(131, 132), 66(131, 132), *77*
Little, H. N., 200(63, 66), *205*
Lloyd-Jones, C. P., 6–8(19, 20), 9, 11(19), 15–17(19, 20), *46*
Lockhart, J. A., 7(32), 14(32), *46*
Logan, A. V., 7(33), *46*
Loomis, W. E., 221(60), 230(60), 231, *251*
Loos, M. A., 19(97, 98), 21(97, 98), 22(97), 24(97, 98), 28(97, 98, 115), 29(97, 98, 115), 36(135, 137), 39(147), *48*, *49*
Loughman, B. C., 10(36, 37), 11(37, 39), 16(36), *46*, 200, *205*
Loustalot, A. J., 83(11), 85(33), 86(33), 90(11, 33), *109*, 221, 231(57), *251*
Luckiesh, M., 325(6), *360*
Luckwill, L. C., 6–8(19, 20), 9, 11(19), 15–17(19, 20), *46*
Luecke, R. W., 243(139), *253*

M

McCall, E. B., 26(112), *48*
McCall, G. L., 83(10), *109*, 208, *250*
McCalla, D. R., 125(28), *142*
McCarty, M. K., 15(60), *47*
McCollum, J. P., 63(84), 72(84), 73(84), *76*
McCormick, L. L., 72(171), *78*
McCready, C. C., 238(118), *252*
McGahen, J. W., 90(71), 91(71), 93(71), 94(71), *110*, 346(48), *361*
McGregor, A. N., 224(74), *251*
McIntyre, G. I., 217, *250*
McKennon, K., 211(26), 212(26), *250*
McLane, S. R., 188(7), *204*, 299(2), 303(18), 308(57), 309(57), *317–319*
McMahon, R. E., 105(95, 96), 106(96), *111*, 258(26), 259(26), *281*
McRae, D. H., 133(72), 134(59a, 72), 136(59a), 138(72), 140(72), *143*, *144*
MacRae, I. C., 30(120), 31(120), 38(120, 145, 146), 40(145, 146, 150, 151), 41(120), *48*, *49*, 72(170), *78*, 160(22), *164*, 307(51), 308(51), *319*

McWhorter, C. G., 87(47), *109*, 198(57), 199(57, 59), *205*, *250*
Magalhaes, A. C., 311(77), 312(77), *319*
Magee, L. A., 221, 224(62), 229(91), 233, *251*, *252*
Maier, N. A., 357(97), *362*
Mann, J. D., 62(68), *76*, 89(70), *110*, 183, *185*, 347(52), 354(52), *361*
Margoliash, E., 201(74), *205*
Margulies, M. M., 203(89), *206*
Marinos, N. G., 6(31), 15(31), 18(31), *46*
Marion, L., 85(27), *142*
Markus, K., 6–8(27), 15(27), 18(27), *46*
Marsh, H. V., 203(86), *206*
Marshall, F. J., 258(26), 259, *281*
Marth, P. C., 18(69), *47*
Martin, J. P., 348(61), *362*
Mason, G. W., 310(64), *319*
Mason, H. S., 107(108), *111*, 131(53), *143*
Massicot, J., 85(27), *142*
Massini, P., 131(50), *143*, 188(6), 189, 191(16), 192(6, 16), 193, 197(16), 203(16), *204*, *206*, 314(91), 315(91), *320*
Matrone, G., 203(86), *206*
Matsuda, K., 202(84), 203(84), *206*
Matsunaka, S., 138(100a), *145*
Matthews, A., 348(62), *362*
Mattson, A. M., 65(133, 134), 69(135), *78*
May, L. H., 6(31), 15(31), 18(31), *46*
Mayer, F., 212(36), 213(36), *250*
Mayeux, J. V., 229, *251*
Maynard, E. A., 104(112), *111*
Meagher, W. R., 14, 15, *47*
Mees, G. C., 295(52, 54), *298*
Meikle, R. W., 132(57), *143*, 245, *253*
Mellor, R. S., 339, *361*
Menzer, R. E., 106(102), *111*, 128(42), *143*
Mercer, F. V., 203(91), *206*
Merkle, M. G., 295(55), *298*
Metcalf, R. L., 119(6), 120(6, 7), 123(7, 16), 130(46), 138(99), 139(13a), *142*, *143*, *145*
Meyers, L., 295(66), 296(66), *298*
Michaelis, L., 283(2), 294, *296*
Miller, C. S., 14(56), *47*, 188, 191(14), 192(14), 197(14), 203(14), *204*, 284(19), *297*
Miller, C. W., 315(95), *320*
Miller, J. H., 213(43), *250*
Miller, L. P., 131(49a, 49b), *143*
Miller, S. R., 241, *252*
Minarik, C. E., 207(5), *249*
Minshall, W. H., 64(107), *77*, 85(32), *109*, 347(51), *361*
Minton, E. B., 202(79), *205*
Minyard, V., 336, *361*
Mitchell, C. B., 308(57), 309(57), *319*
Mitchell, J. W., 11(44, 45), 18(69, 72), 42(44, 45, 157, 158), *46*, *47*, *49*, 309(60), 311(67), 312(60), *319*
Mitchell, L. C., 337, 338, 341, 344, 345, 347–349, 352, 354, 356(22), 358, *361*
Mitoma, Ch., 107(107), *111*
Molnar, J., 335(16), 348(16), *361*
Monod, J., 227, *251*
Montgomery, M. L., 6(16), 19(16), *46*, 56(12, 24), 65(12, 24, 121, 122), 67(24, 146), 69(24), 73(24, 121, 122), 74(24), *75*, *77*, 95(80), *110*, 132(65), *144*, 160(20), *164*, 189(15), *204*, 210(16), 211(26), 212(26, 27), 238(16), *250*, 303(26), 304(26), 311(73), 312(73), 314(93), *318–320*
Moore, W. E. C., 229(95, 96), *252*
Moreland, D. E., 6(13), 9(35), 16(35), 36(35), 39(35), *46*, 65(126), 67(126, 147), 72(126), 73(126), *77*, *78*, 132(61), *144*
Morgan, C. B., 284(17), *297*
Morgan, P. W., 6–8(24), 14(24), 16(24), 17(24), *46*
Morré, D. J., 41(155), *49*
Morton, H. L., 15(63), *47*
Moss, P., 20(86), 25(86), *48*
Mostafa, I. Y., 133(74), *144*
Muelder, W. W., 212(31), 231(31), 217(31), 238(31), *250*
Mueller, P. W., 56(25, 26), 68(26, 162), 69(25, 26, 162), 71(26), 73(26), 74(26), *75*, *78*
Mulens, R., 203(91), *206*
Munakata, K., 349(64, 65), 358(64, 65), 359(101), *362*, *363*
Munnecke, D. E., 348(61), *362*

Muzik, T. J., 83(11), 85(33), 86(33), 90(11, 33), *109*, 189, *204*
Myers, L., 88(57), *110*

N

Nair, P. M., 125(26), *142*
Nalewaja, J. D., 152, 153, *164*
Nash, R. G., 56(18), *75*
Nashed, R. B., 95, 99, *110*
Naylor, A. W., 191(34, 40), 192(40), 197(34, 40), 198, 199, 203(34), *204, 205*
Neal, M., 230(100), *252*
Negi, N. S., 65(127), 67(127), 77, 262(33), 277(41), 278, 279(42), *281, 282*, 285(29), 290(29, 47), 291(29), 292(29), *297*, 356(91), *362*
Neilands, J. B., 212(28), *250*
Neish, A. C., 125(28, 29), *142*, 303(9), *318*
Nery, R., 128, *143*
Neufeld, C. H. H., 11(44, 45), 42(44, 45), *46*
Newman, A. S., 18(71, 74, 75), 19(87), 20(87), 22(74), 23(74), 24(87), *47, 48*, 134(83), *144*, 222, 227, *251*
Ney, R. E., 42(156), *49*
Niessen, H., 131(48), *143*
Nimmo, W. B., 313–315(90), *320*
Norman, A. G., 79(1), *108*, 207, *249*
Norman, R. O. C., 19(107), 26(107), *48*
Norris, J. F., 313(83), *319*
Norris, L. A., 6–8(26), 14(26), 16(26), 18(26, 66), 31(26), 36(136), *46, 47, 49*
North, J. C., 131(53), *143*
Novogrodsky, A., 201(74), *205*
Noyes, W. A., Jr., 335, *361*
Nutman, P. S., 18(67), *47*

O

Ochoa, S., 170, *185*
Ogle, R. E., 90(72), *110*, 135(85), *144*, 221, 231(58), *251*
Okuyama, T., 353(76), *362*
Ol'dekop, Y. A., 357(97), *362*
Oliver, C., 349(66), *362*
Olsson, E. A., Jr., 238(121), *252*
Onley, J. H., 95(84), 97(84), 100, *110*

Oonnithan, E. S., 125(21), 128(21), *142*
Oppenheim, A., 189(19), 190(19), 200(19), *204*, 352(71), *362*
Orgell, W. H., 202(79), *205*
Osborne, D. R., 61(62), *76*
Osman, M. F., 130(46), *143*
Otten, R. T., 229, *251*

P

Pake, G. E., 295(61), *298*
Pallas, J. E., Jr., 301(4), *318*
Palleroni, N. J., 25(110), *48*
Palmer, R. D., 67(158), *78*
Panner, B. S., 104(112), *111*
Pantos, G., 63(92), *77*
Pardee, A. B., 24(109), *48*
Parka, S. J., 129(44), 130(44), *143*, 258(17–20), 261–263(19), 266(19, 20), 269(18, 19), 270(19), *281*
Parker, C. A., 303(82), 313(82), *319*, 335(13), *361*
Parkins, M. D., 308(57), 309(57), *319*
Parochetti, J. V., 134(84), 135(84, 85a), *144*
Pascal, R. M., 5(4), 9(4), 16(4), 31(4), 33–36(4), 38(4), 39(4), *45*
Pate, D. A., 313(87–89), 314(87–89, 92), 315(88, 89), *320*
Paton, D., 317, *320*
Pavlova, N. N., 8(34), *46*
Payne, L. K., Jr., 119(5), 130(45), *142, 143*
Payot, P. H., 56(26), 68(26), 69(26), 71(26), 73(26), 74(26), *75*
Pease, H. L., 94(79), *110*
Penfound, W. T., 336, *361*
Penner, D., 243, 245(145), *253*
Perry, P. W., 284(24), *297*
Petersen, H. I., 21(95, 96), 24(95, 96), *48*
Peterson, J. H., 85(34), *109*
Peterson, J. J., 68(161), *78*
Peterson, P. J., 199, *205*
Petunova, A. A., 65(117), *77*
Pfeiffer, R. K., 242(134), *253*, 310(69), 311(69), *319*
Phillips, W. M., 310(71), *319*
Pieczarka, S. J., 256(6–8), 259(8), *280, 281*
Pitts, J. N., Jr., 322(3), 329, 331(3), 335, 336, *360*

Plaisted, P. H., 65(123–125), 66(124), 67(123–125), 68(124), 69(124), 77
Plimmer, J. R., 189(28), 190(28, 30), 201(30), *204*, 306(43), 307(43, 45), *318*, *319*, 343, 352, *361*, *362*
Ploeg, H. L., 87(45), *109*
Pochon, J., 63(86, 87, 89), *76*
Porter, C. A., 174, 176, 177(11), *185*
Porter, G., 332(12), *361*
Porter, J. R., 161(24), *164*
Posner, H. S., 107(107), *111*
Potts, K. T., 187(1), 188(1), *204*
Powell, R. G., 10(36, 37), 11(37, 39), 16(36), *46*
Pramer, D., 93, *110*, 136(96, 97a), *144*, *145*, 263, *281*
Prasad, R., 213(42), 239(124), 241(42), 242, 243, 244(42), 245(42), 249, *250*, *252*, *253*
Pray, B. O., 135(86), *144*
Prendeville, G. N., 134, 139(78), *144*
Preston, W. H., Jr., 11(44, 45), 42(44, 45, 157), *46*, *49*, 202(79), *205*
Price, L., 203(87, 88), *206*
Pridham, J. B., 107(109), *111*
Probst, G. W., 258(19, 23), 261, 262(19), 263(19), 266(19), 269(19), 270(19), 275(23), *281*
Putala, E. C., 200(63), *205*
Pybus, M. B., 5(4), 9(4), 16(4), 31(4), 33–36(4), 38(4), 39(4), *45*
Pyfrom, H. T., 201(73), *205*

Q

Quastel, J. H., 18(67), *47*, 222, *251*

R

Racusen, D., 188(8), 189(8), 191(8), 192(8), 197(8), 198(8), 203(8), *204*
Ragab, M. T. H., 63(84), 72(84), 73(84), *76*
Rai, G. S., 231(107), 243(143), *252*, *253*
Rake, D. W., 359, *363*
Rakitin, Yu. V., 139(103), *145*
Ram, H. Y., 242, 245(137), *253*
Raman, H. L., 299(2), *317*
Rao, D. V., 345(45), *361*

Rapoport, L., 57(29a–29d), 61(29e), *75*
Raun, A. P., 258(22), 273(22), *281*
Rauser, W. E., 307(52, 53), 308(52, 53), *319*
Raynor, R. N., 240(127), *252*
Rebstock, T. L., 243, *253*
Redemann, C. T., 132(57), *143*, 238(120), 245, *252*, *253*, 343(42), *361*
Reese, C. B., 351, *362*
Reid, J. J., 19(94), 21(94), *48*, 63(88), *76*
Reinhart, J. H., 6(23), 7(23, 32), 8(23), 14(32), 15(59), 16(23), 18(23), *46*, *47*
Renson, J., 126(33), 127(33), *143*
Reynolds, H. T., 130(46), *143*
Reynolds, T. L., 132(66), 133(66), *144*
Rhodes, R. C., 92(75), 104(112), *110*, *111*, 163(27), *164*
Richards, R. F., 230–232(104), *252*
Richardson, L. T., 229, *252*
Richman, B. Q., 65(136), *78*
Richmond, T. R., 243(138), *253*
Riden, J. R., 132(68), 133(68), 136(68), *144*
Riempa, P., 189(24), 190(24), *204*
Ries, S. K., 129(43a), 139, *143*
Ritty, P. M., 339, *361*
Rivett, K. F., 301(16), 317(16), *318*
Roadhouse, F. E. B., 63(76, 79), *76*
Robbins, J. D., 66(140, 141), 71(141), *78*
Robbins, W. W., 240, *252*
Roberts, D. R., 65(116), 67(116), *77*
Roberts, R. N., 19(97), 21(97), 22(97), 24(97), 28(97, 115), 29(97, 115), *48*
Robinson, E. L., 310(70), *319*
Rodriguez-Kabana, R., 262(33), *281*, 287, 297
Rogers, B. J., 41(155), *49*, 191, 200(69), 202(32), *204*, *205*, 241, 243(129), 245(129), *252*
Rogers, E. G., 63(77), *76*
Rogers, R. L., 85(86), 96(86), 97(86), 99, *110*
Rogoff, M. H., 19(94), 21(94), *48*, 106(106), *111*
Rohan, J., 6(10, 11), 7(11), 8(11), 16(11), *46*
Rosen, J. D., 344, *361*
Rosher, P. H., 313–315(85), *319*
Roth, W., 67(144, 145, 153), *78*
Rothberg, S., 107(107), *111*
Rovira, A. D., 38(145), 40(145), *49*

Roy, C., 131(56), *143*
Russell, D. W., 352, *362*
Russell, R. C., 231(106), 232(106), *252*
Rustagi, P. N., 242, 245(137), *253*
Ryskiewich, D. P., 65(123, 125, 137), 66(142), 67(123, 125), 68(137, 142), 69(137), *77, 78*

S

Saburova, P. V., 65(117), *77*
Saggese, E. J., 11(46), 42(46), *46*
St. John, L. E., Jr., 65(131, 132), 66(131, 132), *77*
Salisbury, F. B., 339, *361*
Sand, P. F., 310(70), *319*
San Pietro, A., 89(59), *110*
Sansing, N. G., 65(114), 73(113), *77*
Santelman, P. W., 15(62), 18(64), *47*
Satake, K., 353(76), *362*
Scheinbaum, M. L., 259(27), *281*
Scherff, R. A., 6–8(23), 15(59), 16(23), 18(23), *46, 47*
Schieferstein, R. H., 256–258(12), *281*
Schisler, L. C., 15(59), *47*
Schliebe, K. A., 307(48), *319*
Schmid, A. R., 152(6), 153(6), *164*
Schmidt, E. L., 62(72), 63(72), *76*
Schneller, J., 65(133–135), 69(135), *78*
Schredt, H., 84(25), 85(25, 31), 94(31), *109*
Schreiber, M. M., 134(78), 139(78), *144*, 217, 229(84), *250, 251*
Schultz, D. P., 262(33), 277, 278(45, 48), *281, 282*
Schweizer, E. E., 200(69), *205*
Scott, D. C., 284(25), *297*
Scott, R. A., 244, *253*
Scroggs, R. E., 258(25), *281*
Searle, N. E., 79(2), *108*
Seeley, R. C., 42(159), 43(159), *49*
Segal, H. S., 339(31), *361*
Sell, H. M., 243(139), *253*
Selleck, G. W., 166(3), *185*
Sexton, W. A., 119(4), *142*
Shadbolt, C. A., 85(28), *109*
Shantz, E. M., 11(46), 42(46), *46*
Sharp, S. S., 83(10), *109*
Shavit, N., 295(64), *298*

Shaw, W. C., 6(13), 36, 37(138), *46, 49*, 63(78), 64(78), *76*
Sheets, T. J., 56(18, 27), 62(71), 63(27, 78, 93, 95), 64(78, 98), 65(115), 70(93, 95, 98, 165), 72(93), *75–78*, 83(7), 84(16, 17), 85(7, 16, 17, 83), 89(7), 90(17), 93(83), 94, 95(83), 97(83), 99, *108–110*, 160(23), *164*, 209–211(14), 219(14), 220(14), 222(14), 224(14), 227–230(14), 232–236(14), 246(14), 247(14), *250*, 306(44), 307(44), 310(72), 313(72), 314(94), 316(94), *319, 320*, 342(40), 354, *361, 362*
Shemin, D., 202, *205*
Sherburne, H. R., 84(13, 14), *109*
Shimabukuro, R. H., 64(112), 71(166–168), *77, 78*
Shugar, D., 355(85), *362*
Shuster, L., 105(99), 107(99), *111*
Siegel, A., 202(84), 203(84), *206*
Siegel, J. N., 198(52), *205*
Sijpesteijn, A. K., 131(51, 54), *143*
Sikka, H. C., 63(82, 91), *76, 77*
Skipper, H. D., 61(63, 64), 63(63), 67(63), 70(63), *76*
Slade, P., 287, 290, 291, 292(37), 293(37, 45), *297*, 356(92), 359, *362, 363*
Slife, F. W., 6(28, 29), 7(28, 29), 11(29), 15(29, 61), 16(28), 17(29), 18(29, 61), *46, 47*, 183(15), 184(15), *185*, 188(12), *204*, 303(29, 31, 32), 304(32), 305, *318*
Sloane, L. W., 277(39), *281*
Smale, B. C., 42(158), *49*
Smith, A. E., 290(46), 291(46), *297*
Smith, B. S. W., 20(84), 24(84), 25, 26, *47*
Smith, D. W., 104(112), *111*
Smith, G. N., 212(31, 34), 213(31, 34), 215(34), 217(31), 238(31), *250*
Smith, G. R., 177, 184, *185*
Smith, J. E., 317, *320*
Smith, J. W., 85(83), 93(83), 95(83), 97(83), 99, *110*, 314(94), 316(94), *320*
Smith, K. C., 355(88), *362*
Smith, L. W., 191(36), 192(36), 197(36), 198, *205*, 211(20–22), *250*, 286(35), *297*
Smith, M. S., 36(134), *49*, 310(66), *319*
Smith, W. J., 127(37), *143*
Smolin, E. M., 57(29a–29d), 61(29e), *75*

Solaway, S. B., 257(16), *281*
Solga, J., 65(133, 134), 69(135), *78*
Somers, G. F., 104, *110*
Soper, Q. F., 255(4, 5), 257(15), *280*, *281*
Soundy, M. L., 301(16), 317(16), *318*
Sousa, A. A., 119(5), *142*
Speziale, A. J., 166(1), *185*
Spicher, G., 21(92, 93), *48*
Srinivasan, R., 61(61), *76*
Srivastava, M. G., 200, *205*
Stammbach, K., 56(11, 28), *74*, *75*
Standifer, L. C., Jr., 277, *281*
Stanier, R. Y., 25(110, 111), 27, *48*
Stanovick, R. P., 133(73), 134(73), 139(73), *144*
Stansbury, H. A., Jr., 130(45), 132(67), 133(67), *143*, *144*
Stapp, C., 21(92), *48*
Steenson, T. I., 19(88, 89), 20(88), 21(88, 89), 22(88, 89, 108), 23(88), 24(88), 25, 27(89), 28(89), *48*
Stellmach-Hellwig, R., 222(68), 224(68), 232(68), *251*
Stenberg, V. I., 345(45), *361*
Stevenson, H. A., 255(2), *280*
Still, C. C., 134(81), 137(81), 144
Still, G. G., 89(66), 107(113), *110*, *111*, 132(58, 59), 133(58), 136(59), 137, 138, *143*, *145*
Stoessl, A., 356, *362*
Storherr, R. W., 188(9), *204*
Strickland, A. G., 284(18), 285(18), *297*
Stumpf, P. K., 212(28), 217, *250*
Suess, A., 72(172), *78*
Sullivan, H. R., 105(96), 106(96), *111*
Sumner, J. B., 104, *110*
Sund, K. A., 188, 189(10), 200(63, 66), 201, *204*, *205*
Sutherland, M. L., 299(2), 303(17, 30), 304(30), 307(17), 308(17), *317*, *318*
Swan, D. G., 303(31, 32), 304(32), 305, *318*
Swanson, C. P., 79(1), *108*
Swanson, C. R., 89, 97(85), 101, *110*, 132(57a, 69), 133(69), *143*, *144*, 302(3), 303(28, 33, 34, 36), 304(28, 33, 34, 36), 305(33, 41), *318*
Swanson, H. R., 89, 97(85), 101, *110*, 303(28, 33), 304(28, 33), 305(33), *318*

Sweetser, P. B., 88(55), 89(62), 95, *109*, *110*, *362*
Swingle, M. C., 83(10), *109*
Switzer, C. M., 243(144), 245(144), *253*, 307(52, 53), 308(52, 53), *319*
Symonds, K. V., 30(117), *48*
Synerholm, M. E., 5(2), 31, 32(132), *45*, *49*
Szabo, S. S., 41(153), *49*
Székely, G., 56(11, 28), *74*, *75*

T

Takacs, T., 63(92), *77*
Takehara, H., 357, *363*
Talavdekar, R. V., 61(61), *76*
Talbert, R. E., 63(81), *76*, 277, *282*, 308(55), 309(55), *319*
Tamas, I., 295(57), *298*
Tanegawa, K., 134(79), 137(79, 80), 138(80), 140(80), *144*
Tang, C. S., 340(32), *361*
Tardieux, P., 63(86, 87), *76*
Tatham, P. B., 284(12), *296*
Taylor, H. F., 5(3, 4), 9(4), 16(4), 31(3, 4, 130), 32(133), 33(3, 4), 34(4), 35(4), 36(3, 4), 38(4, 144), 39(4, 144), 42(3, 159), 43(3, 159), *45*, *49*
Taylor, T. D., 284(6, 23), *296*, *297*
Taylorson, R. B., 348(60), *362*
Templeman, W. G., 5(5), *45*, 119(4), *142*
Tepe, J. B., 129(44), 130(44), *143*, 258(18–20, 25), 261(19), 262, 263(19), 266(19, 20), 269(18, 19), 270(19), *281*
Theisen, P., 152(8, 9), 158(14), *164*
Thiegs, B. J., 221(59), 222(61), 224(61), 231(59), 236, *251*
Thimann, K. V., 310(65), *319*
Thomas, E. W., 10, 11(37, 39), 16, *46*
Thomas, J. R., 18(74, 75), 19, 22(74), 23(74), *47*
Thompson, H. E., 79, *108*
Thompson, H. W., 357(95), *362*
Thornton, H. G., 18(67), *47*
Thornton, M. L., 65–69(124), *77*
Thorpe, W. V., 101(88), *110*
Thrower, L. B., 286(36), *297*
Thrower, S. L., 286(36), *297*

Tibbetts, T. W., 212, 213, *250*
Tilles, H., 148, *164*
Timmons, F. L., 62(74), *76*, 89(68, 69), *110*, 347(53, 59), 354(82), *361, 362*
Todd, C. W., 79(2, 3), 88(55), 89(62), *108–110*
Tomlinson, T. E., 294(50, 51), 295(52), *297, 298*
Toornman, B. V., 207, *249*
Towers, G. H. N., 131(55, 56), *143*, 303(9), *318*
Treharne, R. W., 88(56), *110*
Trotman-Dickenson, A. F., 323(4), *360*
Tsou, T. M., 249(155), *253*
Turner, J. L., 284(6), *296*
Tutass, H. O., 336, 338, 343(21), 351, *361*

U

Udenfriend, S., 107(107), *111*, 126 (32–34), 127(33), 136(34), *143*
Uehleke, H., 107(110), *111*
Uejima, T., 134(79), 137(79, 80), 138(80), 140(80), *144*
Ugochukwu, E. N., 317(102), *320*, 351, *362*
Uhlig, S. K., 63(94), 65(119), *77*
Upchurch, R. P., 84(15), *109*, 284(24), *297*, 307(50), 308(50), 313(50), *319*

V

Vandenborn, W. H., 311(74), 75), 312(74, 75), *319*
Van der Kerk, G. J. M., 131(51, 54), *143*
Van der Schans, C., 258(19), 261–263(19), 266(19), 269(19), 270(19), *281*
van der Veen, R., 87, *109*
van der Zweep, W., 284(13), *297*
Vanneste, M., 131(53), *143*
van Oorschot, J. L. P., 64(108, 110), *77*, 89, *110*, 246, *253*, 295(56), *298*
van Overbeek, J., 238(119), 240(125), *252*
van Schaik, P., 230(100), *252*
Varga, L., 63(92), *77*
Varner, J. E., 184, *185*
Venis, M. A., 310(61–63), *319*
Venkataraman, K., 61(61), *76*
Verloop, A., 313–315(90), *320*

Vernetti, J., 160(20), *164*
Vernon, L. P., 88(56), *110*
Vincent, P. M., 166(3), *185*
Vining, L. C., 125(26), *142*
Virtanen, A. I., 67(149–152), *78*
Vlitos, A. J., 44(161, 162, 164), *49*
Voss, G., 86(44), 93(76), 95(76), 97(44), 98(76), 99(44, 76), 106(76), *109, 110*

W

Wagner, D. G., 65(131, 132), 66(131, 132), *77*
Wahlroos, O., 67(149), *78*
Wain, R. L., 5(3, 4), 9(4), 16(4), 31(130), 32(124, 133), 33(3, 4, 124, 125), 34(4), 35(4), 36(3, 4, 125–127, 134), 37(124, 126, 127), 38(4, 126, 127, 144), 39(4, 144), 41(128, 129), 42(3, 159), 43(3, 159), *45, 48, 49*, 241(128), *252*, 310(66), 316(100), 317(102, 103), *319, 320*, 351(68), *362*
Walker, N., 19(88, 89), 20(88), 21(88, 89), 22(88, 89, 108), 23(88), 24(88), 25, 27(89), 28(89), *48*
Walker, R. L., 18(75), 19(87), 20(87), 24(87), *48*, 227, *251*
Wang, S. Y., 355(87), *362*
Warner, L. C., 303(35), 307(35), 308(35), *318*
Warner, R. G., 65(132), 66(132), *77*
Warren, G. F., 18(73), *47*, 84(21), 90(72), *109, 110*, 134(78, 84), 135(84–85a), 139(78), *144, 145*, 221, 230(101, 102), 231(58, 102), *251, 252*, 259, *281*, 284(11), *296*, 303(21, 25), 304(21), 307(47, 49), *318, 319*, 352, *362*
Wart, D. J., 200, *205*
Wax, L. M., 64(111), *77*
Webb, J. L., 167(4), 170(4), *185*
Weber, J. B., 55, 284(24, 25), *297*
Webley, D. M., 38(141–143), 39(141–143), *49*
Weed, M. B., 83(10), *109*
Weeks, O. B., 21(100), *48*
Weiden, M. H. J., 119(5), 130(45), *142, 143*
Weier, T. E., 202(84), 203(84), *206*
Weierich, A. J., 158(16), *164*

Weinmayr, V., 357(96), *362*

Weintraub, R. L., 6(10, 11, 23), 7(11, 23), 8(11, 23), 14, 15(59), 16(11, 23), 18(23), *45–47*, 207(5), *249*

Weinweber, C. L., 295(55), *298*

Weldon, L. W., 89(68), *110*, 284(7), *296*, 347(53), *361*

Welker, W. V., Jr., 347(54), *362*

Wells, A. A., 322(1), 336(1), 345(1), 352(1), 357(1), *360*

Wessels, J. S. C., 87, *109*

Weyter, F. W., 199(54), *205*

White, D. P., 64(106), *77*

White, J. L., 284(20), *297*, 324(5), *360*

Whitenberg, D. C., 65(128), 69(128), 73(128), *77*

Whiteside, J. S., 39(148), *49*

Whiting, F. L., 85(28), *109*

Wiater, A., 198(53), 201(53), *205*

Wicks, G. A., 310(67), 311(67), *319*

Wierzchowski, K. L., 355(85), *362*

Wightman, F., 5(3, 4), 9(4), 16(4), 31(3, 4, 125, 130), 33(3, 4, 125), 34(4), 35(4), 36(3, 4, 125), 38(4), 39(4), 42(3, 159), 43(3, 159), *45, 48, 49*, 241(128), *252*

Wilcox, M., 9(35), 16(35), 36(35), 39(35), *46*

Wilkinson, R. E., 239, 241, *252*

Williams, A. K., 199, *205*

Williams, C. H., 139(101), *145*

Williams, C. T., 106(105), *111*

Williams, E. A., 132(57), *143*

Williams, E. F., 188(11), *204*

Williams, M. C., 6(28), 7(28), 16(28), *46*

Williams, P. P., 276, *281*

Williams, R. T., 132(70), *144*, 161, *164*

Wilson, C. L., 166(2), *185*

Wilson, G. B., 249(155), *253*

Wilson, H. F., 133(72), 134(59a, 72), 136(59a), 138(72), 140(72), *143, 144*

Winston, A. W., 339, *361*

Winterlin, W. L., 346(47), *361*

Withrow, R. B., 203(87), *206*

Witkop, B., 126(33, 34), 127(33, 34), 136(34), *143*

Witman, E. D., 135(86), *144*

Wolf, F. T., 199(58), 200(58), 201(77), 202(58, 77), *205*

Wolff, J. B., 203(87), *206*

Wood, J. W., 11(43), 17(43), 42(43), *46*

Woodcock, D., 11(40), 19(40, 103–106), 26(40, 103–106), 38(103), 39(103), *46, 48*

Woodford, E. K., 4(1), 5(1), *45*, 238(118), *252*

Worsham, A. D., 229, *251*

Worth, H. M., 258(17), *281*

Wright, A. N., 316(97, 98), *320*

Wright, M. E., 277(39), *281*

Wright, M. J., 37(140), *49*

Wright, W. L., 255(4, 5), 256(6–8), 259(8), *280, 281*, 352, *362*

Y

Yamaguchi, S., 6(29), 7(29), 11(29), 15–18(29), *46*, 85(35, 36, 43), 86(43), 87(43), *109*, 152(11), *164*, 189(19), 190(19), 200(19), *204*, 286(31), *297*, 352(71), *362*

Yeatman, J. N., 7(32), 14(32), *46*

Yeo, R. R., 284(14), *297*

Yih, R. Y., 133(72), 134(72), 136(59a), 138(72), 140(72), *143, 144*

Yip, G., 42(156), *49*, 95(84), 97(84), 100(84), *110*

Yost, J. F., 188(11), *204*

Yu, T. C., 148, 153(2), *164*

Yuen, Q. H., 84(18, 19), 85(18, 19), *109*

Yuen, S. H., 284(17), 285(28, 30), *297*

Z

Zahnley, J. W., 208, *250*

Zaki, M. A., 317(105), *320*

Zaltzman-Nirenberg, P., 126(34), 127(34), 136(34), *143*

Zayed, S. M. A. D., 133(74), *144*

Zelitch, I., 170, *185*

Zemanek, I. J., 58(40), *75*

Zemskaya, U. A., 128(39), 139(103), *143, 145*

Zimmerman, P. W., 5(2), 31, 32(132), *45, 49*, 208, *249*, 299(1), 309, *317*

Zobell, C. E., 218(52), *251*

Zwahlen, K. D., 257(16), *281*

Zweig, G., 295(53, 57, 63, 64), *298*

Subject Index

A

Absorption, 18, 36, 64, 85–89, 148, 154, 167–178, 212, 230, 259, 286, 302–317, 324
Acetanilide, 126, 345
Acetic acid, 31
2-Acetylamino fluorene, 128
Acetylation, 60
4-Acetylbenzoic acid, 343
Achromobacter, 20, 24–28
Acid hydrolysis, 197
Acrolein, 172
Acrostalagmus, 224
Actinometers, 334
Activation, 44–45, 70–71, 190
Acylanilides, 119
Acylation, 60
Acyl hydrolase, 141
Adaptation, microbial, 19–25
Adenine, 199–200
Adenosine triphosphate, 35
ADP, 88
Adsorption, 84–89, 135, 189, 307–317
Aerobic soils, 263
Agrobacterium, 221, 224
Alanine, 131, 162, 192
β-, 243, 246–249
Alcaligenes, 224
Alfalfa, 9, 36–40, 152–153, 197, 268
Alkylation, 183, 192, 201, 212
Alkylthiols, 58
2-Alkylthio-4,6-bisalkoxyalkylamino-s-triazines, 56
Alligator weed, 286, 314
Alternaria sp., 222
Alternanthera philoxeroides, 286, 314
Allyl alcohol, 172
Amaryllidaceae, 125
Ametryne, 54
Ammelide, 70
Ammeline, 71
Amiben (3-amino-2,5-dichlorobenzoic acid), 132, 299, 303–309, 342

Amic acid, 349
Amidase, 137, 139
Amides, 41–42, 105, 124, 308
Amines, 351
Amino acids, 12, 13, 131, 199
Aminoacyl-sRNA, 183
3-Amino-5-chlorobenzoic acid, 343
3-Amino-2-chloro-5-hydroxybenzoic acid, 343
3-Amino-5-chlorosalicylic acid, 343
3-Amino-2,5-dichlorobenzoic acid, *see* Amiben
4-Amino-5-imidazole carboxamide, 200
δ-Amino levulinic acid, 202
Amitrole, 187–204, 352
Ammonium thiocyanate, 197
Amylase, 184
Anaerobic soils, 269
Anilines, 93–94, 100, 104, 107, 113–145, 175, 255
Animal metabolism, aliphatic acids, 217
dinitroanilines, 273
methyl- and phenylcarbamates, 125
s-triazines, 65–72
ureas, 101–104
Apple, 6–8, 15–17
Arc light, 326–327
Arthrobacter, 21, 24, 28–30, 221–224
Arylamidase, 139
Arylamine *N*-glucosyltransferase, 132, 305
Aspartic acid, 11, 44, 131
Aspergillus, 70, 91, 224
Aspergillus niger, 11, 19, 26, 38–39, 262
3-ATAL [3-(3-amino-1,2,4-triazole-1-yl)-2-aminopropionic acid], 192, 197, 199
ATP, 35, 88
Atratone, 53
Atrazine, 52, 353
ATX, 192
Avena, 277, 309
Azak, 346
Azetidine-2-carboxylic acid, 199

Azide, sodium, 18
2-Azido-4-amino-6-alkylthio-*s*-triazines, 56
2-Azido-4-*sec*-butylamino-6-ethylamino-*s*-triazine, 56
2-Azido-4,6-diamino-*s*-triazines, 56
2-Azido-4-isopropylamino-6-methylthio-*s*-triazine, 56
Azodrin, 129
Azo dyes, 188, 192
Azolla carolina Willd., 285

B

Bacillus, 44, 91, 224
Bacterium globiforme, 21
Bacteroides ruminicola, 276
Banol, 113–145
Barban, 113–145
Barley, 8–9, 41, 171, 189, 303–310
Barnyard grass, 138, 141
Base ratios, 200
Beans, 6–18, 36, 41, 69, 73, 86, 189, 197–198, 287, 291, 310
Bedstraw (*Galium aparine*), 7–8, 15–16, 31
Benefin, 256
Benzaldehyde, 340
Benzamide, 302
1,2,4-Benzetriol, 336
Benzoic acid, 302–303, 340–344
Benzoylasparagine, 302
Benzoylaspartic acid, 302
Benzyl alcohol, 339
Benzyl methylcarbamate, 120
Bermuda buttercup (*Oxalis pes-caprae*), 14, 18
Bidrin, 113–145
Biguanide, 74
Bindweed, 197
Bioassay, 158, 167–168, 241, 262, 310
N,N'-Bisacylamido-*s*-triazines, 61
Birdsfoot trefoil, 36–37
Biuret, 74
Blackjack oak, 7
Bluegrass, 311
Bond strengths, 323
Bromacil, 354
Bromegrass, 37, 166
4-Bromo-2-chlorophenoxyacetic acid, 20–21, 24

3-(*p*-Bromophenyl)-1-methoxy-1-methylurea (metobromuron), 79–111
3-(4-Bromophenyl)-1-methoxyurea, 99
3-(4-Bromophenyl)-1-methylurea, 99
4-Bromophenylurea, 99
Bromoxynil, 302, 316, 317, 351
Buckwheat, 311, 312
Butoxyethanol ester, 41
Buturon, 79–111
Butyl ester, 41–42
Butyric acid, 31, 40

C

Cabbage, 171
Calabar bean, 119
Canada thistle, 197–198, 311
Caproic acid, 31
Caprylic acid, 31
Carbamates, 105, 113–164
Carbamic acid, 117
Carbanilates, 113–145
Carbanilic acid, 117
Carbaryl, 113–145
Carbomethylene (ketene), 60
Carbon disulfide, 161
N-(3-Carboxy-2,5-dichlorophenyl)glucosylamine, 132
Carboxylase, 245
Carrots, 36, 69, 73, 266, 304
Castor beans, 41
Catalase, 201, 295
Catechols, 24
Catha edulis, 127
CDAA, 166–173
CDEC, 151, 158, 348
Celery, 36
Cell division, 200
Charlock, 36
Cheatgrass, 166
Chemical and physical properties, *see also specific herbicides*
 aliphatic acids, 208
 amitrole, 188
 benzoic acids, 300
 chloroacetamides, 166
 dinitroanilines, 256
 dipyridyls, 283
 methyl- and phenylcarbamates, 113–120
 phenoxyalkanoic acids, 1–6
 thiolcarbamates, 147

s-triazines, 51–56
ureas, 80–82
Chenopodiaceae, 166
Cherry, 15
Chlorazine, 71
Chlorbromuron, 79–111
Chlorella, 95
Chloride shift, 11, 26, 127
Chloroacetamides, 165–185
2-Chloro-4-acetamido-6-amino-*s*-triazines, 60
2-Chloroacetic acid, 167–168, 178
2-Chloro-4-acylamido-6-amino-*s*-triazines, 60
4-Chloro-4'-amino-diphenylether, 91
2-Chloro-4-amino-6-ethylamino-*s*-triazine, 70–71
2-Chloro-4-amino-6-isopropylamino-*s*-triazine, 71
Chloroanilines, 93, 121, 132–137
4-Chlorobenzoic acid, 342
2-Chloro-4,6-bisamino-*s*-triazine, 57–58, 71
2-Chloro-4,6-bis(ethylamino)-*s*-triazine (simazine), 51–78
2-Chloro-4,6-bis(isopropylamino)-*s*-triazine(propazine), 51–78
3-(3-Chloro-4-bromophenyl)-1-methoxy-1-methylurea (chlorbromuron), 79–111
4-Chloro-2-butynyl-*m*-chlorocarbanilate (Barban), 113–145
4-Chlorocatechol, 25–28, 40
5-Chloro-*o*-cresol, 26
2-Chloro-*N,N*-diallylacetamide, *see* CDAA
2-Chloro-4-diethylamino-6-ethylamino-*s*-triazine (trietazine), 51–78
2-Chloro-4-diethylamino-6-isopropyl-amino-*s*-triazine(ipazine), 71
2-Chloro-4-ethylamino-6-isopropylamino-*s*-triazine (atrazine), 51–78
2-Chloro-4-fluorophenoxyacetic acid, 8, 15
Chlorohydroquinone, 30
2-Chloro-4-hydroxyphenoxyacetic acid, 10–11, 337
4-Chloro-2-hydroxyphenoxyacetic acid, 336

2-Chloro-*N*-isopropylacetanilide, 166, 174–177
5-Chloro-3-methylcatechol, 26–27
4-Chloro-2-methyl phenol, 24, 26
α-Chloromuconic acid, 26, 28–29
β-Chloromuconic acid, 25, 28
2-Chlorophenol, 29
4-Chlorophenol, 27–29
2-Chlorophenoxyacetic acid, *see* 2-CPA
3-Chlorophenoxyacetic acid, 30
4-Chlorophenoxyacetic acid, *see* 4-CPA
2-Chlorophenoxyalkanoic acid, 38
4-Chloro-α-phenoxycaproic acid, 41
3-[4-(*p*-Chlorophenoxy)-phenyl]-1,1-dimethylurea (chloroxuron), 79–111, 347
3-(4-Chlorophenoxy)phenyl-1-methyl-urea, 91
3-(4-Chlorophenoxy)phenylurea, 91
p-Chlorophenylalanine, 126
m-Chlorophenylcarbamic acid, 121
3-(*p*-Chlorophenyl)-1,1-dimethylurea (monuron), 79–111
3-(*p*-Chlorophenyl)-1-methoxy-1-methyl-urea (monolinuron), 79–111
3-(*p*-Chlorophenyl)-1-methyl-1-(1-methyl-2-propylurea) (buturon), 79–111
Chlorophyll synthesis, 201
Chloroplasts, 202–203, 295, 314
Chlorosis, 189, 238
2-Chloro-4,6-tetraethylamino-*s*-triazine (chlorazine), 71
Chlorotriazines, 57–68
3-Chlorotyrosine, 127
Chloroxuron, 79–111, 347
Chlorthiamid, 302, 316
Cholinesterase, 120, 123, 138–139
CIPC, 113–145, 345
Citric acid, 162–163
Citrus, 14–15
Clays, 158, 230, 307, 313–314
Clonostachys, 221, 224
Clostridium pasteurianum Winogradsky, 290
C_1 metabolism, 199
Clover, 36
Cocklebur, 7
Coenzyme A, 35, 247
Coix lacrima jobi L., 71

Coletricium, 125
Competitive inhibition, 245
Complexes, 12, 14–15, 17, 95–96, 302, 304, 312
Compositae, 166
Conjugates, 12, 14, 69, 95–96, 106, 131–133, 188–198; *see also* Complexes
Conjugation, 6, 11–14, 17, 44, 100, 125
Corynebacterium, 21, 289
Corn, 7–12, 17, 37, 41, 58, 67–74, 95–101, 154–156, 166–181, 188, 199, 277, 291, 310
Cotton, 7–8, 14–17, 37, 64–73, 95–101, 266, 277
2-CPA (2-chlorophenoxyacetic acid), 4, 10, 15–30
4-CPA (4-chlorophenoxyacetic acid), 4, 15–16, 20–30, 42
Crabgrass, 99, 120, 166, 262
Creeping thistle, 36
Cross-adaptation, 23
Crotonamides, 106
Crotonic acid, 40
Cucumber, 7–17, 41, 97–99, 178, 277, 303–314
Currants, 6–11, 15–18
Cyanamid, 190
Cyanuric acid, 73
Cyanuric chloride, 61
Cycluron (3-cyclooctyl-1,1-dimethylurea), 79–111
Cyperus rotundus L., 311
Cysteic acid, 152
Cysteine, 153, 241
Cystine, 152–153
Cytosine, 200

D

2,4-D (2,4-dichlorophenoxyacetic acid), 1–49, 336
2,5-D (2,5-dichlorophenoxyacetic acid), 4, 23, 30, 35
2,6-D (2,6-dichlorophenoxyacetic acid), 4, 10, 20–21
Dacthal, 343
Dalapon, 207–253, 341
2,4-DB [4-(2,4-dichlorophenoxy)butyric acid], 1–49, 338
DCU, 347
Dealkoxylation, 99–100

Dealkylation, 69–74, 96–108, 128–139, 163, 258–268
Deamination, 92
Decamethylene diguanidine, 310
Decarboxylation, 7–9, 16, 29, 92, 313
Dehalogenase, 232
Dehalogenation, 217, 246
Dehydrochlorination, 211
Deiodination, 317
Demethoxylation, 99–108
Demethylation, 92–108, 289
Desorption, 84
Desiccants, 284
Diallate, 151
Diallylamine, 172
2,4-Dibromophenoxyacetic acid, 20–21, 24
2,6-Di-*t*-butyl 4-methylphenol, 120
Dicamba, 302, 311–313, 343
Dichlobenil, 302, 313–316
Dichlone, 357
3,4-Dichloroaniline, 91–93, 100, 104, 132–138
2,4-Dichloroanisole, 9, 29
Dichloroazobenzene, 136
2,5-Dichlorobenzoic acid, 311
2,6-Dichlorobenzoic acid, 315–316
3,4-Dichlorobenzyl methylcarbamate (UC 22463), 120
3,4-Dichlorobutyric acid, 38
3,5-Dichlorocatechol, 26–29
2,3-Dichloro-4-hydroxyphenoxyacetic acid, 11, 14
2,5-Dichloro-4-hydroxyphenoxyacetic acid, 11, 14, 26
3,4-Dichloromethylvaleranilide, 134
3,4-Dichloronitrobenzene, 100
2,4-Dichlorophenol, 8–9, 24–32, 39–43, 337
3,4-Dichlorophenol, 104
2,4-Dichlorophenoxyacetic acid, *see* 2,4-D
2,5-Dichlorophenoxyacetic acid, *see* 2,5-D
2,6-Dichlorophenoxyacetic acid, *see* 2,6-D
2,4-Dichlorophenoxyacetonitrile, 43
2,4-Dichlorophenoxyacetylaspartic acid, 11–12, 17
ω-(2,4-Dichlorophenoxy)alkane nitriles, 42–43
2,4-Dichlorophenoxyalkanoic acids, 32

4-(2,4-Dichlorophenoxy)butyric acid, *see* 2,4-DB
2,5-Dichlorophenoxybutyric acid, 35
3,4-Dichlorophenoxybutyric acid, 38
2,4-Dichloro-α-phenoxycaproic acid, 41
2,5-Dichlorophenoxycaproic acid, 33
2,4-Dichlorophenoxycrotonic acid, 39
2,4-Dichlorophenoxyethanol, 44
2,4-Dichlorophenoxyethyl sulfate, *see* Sodium 2,4-dichlorophenoxyethyl sulfate
2-(2,4-Dichlorophenoxy)propionic acid (2,4-DP or dichlorprop), 1–49
3-(3,4-Dichlorophenyl)-1-butyl-1-methyl-urea (neburon), 79–111
3-(3,4-Dichlorophenyl)-1,1-dimethylurea (diuron), 79–111, 126, 129
N-(3,4-Dichlorophenyl)glucosylamine, 132
3-(3,4-Dichlorophenyl)-1-methoxy-1-methylurea (linuron), 79–111
3-(3,4-Dichlorophenyl)-1-methoxyurea, 99
3-(3,4-Dichlorophenyl)-1-methylurea, 92, 104
3,4-Dichlorophenylurea, 92
3′,4-Dichloropropionanilide, 93
3,6-Dichlorosalicylic acid, 312
Dichlorprop (2,4-DP), *see* 2-(2,4-Dichlorophenoxy)propionic acid
Dicrotophos, 106
2,4-Difluorophenoxyacetic acid, 7–8
5,6-Dihydro-5,6-dihydroxynaphthyl methylcarbamate, 133
2,4-Dihydroxy-6-amino-*s*-triazine (ammelide), 70
2,4-Dihydroxy-7-methoxy-1,4-benzoxazin-3-one (MBOA), 67–69
2-(3,4-Dihydroxyphenyl)ethyl amine, 127
N,*N*-Dimethylcarbamates, 106
N,*N*-Dimethyldiphenylacetamide, 106
2,4-Dimethylphenoxyacetic acid, 30–31
Dimethyl sulfoxide, 312
2,6-Dinitro-*N*,*N*-dipropyl-*p*-toluidine, *see* Dipropalin
2,4-Dinitro-6-methylphenol, 335
Dinoben, 302–309
Diphenamid, 113–145, 344
3,5-Diphenyl-4-hydroxybenzonitrile, 317
s-Diphenylurea, 346

Dipropalin (2,6-dinitro-*N*,*N*-dipropyl-*p*-toluidine), 256
4-(Dipropylamino)-3,5-dinitrobenzoic acid, 267
Dipyridyls, *see* Diquat, Paraquat
Diquat, 283–298, 356
Dispersion, 325
Dithiocarbamates, 131, 348
Diuron, 79–111, 116, 129
DMTT, 348
DNA, 200, 278
2,4-DP (dichlorprop), *see* 2-(2,4-Dichlorophenoxy)propionic acid

E

E.C. 3.5.1.a, 137
Electrochromatography, 288
Electronic effects, 35
Electron-transfer, 83
Electron transport, 296
Elm, 7
Endothal, 341
Enzymes, 36, 22–24, 120–125, 132–141, 156, 190, 201, 227
EPTC, 147–163, 348
Erbon, 232
Escherichia coli, 199
Esterase, 41, 137, 139
Esters and ester derivatives, 11–18, 41–43, 308, 339
Ether cleavage and linkage, 30, 38, 40
Ethylcarbamate, 118, 128
Ethyl carbanilate (phenylurethane), 119
Ethylene oxide, 189
Ethyl ester, 42
Exchange-energy binding, 240
Extracellular enzymes, 190

F

FAD, 35
Fat hen, 36
Fatty acid peroxidase, 201
Fenac, 339
Fenton's reagent, 190
Fenuron, 79–111, 345
Ferredoxin, 295
Ficin, 95
Flash photolysis, 332
Flavin adenine dinucleotide, 35

Flavins, 200
Flavobacterium, 21, 24, 29, 40, 221, 224
Flax, 32–37, 171
Fluometuron, 79–111
4-Fluorophenoxyacetic acid, 7
FMN (flavin mononucleotide), 89
Forage, 36–37, 42
Formic acid, 189, 192
Foxtail, 166
Free radicals, 189–192, 201, 284–285,
    294, 317, 332, 385
Freundlich adsorption, 84
Fructose, 191
Fugopyrum tatoricum, 125
Fusarium, 67, 262, 315

G

Galium aparine, see Bedstraw
Gametocides, 244
Gaultheria procumbens, 303
Gentitobiose, 131
Geotrichum, 315
Gibberellic acid, 184
Glucose, 44, 131, 191
β-Glucosidase, 11, 131, 133
Glucosides, 10–12, 67, 131–133
N-Glucosyl amiben, 304
Glucuronides, 104–107
Glucuronyl transferase, 106–107
Glutathione, 183, 241
Glyceric acid, 167–168
Glycine, 192, 199–200
Glycolic acid, 167–170, 178, 341
Glycosides, 12, 304
Glyoxylate, 192
Glyoxylic acid, 168–170
Grapes, 37
Growth responses, 33–34
Guanine, 200

H

Hemiacetal, 30
3-(Hexahydro-4,7-methanoindan-5-*yl*)-
    1,1-dimethylurea (norea), 79–111
Histidine, 198–199
Honeysuckle, 197
Hordeum diatechum, 125
Humic acid, 337, 349
Hydroelastic reaction, 234

Hydrogen bonding, 210
Hydrogen peroxide, 295
Hydrolysis, 41–43, 57–60, 94, 97, 161
Hydroquinone, 29
β-Hydroxyacyl–coenzyme A thioesters,
    39
β-Hydroxyaliphatic acid–coenzyme A
    thioester, 35
2-Hydroxy-4-amino-6-ethylamino-*s*-tria-
    zine, 71
4-Hydroxyanisole, 29
Hydroxyatrazine, 61, 67–68, 73
N-Hydroxybarban, 133
4-Hydroxybenzoic acid, 303, 342
N-Hydroxybenzoxazinones, 61
2-Hydroxy-4,6-bisamino-*s*-triazine (am-
    meline), 57–58, 71
2-Hydroxy-4-chlorophenoxyacetic acid
    (2-OH-4-CPA), 4, 20–26
3-Hydroxy-4-chlorophenoxyacetic acid,
    26
3-, 5-, and 6-Hydroxy-2-chlorophenoxy-
    acetic acid, 26
4-Hydroxy-2-chlorophenoxyacetic acid,
    12, 26
3-(2-Hydroxy-4-chlorophenyl)urea, 102
3-(3-Hydroxy-4-chlorophenyl)urea, 102
Hydroxy-2,4-dichlorophenoxyacetic acid,
    6, 9
6-Hydroxy-2,4-dichlorophenoxyacetic acid
    (6-OH-2,4-D), 4, 20–26
β-Hydroxy-2,4-dichlorophenoxybutyric
    acid, 36
β-Hydroxy-2,5-dichlorophenoxybutyric
    acid, 35
3-(2-Hydroxy-4,5-dichlorophenyl)urea,
    103
3-(2-Hydroxy-3,4-dichlorophenyl)urea,
    103
N-Hydroxyethyl carbamate, 128
N-Hydroxy IPC, 128
Hydroxylamine, 100
Hydroxylases, 127
Hydroxylation, 6, 9–11, 16, 19, 26, 36–
    39, 44, 101–109, 124–128, 133, 137,
    142, 302
5-Hydroxy-2-methoxy-3,5-dichlorobenzoic
    acid, 312

N-Hydroxymethylamine, 105
6-Hydroxy-2-methyl-4-chlorophenoxy-
    acetic acid (6-OH-MCPA), 4, 26–
    27
4- and 5-Hydroxy-1-naphthyl methylcar-
    bamate, 126
2-Hydroxyphenoxyacetic acid, 26, 39
3-Hydroxyphenoxyacetic acid, 26
4-Hydroxyphenoxyacetic acid (4-OH-
    PA), 4, 10, 20–21, 26, 39
β-Hydroxyphenoxybutyric acid, 39
3-(2-Hydroxyphenoxy)propionic acid, 39
3-(4-Hydroxyphenoxy)propionic acid, 39
Hydroxypropazine, 65, 68–69
Hydroxysimazine, 68, 71
3-Hydroxy-2,4,6-trichlorophenoxyacetic
    acid, 11

I

Imidazoleglycerol, 198
Imidazoleglycerol phosphate dehydrase,
    198
Imino hydrogen, 188
Imperata cylindrica L., 71
Indoleacetic acid, 277
Indole-3-acetic acid, 340
Indole-3-aldehyde, 340
Indole-3-glycolic acid, 340
Inductive effect, 208
Inhibition, 156, 228, 245, 277, 288
Inhibitors, 241
Ioxynil, 302, 316–317, 351
Ipazine, 67, 71
IPC, 113–145, 346
Irradiation, 62, 331
Ironweed, 15
Isocil, 354
Isocyanate, 122
Isopropanol, 121, 124, 137
N-Isopropylaniline, 175
Isopropyl *N*-(3-chlorophenyl)carbamate
    (CIPC), 119, 345
Isopropyl ester, 41
Isopropyl *N*-phenylcarbamate (IPC), 119
Isoriboflavin, 201

J

Jimsonweed, 7, 15
Johnson grass, 67, 277, 304

K

Ketene (carbomethylene), 60
Kidney bean, 154
Krebs cycle, 162
Kynurenin, 25

L

Lachnospira multiparus, 276
Lactic acid, 158, 167–168
Lag phase, 19, 22–23, 70–72, 93–94, 190
Leaching, 89, 135, 166, 230, 261–262,
    308–309, 313–315
Lemna minor, 241, 243, 285
Lemons, 15, 41
Leucine, 183
Lignin complex, 134
Lilac, 6, 15
Linuron, 79–111
α-Lipoic acid, 183
Lipophilicity, 240

M

Maleic hydrazide, 131, 356
Maple, 7–8, 14–18, 31, 36
MBOA (2,4-dihydroxy-7-methoxy-1,4-
    benzoxazin-3-one), 67–69
MCPA, *see* 2-Methyl-4-chlorophenoxy-
    acetic acid
MCPB, *see* 4-(2-Methyl-4-chlorophen-
    oxy)butyric acid
MCPP (mecoprop), *see* 2-(2-Methyl-4-
    chlorophenoxy)propionic acid
Mecoprop (MCPP), *see* 2-(2-Methyl-4-
    chlorophenoxy)propionic acid
Membrane permeability, 241
Mercaptans, 161, 163
2-Mercapto-4,6-bisamino-*s*-triazines, 59
Meristematic activity, 244
Mesquite, 15
Mesurol, 113–145
Methionine, 152
Methionine sulfone, 152
2-Methoxy-4,6-bisamino-*s*-triazines, 72
2-Methoxy-4,6-bis(isopropylamino)-*s*-
    triazine (prometone), 51–78
2-Methoxy-4,6-diamino-*s*-triazines, 57–59
2-Methoxy-4-ethylamino-6-isopropyl-
    amino-*s*-triazine (atratone), 51–78
Methoxymethylamine, 91

Methoxytriazines, 58–61, 68
Methylamine, 117–118, 123
Methylamine hydrochloride, 291
N-Methylcarbamates, 106, 113–145
Methylcarbamic acid, 117–118, 123
α-Methyl-γ-carboxymethylene-Δ^α-butenol-
    ide, 26–27
1-Methyl-4,4'-carboxypyridinium chloride,
    290
1-Methyl-4-carboxypyridinium ion, 288,
    291
α-Methyl-γ-chloromuconic acid, 27
2-Methyl-4-chlorophenol, 26–29
2-Methyl-4-chlorophenoxyacetic acid
    (MCPA), 1–49
4-(2-Methyl-4-chlorophenoxy)butyric
    acid (MCPB), 1–49
ε-(2-Methyl-4-chlorophenoxy)-ε-methyl-
    caproic acid, 39
2-(2-Methyl-4-chlorophenoxy)propionic
    acid (MCPP or mecoprop), 1–49
1-Methyl-4,4'-dipyridinium ion, 288
N'-Methyl-N-hydroxymethylamide, 129
3-Methylindole, 340
α-Methylmaleylacetic acid, 27
2-Methylphenoxybutyric acid, 38
2-Methylthio-4,6-bis(isopropylamino)-s-
    triazine (prometryne), 51–78
2-Methylthio-4,6-bis-γ-methoxypropyl-
    amino-s-triazines, 56
2-Methylthio-4,6-diamino-s-triazines, 57–
    60
2-Methylthio-4-ethylamino-6-t-butyl-
    amino-s-triazine, 51–78
2-Methylthio-4-ethylamino-6-isopropyl-
    amino-s-triazine (ametryne), 51–78
2-Methylthio-4-isopropylamino-6-γ-meth-
    oxypropylamino-s-triazine, 51–78
2-Methylthio-4-methylamino-6-isopropyl-
    amino-s-triazine, 51–78
Methylthiotriazines, 59–61, 69
Metobromuron, 79–111
Microbial degradation, 18–31, 89–95
Microbial metabolism, 160–162, 189, 262,
    307, 313
    aliphatic acids, 221
    benzoic acids, 307, 311–317
    dinitroanilines, 262, 269
    dipyridyls, 287
    thiolcarbamates, 158

Micrococcus, 38, 224
Microsomes, 163
Mitochondria, 243, 278
Mode of action, aliphatic acids, 238–249
    amitrole, 198–204
    chloroacetamides, 182–184
    dinitroanilines, 277–279
    dipyridyls, 294–296
    ureas, 87–89
Molinate, 151, 158
N-Monoacylamido-s-triazines, 61
Monallylamine, 172
Monocrotophos, 106
Monolinuron, 79–111
Monuron, 79–111, 347
Morning glory, 277, 304
Mung bean, 153–157, 166
Mustard, 277
Mutation, 22, 227
Mycoplana sp., 20

N

NAD, 35
NADPH, 29, 88, 105–106
NADPH$_2$, 125
Naphthaleneacetic acid, 340
α-Naphthol, 133
1-Naphthylcarbinol, 340
1-Naphthyl hydroxymethylcarbamate, 124
Neburon, 79–111
Neocosmospora vasinfecta, 288
Nettle, 36
Nicotinamide adenine dinucleotide, 35
NIH shift, 127
Ninhydrin, 191–192
Nitralin, 256
Nitrification, 229
Nitrogen fixation, 229
Nitrogen metabolism, 243
Nitroprusside–ferrocyanide, 188
Nitration, 60–61
Nitriles and nitrile derivatives, 41–43
N-Nitroethylamino group, 60
p-Nitrophenyl dimethylcarbamate, 125
Nitrosation, 61
Nocardia, 21, 28, 30, 38–41, 220, 224
Noradrenaline, 127
Norea, 79–111
d-Norpseudoephedrine, 127

Nucleic acid metabolism, 199
Nucleic acids, 278
Nucleotides, 200
Nutsedge, 311–312

O

Oak, 15, 18
Oats, 9, 11, 71, 73, 90, 94, 99, 133, 139,
    154, 178, 181, 189, 277, 314
Octyl ester, 41
Onion, 171
Orchard grass, 37
Organic matter, 158, 307, 314
Oxalate, 222
Oxalic acid, 168
Oxalis pes-caprae, 14, 18
Oxidase, mixed function, 107
Oxidation, 59, 161
    α-, 43
    β-, 5, 31–45
    ω-, 33
Oxidative phosphorylation, 278
N-Oxide formation, 107
2-Oxo-4,6-diamino-1,2-dihydro-*s*-triazines,
    57
2-Oxo-1-methyl-1,2-dihydro-*s*-triazines, 59

P

Panicum crus-galli, 137
Panthethine, 247
Pantothenate, 183, 243, 245
Pantothenate-synthesizing enzyme, 246–
    247
Paraquat, 284–298
Parsnips, 36
Partition coefficient, 314
PCP, 349
Peas, 11–43, 69, 73, 154–157, 171, 302,
    304
Peanuts, 9, 268, 277
Pebulate, 148–163
Pectic acid, 14
Penicillium, 91, 221, 224, 315
Peroxidase, 136
Persimmon, 7
Persistence, 85, 158, 160, 189, 261–262,
    293–294, 307–314
Phaseolus vulgaris, 6
Phenols, 24, 29, 33, 37, 131, 348
Phenoxyacetic acids, 1–49

Phenoxyalkanoic acids, 1–49
Phenoxybutyric acids, 1–49
Phenoxycaproic acid, 34
10-Phenoxy-*m*-decanoic acid, 33, 37
Phenoxyheptanoic acid, 34
9-Phenoxynonane-1-carboxylic acid, 33
Phenoxypropionic acids, 1–49
Phenoxyvaleric acids, 34, 39, 41
Phenylacetamides, 106
Phenylacetic acid, 339
Phenylalanine, 125, 127, 141
Phenylalanine hydroxylase, 125
Phenylamide, 119
Phenylcarbamates, 113–145
3-Phenyl-1,1-dimethylurea (fenuron),
    79–111, 345
Phenyl ethylcarbamate, 118
3-Phenyl-1-(2-methylcyclohexyl)urea
    (siduron), 79–111
Phenylureas, 119
Phenylurethane(ethyl-carbanilate), 119
Phospholipase-D, 310
Phosphor, 329
Phosphoramides and phosphoric acid
    crotonamides, 106
N-Phosphorylamido group, 60
Photochemical reactors, 330–331
Photochemistry, 290–293
Photodecomposition, 89, 189, 259, 307,
    317, 321–363
Photosynthetic phosphorylation, 295
Phthalomonoper-acid, 59
Physical properties, *see* Chemical and
    physical properties
Physostigma venenosum, 119
Physostigmine, 119
Picloram, 343
Pine seedlings, 70
Plantain, 97, 101
Plant metabolism, aliphatic acids, 212–
    217
    amitrole, 188–198
    benzoic acids, 302–317
    chloroacetamides, 167–182
    dinitroanilines, 266–268
    dipyridyls, 286–287
    thiolcarbamates, 152- 158
    s-triazines, 64–69
    ureas, 95–101
PMA, 356

Polygonum, 242, 317
Polysulfide ions, 58
Porphobilinogen, 202
Porphyrin synthesis, 202
Potassium azide, 189
Potassium cyanide, 58
Potatoes, 95, 99, 171
Prickly pear, 8, 15–16, 31
Primula acaulis, 303
Proliferation, 227
Proline, 199
Propanil, 113–145
Propylene glycol butyl ester, 41
Prostigmine, 120
Protein complexes, 12–13
Protein synthesis, 183–184, 199, 278
Proteus vulgaris, 245
Pseudomonas, 20–28, 38, 91, 127, 137, 161, 220–224
Pumpkin, 41
Purines, 199–200
Pyrazole, 197
β-Pyrazol-1-yl-α-alanine, 192
Pyrimidines, 200
o-Pyrocatechnic acid, 303
Pyrrole, 202
Pyruvate, 245
Pyruvic acid, 212, 234, 245, 314

Q

Quackgrass, 311
Quantum energy, 322–326
Quinoid formation, 107

R

Rape, 36
Raspberry, 8
Reduction, 258, 269, 273
Reductive dechlorination, 349
Residues, 152, 174, 230, 284
Rhizoctonia solani Kuhn, 287
Riboflavin, 189, 190, 200, 337
Ribosides, 200
Ribosomes, 202
Rice, 37, 132–141
Ring cleavage, 61, 72–74, 188–190, 289
RNA, 200, 278
Ro-Neet, 148, 151
Ryegrass, 167, 182

S

Saccharomyces cerevisiae, 200, 245
Salicylic acid, 303
Salmonella typhimirium, 200
Salvia, 125
Salvinia natans, 242
Sarcina, 91
Satan, 148, 151
Scenedesmus, 89, 200
Sclerotium rolfsii, 262, 287
Sensitization, 338
Sequential induction, 27, 39
Serine, 192, 197, 199
Sesone, *see* Sodium 2,4-dichlorophenoxy-ethyl sulfate
SH group, 212
Side-chain degradation, 6–9
Siduron, 79–111
Silage, 37–38
Silvex, *see* 2-(2,4,5-Trichlorophenoxy)-propionic acid
Simazine, 353
Simultaneous adaptation, 27
Smartweed, 7
SMDC, 150
Sodium azide, 18, 58
Sodium 2,4-dichlorophenoxyethyl sulfate (sesone), 4, 44
Soil moisture, 190
Sorghum, 7–8, 14, 67, 73, 171, 277
Soybeans, 9, 36, 69–73, 97–101, 166–178, 261–277, 303–305
Spectrum, 193–196, 322–324
Spinach, 41, 137
Sporocytophaga congregata, 21
Squash, 303–304
Steric effects, 35
Strawberries, 6–8, 15–17, 171
Streptococcus faecalis, 245
Streptomyces, 21, 38, 224
Streptomycin, 310
Substituted ureas, 79–111
Substitution effects, 294
Succinate, 192
Sugar beet, 171, 243, 304–305
Sulfanilamide, 22
Sulfhydryls, 24, 183, 317
Sulfone, 59, 69, 130–131

Sulfoxide, 60, 69, 130–131
Sulfoxy, 59
Sulfur oxidation, 130–131
Sunflower, 8, 139
Surfactants, 211, 240
Susceptibility, 15–18
Swep, 113–145
Sweet clover, 36
Sweetgum, 7
Sweet potato, 278
Synergism, 197
Synthesis, 148, 166, 257

T

2,4,5-T, see 2,4,5-Trichlorophenoxyacetic
    acid
2,4,6-T, see 2,4,6-Trichlorophenoxyacetic
    acid
Takadiastase, 12
Tautomers, 188
2,4,5-TB, see 4(2,4,5-Trichlorophenoxy)
    butyric acid
2,3,6-TBA, 309–311
TCA, 207–253, 335, 341
Temik, 113–145
Temperature, 153, 190, 231, 306, 332
Terbutol, 113–145
Terephthalic acid, 342
3,3′,4,4′-Tetrachloroazobenzene, 93, 136,
    263
1,2,3,4-Tetrahydro-1-oxo-pyrido-(1,2-*a*)-
    5-pyrazinium ion, 293
Thioester, 35
Thiolcarbamates, 147–164, 348
Thymine, 355
Thyroid tumors, 187
TIBA, 341
Timothy, 36–37
3- and 4-Tolylurea, 101
Tomatoes, 12–43, 137, 139, 189, 200,
    277, 286–291, 304–314
N-s-Trazol-3-yl-glucosylamine, 191
Transesterification, 42
Translocation, 18, 36–37, 64, 85–87, 152,
    286, 302–317
Transpiration, 314
Transthiolation, 161
Triallate, 151
s-Triazines, 51–78

N-Trichloromethylthio group, 60
2,4,5-Trichlorophenol, 8, 16
2,4,5-Trichlorophenoxyacetic acid (2,4,5-
    T), 1–49, 338
2,4,6-Trichlorophenoxyacetic acid (2,4,6-
    T), 4, 10–11
4-(2,4,5)-Trichlorophenoxy)butyric acid
    (2,4,5-TB), 1–49
2-(2,4,5-Trichlorophenoxy)propionic acid
    (silvex), 1–49, 338
Trichoderma, 221, 224, 262, 315
Triethylamine, 58
α,α,α-Trifluoro-*N*-butyltoluene-3,4,5-tri-
    amine, 266
α,α,α-Trifluoro-2,6-dinitro-*p*-cresol, 266
α,α,α-Trifluoro-2,6-dinitro-*N*-methyl-*p*-
    toluidine, 259
Trifluoromethylaniline, 94–96, 104
3-(*m*-Trifluoromethylphenyl)-1,1-
    dimethylurea (fluometuron),
    79–111
3-(3-Trifluoromethylphenyl)-1-methyl-
    urea, 96
3-Trifluoromethylphenylurea, 96
α,α,α-Trifluoro-6-nitro-2-nitroso-*p*-tolui-
    dine, 260
α,α,α-Trifluoro-5-nitro-*N*-propyltoluene-
    3,4-diamine, 263
α,α,α-Trifluoro-*N*-propyltoluene-3,4,5-
    triamine, 270
α,α,α-Trifluorotoluene-3,4,5-triamine, 262
Trifluralin, 255–282, 352
Trimethylamine, 58
Triphosphopyridine nucleotide, 125
Triticum vulgare, 125
Tryptophan, 24–25
Tyrosine, 125, 127, 141

U

UDP-glucose (uridine diphosphate-5′-glu-
    cose), 305
Unknown III, 198
Uptake, see Absorption
Urea photolysis, 347
Ureas, 79–111, 190
Urease, 104
Urethanes, 113–145
UV light, 62, 326

V

Vernolate, 148–163
Vicia, 101, 128
Volatility, 158, 173, 232, 285, 290, 336
Volatilization, 89, 134–135, 259, 307,
    313–314

W

Wax formation, 242
Wheat, 11–18, 32–43, 67–68, 133, 153–
    157, 200, 302, 311

Wolffia columbiana Karst., 285

X

Xanthomonas, 91

Y

Yellow foxtail, 242

Z

Zectran, 113–145

49969